CW00538267

White Gold?

Scotland's Dairying in the past

(with particular reference to the West of Scotland)

by

Adam Gray

Adam Gray
15.12.95

ISBN 1 872350 76 3

Typeset & Published on behalf of Adam Gray
by G.C. Book Publishers Ltd
17 North Main Street
Wigtown
Scotland DG8 9HL
and printed by Cromwell Press,
Broughton Gifford
Melksham, Wiltshire

ACKNOWLEDGEMENTS.

The production of White Gold? required advice and assistance. To those who were involved I am truly grateful – especially to Innes McLeod and Jack Lawson who gave me the impetus to develop the germ of an idea which I had been nurturing for some time. My thanks are due to Professor George Houston, Gavin Sprott, Adam McCartney, Tim Russell and Marie Aitken for the benefit of their knowledge and experience from their individual standpoints.

Professor Ian Cunningham is due special praise for his advice and painstaking corrections of the final manuscript.

My thanks are also due to Scottish Pride Co. Ltd. for their generous support towards producing this book.

Finally, this germ of an idea would not have reached fruition over a period of time, if it had not been for the patience and tolerance of my wife Elaine and my sons Adam, Bruce and Peter whom I sincerely thank.

CONTENTS

PREFACE

Many books have been written about all aspects of dairying. This is an endeavour to produce a book which will be to my fellow dairy farmers and of course to anyone else who is interested, an informative account of how dairy farming has developed over the years, "that they might know."

There have been a lot of changes since I was drafted as a schoolboy in to being a 'relief stirrer' of the cheese vat while the curds were cooking, to becoming a Director of the Scottish Milk Marketing Board and subsequently a Director of Scottish Pride Company Limited. There have been more changes in dairying over the forty five year period since 1950 than in the previous 130, when it became an established economic entity.

Generations of farmers and their families have maintained their livelihood at the tail of the dairy cow. The late J.B. Sproat of Lennox Plunton, Borgue, when he was over eighty, told me in 1947 – 'Stick to the dairy cow, she replaces herself and forebye, she always gives you something else to sell.'

This is a gathering together of some information about dairying in the past. With personal limitations on research and literary experience, it is admitted that many authorities have been consulted and liberally quoted from the sources listed in the Bibliography. Old family papers and press cuttings have also been referred to.

To publishers who have allowed me to quote liberally, I am truly grateful. To those whom I have been unable to contact, should there be a digression on copyright, I now apologise.

The mind sometimes 'boggled' at the enormity of this task and it is incomplete. If in some way it gives a measure of a better understanding of the dairy industry, then satisfaction will have been derived for the work and also the personal interest it stimulated.

One eminent authority on human nutrition has written, 'without milk the white race cannot survive.' But it has also been said that 'The human species is unique in that it continues to ingest milk long after its normal weaning age'– Allan Fraser. The difficulties of survival without milk can be shown by pointing out that, when the Mayflower arrived in America, no cattle were on board and the landing was almost a failure because all the children under two years of age at the time of landing died. To those involved, milk was White Gold.

INTRODUCTION

Pope Pius XI was correct when he said in 1920 that, 'milk is one of the most marvellous and precious products of nature, which Almighty God has placed at the disposal of mankind.'

It is guessed that man began to appreciate this truth of His Holiness as far back as 4,000 B.C., when he learned to domesticate animals and by 2,000 B.C., several recognisable different breeds existed. (Zeuner, 1827.)

There are some 48 references to it in the Bible, 43 of these in the Old Testament. Abraham offered milk to the three angels who promised him a son in his old age; 'and he took butter and milk and the calf which had been dressed and he set it before them.' It is alleged that Cleopatra bathed regularly in milk supposedly asses milk which must have been a laborious task for the slave hand milkers.

Milk in early days was produced mainly from sheep and goats. They were more easily herded by man and dog. Cattle by virtue of their superior strength and virility were more difficult to confine and handle and when domesticated were retired for meat, hide and draught purposes It was about the end of the 16th century before cows became established as a primary producing animal. At this time the milk was shared between the needs of the owners of the cow and her hungry calf as still occurs in primitive societies, for example in yak husbandry where calves are allowed to suckle once or twice daily.

'The cow is a noble representative of motherhood in the animal creation. Successful dairying means among other things, the making merchandise of the motherhood of the cow. He who is not wise into his own salvation here will suffer.' (Hoard's Dairyman, U.S.A.)

S.R. Crockett (1904) says in *'Raiderland'* that; 'In the early part of the 18th century, the common of Galloway lived in the utmost simplicity, if it is simplicity to live in a but and ben with the cow. In many of the smaller houses there was no division between the part of the dwelling used for the family and that occupied by Crummie the cow and Gussie the pig. 'The clartier the cosier' was we fear a Galloway maxim which was held in good repute even in the early part of the 18th century among a considerable section of the common folk.'

Cleanliness would be difficult to practise in a smokey chimneyless house, where the daylight was admitted via the open door or through holes at the gable end of the roof, which were sometimes covered over with a cow's placenta to keep out the wind.

Robert Burns described such a house in his poem the 'Vision'.

There lonely by the ingle cheek
I sat and eyed the spewing reek
That filled wi' hoast-provocating smeek the auld clay biggin',
An' heard the restless rattons squeak
Abune the riggin'.

It could be said that dairying in Scotland began in the 'but and ben'. The 'but' was where the peasant farmer lived and ate with his family along with any hired help. The 'ben' was where he slept with his wife usually in a box bed in the corner while the children slept on the floor near the fire.In spite of what Crockett says, it was usual that the livestock was sectioned off with a wooden partition under the same roof.

About the earliest encouragement to increase milk production was in 1214 when there was legislation in the time of Alexander II that if any peasant was rich enough to have four cows he should get land from his lord to plough and sow. This was an era when everyman's wealth was in stockcattle, goats, sheep, fowl with access to game –
deer, fish, etc.From Anglo-Norman times the 'fermtoun' was the focal centre of land layout known as the 'infield' and 'outfield'. Briefly, the 'infield' which was the better land near the settlement, was continually cropped in a form of rotation. In Galloway this was sometimes called the 'Fey'. To maintain its fertility a compost of the farmyard manure of the farmstead plus anything remotely associated with animals, horn shavings, woollen rags, pairings of leather, peat earth reduced to ashes, coal ashes and soot were preserved and put on the stubble after harvest. Where it was accessible seaweed was carried in creels by women on to it. Even in those days it was realised that there was nothing more honest than the good earth, 'You just get out of it what you put into it'. On areas which received insufficient manure, the crops degenerated into weeds and thistles. At this point they were left fallow for a year.

The further away 'outfield' had areas cropped cultivated and rested alternately, often in crops for three years followed by three years in pasture by which fertility was maintained by grazing cattle.

If land in three years 'out' and three years 'in'
'Twill keep in good heart till the deil goes blin'.

Beyond this there were large areas of unenclosed 'common' grazings where cattle were grazed in the summertime and herded by boys, women and old men. For more detail on the management of those 'fields', Fenton, A. (1976) is an excellent reference.

The word 'toun' still remains in its changed form 'town' or in place names, Kirkton, Chapelton which were associated with the church or on other places such as Hilton, Roberton and Easternton etc. It is interesting to note that in Kirkcudbrightshire there are in several parishes farms named Ingleston. Ingleston of Borgue, Ingleston of Gelston, Ingleston of Irongray, Ingleston of New Abbey and Ingleston of Twynholm. This suggests that detachments of Angles must have sailed up the estuaries of the Dee and the Nith. The Angles were farmers rather than warriors.

From the beginning of the 18th century onwards there was a dire necessity for more food due to a rapidly increasing population. The birth rate rose while the death rate fell due to better medical knowledge, better water supplies, better sanitation and a rising standard of living following the agricultural and industrial revolutions. 'For every mouth God sent a pair of hands.'

'The coincidence of the acceleration of agricultural and industrial output in the second half of the 18th century with that of the growth of Britain's population is so striking that it is tempting to ask whether the needs of the much increased population caused the fruitful changes in agriculture and industry or whether the improved farming and industry made possible the larger population.' It has been said that the Agricultural Revolution and the Industrial Revolution ran concurrently.

From that time onwards this country turned from being a net exporter of grain to being a net importer. This meant that manufacturing goods had to be sold abroad to pay for food to feed the nation. This was the beginning of the long drawn out debates on how this was to be practically and economically achieved.

Prior to the 17th century there was little progress in farming in Scotland apart from the endeavours of monks in certain areas such as in the South and East. The Cistercian monks who came from Burgundy to the south of Scotland in the 12th century employed a large number of lay brethren to work their land and fish along the Solway coast. They made cheese and butter to supply Dumfries and Kirkcudbright, both well known ports. They also owned large tracts of land in Glenkens, Kirkmabreck and Corsock where they produced large quantities of wool with a high reputation for quality which was shipped to Holland and France in return for wines, brandy and other luxuries. Grain, wool, fish such as lobster and salmon and honey from large apiaries found a ready market in the expanding towns of northern England.

Introduction

From the time of the dissolution of the monasteries till after the Covenanting feuds, there was little progress made in the improvement of agriculture. In this period it was a case of defence and survival for everyone. Communities were centred round castles, fortified houses and churches.

Until land was enclosed, the main income from agriculture in Scotland came from rearing cattle and sheep and growing poor crops of grain. After the Union of Parliaments there developed an extensive cattle trade into England to supply beef to the expanding English population, especially in London.

This trade declined quite rapidly with the advent of the steamship followed by the railways. This was further aggravated by the fall in grain and beef prices following the French wars which encouraged the expansion of dairying in Scotland.

This expansion in dairying became very necessary especially in the West of Scotland where the population rose from 149,000 to 234,000 between 1755–1821. (Mitchelle & Deane, 1962.) It is noteworthy that this was largely due to the fortuitous fact that their strategic trading position was between the Old World of Europe and the New World of America. They were at the crossroads of international trade coinciding with the industrial revolution.

From c.1750–1820, there was a substantial increase in population especially in the West of Scotland, e,g. Glasgow 31,000–147,000; Paisley 6,800–47,000; Kilmarnock 4,400–12,000; Greenock 2,000–27,000; Falkirk 3,9000–11,000.

It was said that Glasgow until the middle of the 18th century was a 'demure little town with a university and a cathedral.' Glasgow developed rapidly with the successive trades of linen, tobacco, cotton and heavy engineering principally the shipbuilding industry. These were greatly facilitated by the widening of the river Clyde in the early 1770s.

The continuation of a dairy industry was never in doubt as a result of what has often been described as the 'Improvement Movement'. In Scotland this was led by the 'Honourable the Society of Improvers in the Knowledge of Agriculture in Scotland' which was founded in Edinburgh on 8th June 1723. Thomas Hope of Rankeillor was elected president and Robert Maxwell of Arkland, Kirkpatrick Durham, Kirkcudbrightshire was a very enthusiastic secretary. Its objective was to see 'how much the right husbandry and improvement of the ground is neglected, partly through from the want of skill in those who make a profession thereof and partly from the want of encouragement for making proper experiments and improvements.'

This was the forerunner of the Royal Agricultural Society of Scotland established in 1784 and became a real influence on the 'Improvement Hovement' in Scotland when it decided to award 'premiums in money, medals and otherwise, for various facets of agriculture.' The medals were for people of rank and property and cash for those engaged in trade and manufacture which included dairy produce. How Scottish agriculture in general and dairying in particular benefited from this influence is well recorded in the Transactions of the Society at the time when new crop rotations, new machinery and improved livestock breeding were adopted.

From this time forward farming improved and dairying progressed. The account of it herein unfolds in two parts. Chapters 1–8 takes the progress of the dairy industry in Scotland from early days to Britain's entry into the Common Market with emphasis on its development in the former Scottish Milk Marketing Board area from where 86% of the country's milk is produced. Chapters 9–23 are devoted to other aspects of dairying.

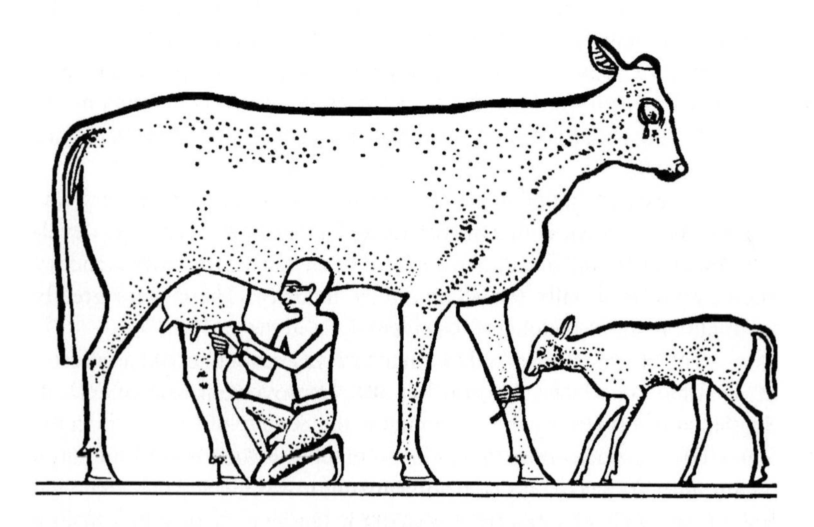

Fig 1 Hornless cow, with calf tied to foot. From coffin of Kawit. 11th dynasty, c2050 B.C.

CHAPTER 1

TOWN DAIRIES

Because milk was so perishable, supplies depended on how long it would keep sweet between the cow and the consumer in an unadulterated and unpasteurised state. As the roads were very poor and there were no railways, the areas of supply depended on the time it took a horse to walk slowly from the farm to the town to make milk available to the housewife in the morning. It was a slow and inadequate transport system to meet the increasing demands thus creating the rise of town dairies.

In many places milk reached the public by small dairy farmers driving cows round the streets with milkers on hand to put the milk straight into the customers jugs. Where there were only a few houses milk could be bought from a cow or goat lead from door to door, 'milked while you wait.' In other places the herds were driven into a milking shed behind a shop in a street and the milk would be got from someone carrying the milk on a yoke.

To improve these circumstances entrepreneurial dairymen set up cow sheds within the boundaries of the larger towns. Some of them rented or owned land within the suburbs of the towns. The milk produced came from herds of varying size. Some had a few cows serving a number of streets nearby, whereas the larger herds extended to several hundred.

At one time town milk came from rather wretched beasts from various breeds and crosses, the Shorthorn being the more popular. Cow keepers in and around towns cared little for pedigrees or even good commercial breeding. The herd replacements were often calved, milked for a year and sold to the butcher, hence the term 'flying herds.' In England where town dairies were well established by the end of the seventeenth century, many of the large dairies were filled with cows from overseas, from Western Ireland, the Low Countries and the Baltic. (Orwin & Whetham, 1946.)

The milk so produced was put into vessels far from clean, kept in an atmosphere which was by no means pure. There were no laws for hygiene nor measures by which milk was to be sold. 'Every man did what was right in his own eyes.' Before reaching the consumer milk was frequently diluted or adulterated by the 'cow with the iron tail', i.e. a water pump!

Two well known dairies of the last century are worthy of mention, belonging to Mr Carmichael and Mr William Harley. It was the progressive town dairies which were to become the focus of new management techniques; of hygienic milking practice, treatment and delivery of milk and housing systems, all ahead of their time and ultimately to have a persuasive influence throughout the dairy industry as it developed.

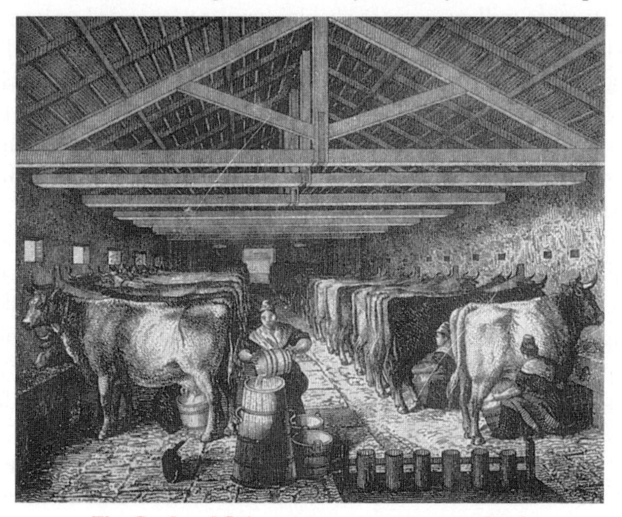

Fig 2. An 18th century town cowshed

There was a 1000 cow dairy owned by Mr Carmichael situated at Port Dundas, Glasgow on the banks of the Forth and Clyde canal. His nephew in an article in the Scottish Farmer, June 13th, 1970 says, 'A whole army of dairymaids lived in rooms above the stalls and every day other milkers came from districts such as Possilpark and Maryhill. Yields from cows which were mostly Ayrshire, Shorthorn and a few big framed Dutch Friesians, which at the time were just beginning to be imported from Holland, were not much behind present day standards. (1970.)

The cows were kept in three large byres, a lot of horses were used for mucking out and pulling the carts from which the milk was sold in the city. The dung was scattered on the fields surrounding the three byres, while the liquid waste was pumped into the Forth and Clyde canal. The calves caused no problem as they were delivered to a nearby slaughterhouse in Milton street. They were simply driven down there by herdsmen– just a ten minute job.'

The article also mentions that 'there was stiff competition from dairies in Ashfield street and Hamilton Hill which at that time were surrounded by green fields.' By the fact that cows were allowed access to the greater comfort of the green fields, they would produce more milk and have a longer milking life compared with those tied all the time in their filthy hovels in narrow lanes, so enabling milk to be sold at a lower price.

Fig 3. An 18th century country cowshed

WILLIAM HARLEY

William Harley was a 'personne extraordinaire.' He set up a town dairy system which was to achieve international fame. He was born in 1770 at Glendevon, Perthshire. He lost his parents in early childhood and was brought up by his paternal grandmother, 'on the proverbial oatmeal and Shorter Catechism.' He next worked for a maternal uncle, a Mr Blyth, who was a weaver of satinettes in Kinross and also a manufacturer of brown linen. After serving his apprenticeship there he moved into Glasgow in 1789 and worked for a cotton manufacturer.

In 1790 he decided to commence for himself as a textile manufacturer in premises on the corner of Frederick Street and George Square. In 1793 he introduced turkey red checked gingham which was extremely popular, so popular that his business expanded dramatically in London, America and the West Indies. He made a fortune.

In that era Glasgow was a large town like any other 'country town' with a population over 60,000. There was a labyrinth of narrow lanes opening onto main streets. Thatched houses were common with their kailyards stretching behind, a portion of which was always reserved for flowers. The wealthy tobacco lords were beginning to build handsome mansions in Buchanan and Queen Streets. The town was developing rapidly.

Prior to Glasgow having a police force about 1800, William Harley joined his fellow citizens to keep the peace 'where there were scenes of vice and depravity.'

His Christian upbringing had a great influence on his life. He had a great compassion for underprivileged children. He organised schools on Sunday evenings; some with 400 in number. He paid his own staff extra to encourage them to attend and teach the children about the Bible. He often reflected how this project gave him 'indescribable satisfaction, that he was a humble instrument in setting afloat this accessible channel to virtuous knowledge.'

'Knowledge was proud that they learned so much,
Wisdom was humble that they knew no more.'

His dedication to the well-being of his fellow man and to Glasgow knew no bounds. He bought Blythswood Hill and built there pleasure gardens with a large summer house on top of a 30 foot tower and charged the public to see a view over Glasgow. He launched into massive building schemes which are now St Vincent Street, Renfrew Street, Bath Street, West Nile Street and Sauchiehall Street. Unfortunately he was unable to hold the feu duties during the depression after the Napoleonic Wars which contributed to his ultimate bankruptcy.

It is not surprising as William Harley was a 'good christian living man,' he had an abhorrence of dirt and poor hygiene. Supplying clean water was an obsession with him.

It was fortunate that the water table in many parts was relatively high. This enabled the aristocracy and the meritocracy to build their houses where they could get water from wells in their gardens. Some houses were built nearby to streams. In Glasgow there were only about 30 public wells scattered throughout the city. In the more salubrious parts servants, many of whom came from the Highlands, foregathered at these wells, 'their noise became a public nuisance.' In other parts of the city it was 'the wives and weans' that drew and carried the water. In a dry summer when the wells went dry, the water was carried from the river where all the poorer people obtained their water. He was advised that he should charge double to haul water from the river, but typical of the man he refused to do so, 'out of regard for the poor'. He kept the price the same, namely, a penny for the 'gang', (a certain quantity) and a bawbee for the 'stoup' (stopping).

A very large supply of spring water was discovered at William Harley's residence at Willowbank. There he sank a series of wells and built a very large storage tank at the corner of West Nile Street and Bath Street to which the water from these wells gravitated. He organised a number of horses and carts to distribute the water. He divided the city into districts to which carts were sent at a certain time. The inhabitants were warned of their approach by the ringing of hand bells.

In his desire that the citizens should be more hygienic he erected in 1803 public swimming baths at the corner of West Nile Street and Bath Street next to the large tank which supplied drinking water. Its size was comparable to today's standards. The swimming bath for men was 40ft. long and 20ft. wide and four and a half feet deep. The ladies' pool was half that size and the one for the boys' and girls' was 12ft. x 10ft. In addition, there was a series of baths and showers. The avenue leading to the ladies' bath house was lined with shrubberies.

In spite of the fact that very few inhabitants of Glasgow had good washing facilities, the novelty of using the baths passed and they became a 'white elephant', like the pleasure gardens on Blythswood Hill. 'Our forefathers ideas of personal cleanliness was far from perfect.' At least we know how Bath Street got its name!

THE HARLIAN DAIRY SYSTEM

When the public baths were popular, there was a modicum of demand after abolutions 'to be furnished with a little new milk.' To satisfy this need William Harley supplied a cow. When this encouraged more milk to be drunk, he built a byre at Willowbank to accommodate 24 cows. As a result of this, the demand for refreshing wholesome milk grew very quickly. As with clean water, he quickly realised that there was a need for clean, unadulterated milk, efficiently produced under hygienic conditions.

As he was a man who never did things by half measures, he launched into erecting what was called "the Grand Byre", which held 260 cows. This splendid commodious building was in many respects up to present day standards. It was erected on arches with underfloor cellars to store the dung. It was situated on a square with Bath Street in the south, Sauchiehall Street in the north, West Nile Street in the east and Renfield in the west. 'This 'monster dairy' lies among a frowning forest of chimneys.....past a manufactory where horses are boiled into glue by the score.' (Dixon, 1912.)

William Harley was very conscious of the vast loss of nutrients from the farm manure due to bad methods of storage, a problem that is still with us today. His precept was 'nothing should be lost.' He made calculations on the financial benefits of well stored farmyard manure.

'A merciful man regardeth the life of his beast.'

In the Grand Byre due consideration was given to the welfare of the animals. The traditional method of tying up a cow was by "fixing the neck of the animal between two stakes similar in appearance to that of a culprit in a pillory, thus preventing the animal from carrying out its natural want of licking itself. 'Licking' contributes to free perspiration and increases the circulation of blood thus promoting general health.√ William Harley patented a chain swivel method which gave the cows more freedom to lick themselves.

Because so many visitors came from all over the country to see the Grand Byre he said that it was 'productive of a double evil, that of interrupting the servants and disturbing the cattle.' As a result he erected a balcony 'from which a bird's eye view of the whole interior of the cow house and its hundreds of cows could be obtained at a glance, without producing the slightest annoyance or inconvenience either to the servants or the cattle.' From this viewpoint, 'princes, noblemen and gentlemen from almost every quarter of the globe, could stand and admire for the price of a shilling ticket, the lines of cows below them being fed four times a day from feed trolleys – on the Scots principle that 'a coo milks by the mou'. A viewer's gallery is only seen at the present day in the most up to date modern dairy premises, but without a charge!

Among the many visitors who came was a deputation from the Highland Society, the forerunner of the present Royal Highland and Agricultural Society. It was so impressed that a suitable inscribed plaque was presented to William Harley.

As he developed his dairy enterprise, William Harley thought long and hard on how to devise improvements for the countryside. He studied modern methods of ploughing, draining, road making, grassland management, etc. He selected grasses for one year leys. This grass seed was sown early and liberally irrigated with urine throughout the season by a device described as 'similar to a fire engine pump.' According to

William Harley he could cut this grass five times in a season, something which is hard to accomplish even with today's modern methods of grassland management.

He practised the 'Soiling System' evolved by Mr Curwen. This claimed that if the manure produced by the cows confined to the buildings was always returned to the ground from which the fodder requirements were taken, the produce from one acre well cultivated when cut and carried will go further than five acres of pasture.

His other activities pertaining to the countryside included, growing strawberries and other fruits at Garnet Hill with success. Methods were devised of preventing hares from attacking the bark of trees in the wintertime. He laid guidelines on how to plant and raise thorn and beech hedges which would be impenetrable to cattle. He made a study of caterpillars and 'the making of liquids for the destruction of these horrible little pests.'

DAIRY MANAGEMENT

'It requires a keen perception, watchful care, a human heart and abundant energy to succeed with dairy cows.' (Hoard.)

William Harley's cow and dairy management was quite unique and so far ahead of his time. The principles he laid then, as indicated earlier are the basis for present day management, his attitude to hygiene, to treatment and delivery of milk, to housing and milk recording. However, it took a long time for those principles to be generally accepted, a phenomenon not uncommon throughout the history of agriculture.

He experimented with various breeds and crosses but preferred the newly improved Ayrshires. Like many of today's breeders, he thought they were the most economical producers of milk. Not so many would agree with him that they were excellent producers of beef, although compared with the other cattle of the time they probably would be. He claimed that the carcases produced lots of tallow which was valuable for soap and candle making etc.

While William Harley would have preferred a self contained herd to reduce the risk of introducing disease, he had to have a 'flying herd' because of the demand for his milk and the necessity to have a regular daily supply of milk available. This meant that he had to buy in cows, milk them until they dropped below a certain yield and sell them and thus not rear any replacements. He usually bought 7–10 year old cows costing £8–10 each,which were able to produce at their peak 25–30 quarts per day, a considerable yield considering that the average weight was 35–50 English stones. These cows were often supplied by dealers including ladies. 'Mrs Dunlop drove up and down the country in a gig, buying up cows which she exposed for sale each Wednesday in Glasgow.' (Becker, 1973.)

When the cows were culled they were transferred to the dark cellars below the byres to fatten. He put these cows in calf because he thought that they would fatten more readily. A thought that still prevails. Other town dairymen sent their cows to be served by the bulls at Willowbank and their service date duly recorded for which they charged 5s.

The seller, the purchase price, the colour, age of cow, whether or not it was in calf and the cast sale price were all meticulously recorded. William Harley bought his cows in calf because he did not agree with 'hafting', i.e. allowing the milk to remain on the cow after she was calved for a considerable time before being sold. Because this was a great discomfort to the cow, he strongly advocated that legal action should be taken against such a cruel practice. Before the newly purchased cows were milked they were 'curried down' (groomed) and the whisk of their tail cut off, 'to prevent lifting dung and water.' 'Fancy cut papers were hung from the roof to attract flies.'

Because the cows were permanently inside, grass, hay, green cut barley, turnips, swedes, cabbages and carrots were carried into the cows, a tedious task. If the grass was short and luxuriant, salt, old hay and straw was fed to prevent bloating. The foods bought were grain, wet distillers grains (draff), bruised beans and ground oilcake. Nine tons of draff per cow were known to be fed in a year. If the grain could be bought at a favourable price, it was stored in excavated pits in the ground. To prevent deterioration, the pits were sealed with mould from sprouted grass seed. In this way it was said that the grain kept in good condition for two or three years. Glasgow and many of the large towns on the west coast were almost wholly supplied by large importations of foreign baled hay. (T.H.A.S.S. 1899.)

Mashes were the main feed in the winter time. They were fed three times a day followed by dry fodder. It was composed of steamed potatoes, turnips, chopped straw and draff with salt being added liberally and 'the whole was vigorously tramped by a byreman naked to the waist.' The 'mashman' ladled 5 Scots pints of mash at each feed into an individual dish in the passages at the head of the cows. The steaming of the forage crops prevented taints in the milk as did the addition of a few spoonfuls of nitre (sodium nitrate) to the milk in the receiving tank.

The food preparation did not depend entirely on manual labour, as there were machines, although primitive, for threshing and chopping straw and slicing turnips and swedes. The latter were essential due to a shortage of water.

All the bought in foods, including hay and straw, were weighed on a weighing machine at the gate. The daily costs were calculated each week. Any dung or urine which was sold was also weighed.

MILKING

'Be thou diligent to know the state of thy flocks and look well to thy herds.'

William Harley's system of dairy management was carried out with great attention to detail.

Each milker was equipped with a towel, stool and a 'luggy'. (a large tin vessel, formerly made of wood.) Every 'two timers' (twice-a-day milker) had a common pail of water for regularly washing the hands and the cow's udders. Every milker was expected to milk 10–12 cows night and morning and they were rotated weekly. The high yielders were milked thrice daily. Individual efficiency was checked. To ensure that the cows were properly milked, each milker had to strip out another milker's cows and a small premium was paid weekly to the milker who produced the greatest amount of milk there from. The cows were groomed daily and all utensils were scalded with steam from a boiler.

The staff was well disciplined. Initially Harley had difficulties instilling into them the necessity for strict hygienic routines in handling of milk from the cow to the consumer. He had to overcome the common 'canna be fashed' attitude of the older workers. As from the 'Cottars of Glenbervie', 'O! We ken weel enough aboot kye and we canna' be fashed wi'thae new fangled ways.' However, the dairymaids were encouraged to sing to the cows while milking as it was believed that it would stimulate production, since "cows are partial to a pleasing sound." This would be more relaxing than the type of music blaring from the radios in the modern parlour!

MILK RECORDING

Usually on a Friday the quantity of milk produced from night and morning milking was weighed and recorded. For this purpose dark staved milking buckets had white staves burnt on them at different levels to give an indication of the individual yields of the cows.

This recording ensured that the right cows were culled for poor performance. It is quite remarkable that it took until 1903 for milk recording to be officially recognised.

DISTRIBUTION

At Willowbank the milk was transferred to what was called the milk office where it was passed over a milk sieve of "finest brass cloth" into a bulk container. From there it was measured into wooden delivery churns fitted with wooden taps, holding 12–18 Scots quarts equivalent to 8–13.5 imperial gallons. In an age when dilution was the rage rather than the exception the churn lids were securely padlocked before dispatch and the air holes in the lids were modified to prevent the introduction of water by the delivery staff. Once filled and sealed the churns were taken to all parts of the city in smart spring pony carts. It was preferred to transport the milk in small spring carts hauled by small ponies to minimise the shaking and agitation which would eventually turn the milk sour.

An innovation was that the milk was supplied to customers from measures on which the quantity was clearly marked on the outside.

About 1818 the milk was retailed in the street at a competitive price of 6d. per Scotch pint equivalent to 2d. per imperial pint. Other measures used 3d. for a quart, a sixth of a pint at 1d. and a twelfth of a pint for a half-penny.

By 1824 the Imperial gallon was generally adopted. Milk sold at the door was called the 'Barn gallon' when a ½ pint more was given for the same price as the Imperial gallon. Similarly, like the modern times 'baker's dozen' a few lbs. of cheese or a few ozs. of butter were 'thrown in'. At first these additions were part of a bargain and then became the custom.This was seen in Kainers' bargains where a stone of cheese was 24lbs.

There was also a brisk trade in the sales of cream, skimmed milk, buttermilk and butter. The cream was usually sold at six times the going rate for fresh whole milk and skimmed milk at half its price. The buttermaking was carried out at Willowbank in a multiple battery of churns driven from a steam engine, this being an innovation at the beginning of the last century. Harley's maxim in the trade was 'Never to undersell but to compete only in regard to quality and sell at a fair price'

To keep a check on the staff and visitors official or unofficial, there was a 'Counting House' situated at the main gate. There was accommoda-

Fig. 4 Hand milking to order!

Fig. 5 Unhygienic methods of milking. Early 18th century

tion in it so that there was someone on duty all the time. Also available were rooms in which the staff changed before going out to deliver the milk. As Regularity, Order and Cleanliness were three indispensable rules to employment at Willowbank, 'the rules to be implicitly obeyed by the servants were that their hair be combed, their hands and face be washed and their dress be clean and neat.' A set of rules hung in each byre and in the milkhouse office so that there was no excuse for anyone being ignorant of them.

William Harley seemed to manage his staff in rather a more autocratic manner than would be allowed today. Each roundsman had an area in the city and the routes were so arranged that they all finished at the same time. For every quarter of an hour a roundsman was late, 'a fine was exacted agreeable to the regulations.' This was to ensure that no one dallied on his round 'in order to evade the less congenial work in the byres.' Breakages and unpaid credit were deducted from their wages. He adopted a crafty method of paying wages. They were paid fortnightly on the Tuesday. This was to minimise the drunkenness on the Saturday night and the absenteeism on Sunday. 'Some on a frolic thought to absent themselves which caused an inconvenience. By paying on a Tuesday also allowed better purchases to be made at the weekly market on Wednesday.'

In those days before there were regulations, the public were quick to note the good quality of Harley's milk and the honest measures by which they were sold. In consequence milk sales rose rapidly. This encouraged other milkmen to improve their standards in order to retain their customers with the result the total consumption of milk in Glasgow rose markedly. In fact Glaswegians were probably the first city dwellers to taste clean sweet milk regularly. The first dairy legislation governing this did not appear till the Adulteration Act of 1860 followed by the Public Health Act of 1875.

True to his philosophy that 'nothing should be lost,' William Harley kept a piggery at Willowbank. The pigs were kept to consume offal from the dairy, and the refuse from farm and garden to turn it all into rich manure. Cinders from ash pits were given daily, as they were supposed to promote digestion and prevent their stomachs becoming distended should they eat or drink too much. The breed kept was a Berkshire-Chinese cross. Like the dairy cows all the sows were groomed using 'Tow and Wool cards.When William Harley's reputation became widespread, his services were in great demand from all over the country, advising on his revolutionary methods of dairying. One of the highlights of his life was in 1829 when he was summoned by Czar Nicholas I of Russia to establish a modern

Fig. 6 Milk sellers. 1826

Fig. 7 Carrying milk with a shoulder-yoke

dairy at St. Petersburg similar to that at Willowbank which the Czar had visited in 1815. Unfortunately on his way to St. Petersburg he collapsed and died in London at the age of 59.

He wrote about himself, 'It may be asked how any single individual could project and properly conduct so many different concerns? It is answered, that it was not from any vain opinion of the competence of his own abilities, but in a judicious division of time and labour and the uniform adoption into every department of that comprehensive "word system." These may be said to have been the regulating powers of his extensive machinery.' The motto throughout his establishment was – 'Every man at his post and doing his duty.'

It is interesting to note the comments of two of his well known contemporaries.

Sir John Sinclair in his general report on Scotland states that, 'If a plan and a minute of the Willowbank system were given, it could easily be adopted in every town in the kingdom. The system is original and not to be met with in any other parts of the kingdom. It can hardly be questioned that many lives are annually lost to the nation for the want of genuine milk, that most nourishing diet.'

William Aiton wrote in 1825, 'Mr Harley has displayed great taste and judgement in the construction of his byres and in everything connected with his dairy. The true superior degree of cleanliness with which his byres, cattle and whole apparatus are kept do him much honour and cannot fail to prove exemplary to others in that branch, where it was of late too much neglected.'

It was tragic that the depression in the economy of the country which followed the Napoleonic Wars, drove William Harley into bankruptcy in 1816, necessitating the sale of Willowbank. He was carried away with the apparent successes of his various enterprises. As happens so often he ultimately stretched his financial resources to the utmost, which made his businesses vulnerable to the adverse economic conditions prevailing. He epitomised the oft quoted saying that 'Success has many fathers, failure is but an orphan child.'

It is also often said that the world is changing faster than our ways of thinking. As far as dairying was concerned, William Harley's thinking was far ahead of the ways of the world. He has been described as the forgotten pioneer. It has been noted how much he contributed to his time and generation, setting standards for others to follow in later years, few knowing from whence they came.

It is fortunate for posterity that in 1829 Harley wrote a book entitled

"The Harlian Dairy System". This gives a view of his outlook in life and an account on how he developed his businesses. There are also some comments on Dutch dairy farming.

In the foregoing, this book has been referred to extensively.

"By 1893 within the Glasgow city boundaries there are 71 licenced byres.The average number being about 740, compared with 786 in 1907. Peter Fyffe, then the chief sanitary inspector, reports that increasing efforts are being made by inspectors to get dairy keepers to adopt covering lids for all counter vessels containing milk or cream. Mr Fyffe is not all enamoured of the method of milk distribution from hand barrows Which has in recent years been imported from England." (Scottish Farmer, 1993.) Neither would William Harley.

Fig 8 Merkland Dairy, Glasgow

EDINBURGH TOWN DAIRIES.

In Edinburgh there were actually more town dairies than in Glasgow although it had a smaller population. This was consequent of the fact that in the more arable counties surrounding Edinburgh, there were fewer dairy farmers. As in many other towns, there were complaints about insufficient supplies of genuine milk. These complaints became more vocal by the well to do, who had tasted good fresh milk whilst they were summering in their country villas or at the summer resorts. On their return to the city they felt the want of that wholesome beverage, it being very difficult to obtain the article unadulterated anywhere in the city.

This lead to the formation of Joint Stock Companies which built dairy premises based on the Harlian system. This naturally upset the older town cow keepers who gave the new establishments 'both skeith and scorn.' Nevertheless the inhabitants of Edinburgh benefited eventually.

'As late as 1927 there were 97 town dairies with 3732 cows in the city of Edinburgh where at one time there were hundreds. Many would be small enterprises with a few cows serving only a nearby street or two with milk.

By 1961 according to the Third Statistical Account there were about 12 herds with about 400 cows.' (Urquart 1979)

FEEDING COSTS

An idea of the feeding costs in a town dairy can be gleaned from a voluminous book, 'Farm Livestock of Great Britain' by Robert Wallace, (1907), which was a hundred years after the Harley Dairy System. The example given quoted almost verbatim, is for a hundred cow dairy in Leith, yielding an average 3 1/2 gallons/cow/day in the summer and 3 gallons in the winter.

The cows were estimated to be 1120 lbs. in weight, costing £22, having had three or four calves. They were milked for one year and sold to the butcher without being quite dry. When such non-pedigree milking Shorthorn cows were kept all season in the house and fed to the highest degree possible, the yield could be made to double that under the natural system.

550 gallons produced per cow in a year, was a common yield for well managed herd towards the end of the nineteenth century.

Food	Cost per Ton.	Total Food (lb.)	Cost pence/day
Draff	22s	33	2
Treacle	105s.	3	1
Peasemeal	150s.	4	3
Compound cake	160s.	4	3 1/4
Water (warm)	-	4	-
Turnips	17s	75	6
Potatoes	25s.	12	1
Hay	40s.	14	3

Description of the food fed:–

Treacle in some form is indispensable as a preventative of stomach staggers resulting from over feeding, the most common ailment of dairy cows under forcing conditions.

Pease meal was made from Canadian peas and it was thought to be less liable to induce bloat.

Compound cakes, while showing an attractive appearance and believed to give good results, were too dear and were suitable for those who did not have the technical knowledge necessary to enable them to buy ingredients separately at market value and mix them at home. Sometimes finely ground indigestible worthless fibre was added under the name of cellulose to keep the price down.

Cotton or linseed cake was fed instead of the compounds. They were sold in the form of large flat slabs and had to be broken down to a palatable size with a machine called a cake mill. This was basically a pair of spiked rollers held in a cast iron frame and turned by a handle. The spiked rollers reduced the slabs to fragments which were collected in a tray at the base.

Yellow turnips were preferred to be fed with their leaves attached during the early part of the season, this was followed about Xmas with stored swedes.

Potatoes were not used if the price rose above 25s. per ton and were fed only in limited quantities once a day, as they were considered more indigestible than turnips and liable to induce bloat. Moreover like mangolds, they produce pale milk which looks poor in quality and unattractive to the consumer.

First cut hay was preferred if the price did not rise above 80s. per ton. When dearer, a proportion of second cut ryegrass at 60s. or oat straw costing 45s. per ton, was substituted. French wheat straw at 42s. per ton was used at times for litter.

The first feed was given at 4a.m. composed of draff only, followed by a basketful of turnips at 5.30a.m. and at 6a.m. a foddering of hay. Milking was carried out from 4a.m. to 6a.m. by women, while men mucked out the byres. The second feeding and second milking began at 9a.m. A mash, at blood heat, consisting of draff, treacle, pease meal and compound cake was given about this time, followed by three turnips each and finally potatoes. The third feeding of mash, turnips and hay, the final milking and cleaning out, began at 3 p.m. At 7p.m., the man in charge looked in to see that all was quiet and the doors were then closed for the night.

If the cow was averaging 3 gallons of milk per day and selling at 10d. per gallon, it made a total of 17/6 per week sold wholesale. When sold at a shilling a gallon, the profit of 2s. net of costs, is too small to support a successful business, so that a larger yield than 3 gallons per day or a larger price than 10d. or 1s. per gallon is necessary, if the flagging business of the town dairy industry is to survive. (Wallace, 1907.)

THE ECLIPSE OF THE TOWN DAIRY

The town dairies served a very useful purpose over many years, making fresh milk available to many people who had no way of obtaining it. Changing circumstances eventually lead to their demise. There were the very serious outbreaks of cattle plague in the 19th century. This led to wholesale slaughter of many town herds which were never replaced. Those which did, had to cope with the introduction of health and hygiene regulations previously mentioned and others introduced later.

The viability of many urban dairies became unsustainable. Several factors mitigated against them. Their costs of production remained high due to having to buy in all the food for the cows and labour was more expensive by £1 to £2 per half year. The poor trading position of the town dairyman was further compounded by cow beef prices falling consequent upon importation, first of frozen beef and later chilled beef from abroad in the late 19th century. Being adjacent to towns, rents for grazing land and ground for growing roots became dearer. Improved roads and the railways allowed transport of milk and dairy products to distant markets and allowed commodities such as lime, kainit and animal feeds to reach farms, leading to new techniques, resulting in a supply of milk more cheaply produced.

CHAPTER 2

COMMUNICATIONS

'Milk must get there'

ROADS

The necessity for town dairies was because of the inadequacy of the roads and the lack of railways.

Although very significant progress had been made in farming during the eighteenth century, general advance was hindered by poor facilities of communications such as bad roads. So much depends on roads therefore, it is remarkable to think that between the departure of the Romans in the fifth century and the middle of the 18th century, no real attempt was made even to imitate the very thorough Roman methods of roadmaking, let alone improve them.

Apart from a few cobbled streets in towns, most roads were without hard surfaces. In Ayrshire during the time of Robert Burns, when an enterprising landlord, Lord Cathcart, offered to supply his tenants with wheeled carts to take their produce to market, they were refused. They were considered useless to travel over the roads with so many potholes. It was said that on the Great North road in England horses as well as men drowned in the potholes after heavy rains.

The means of carriage had to suit the roads. 'In Galloway, for instance, long strings of pack horses bearing sacks and creels carried on the exchange of commodities.' (Trotter, 1901.) The poor state of the roads meant that the severe jolting kept the pace of carts down to that of a snail and it was not conducive for the conveying of milk and butter from the farms to the towns.

At first, roadmaking was done by enterprising proprietors, who contracted the work themselves with the object of opening up their estates. They were so necessary for the progress of enclosing land.

A great impetus to the improving of roads was given at the time of the Jacobite Rebellions.

"If you had seen the roads before they were made,
You would hold up your hands and bless General Wade."

General Wade and his subordinate and successor, General William

Caulfield, were responsible for the making of a large number of roads to facilitate troop movements during the disturbances. The new roads were not always welcomed. The Jacobite clans knew that the roads, which could be used to carry baggage and cannons, might make life difficult for them and they scorned the weakling who used the roads. Even the women folk considered the roads to be for softies and walked alongside them, ignoring the new bridges by wading the burns and rivers.

Moderate efforts in maintaining roads were made in the 17th century, when a Statute for Labour was introduced in 1669, whereby able bodied men had to provide so many days labour in the year. Adjoining landowners were also compelled by statute to clear all the roads between market towns from trees and undergrowth to a space of 200 feet on either side. The object was not only to allow the roads to dry out after rains but also to destroy lurking places for robbers. The adjoining owner was held responsible for any violent crime committed on a road not properly cleared.

It was only after the Turnpike Act was passed in 1751 that any real progress was made. Between 1760 and 1774 there were 452 Turnpike Acts passed and from 1785 to 1800 this number was increased by 643. (Ernle, 1961.) This enabled capital to be raised by subscription or loans which were administered by appointed Turnpike Trusts and the maintenance financed by tolls. The tolls were collected from all road users at turnpikes or tollgates usually positioned at road junctions. The principle being that 'every person ought to contribute to the repair of the roads in proportion to the use they make of the convenience they derive from them.'

Periodically the toll houses were let by auction. It provided a good gamble for anyone who knew of any local development likely to increase the traffic in a certain main road.

Some of the tolls imposed about 1870 were:–

For every horse, ox, or other beast of draught, drawing any coach, chariot, chaise, hearse or any such carriage – each 6d.

For every horse, ox, or other beast of draught drawing a waggon, wain, van, caravan, cart or any other wheeled carriage not on springs, when the number is not exceeding four – each 8d.

When the number shall be three – each 5d.

When the number shall be two or one – each 4d

For every horse, mule or other beast of burden, laden or unladen, not drawing – each 2d.

For every drove of oxen or meat cattle – 10d. per score.

For every drove of horses or fillies unshod – 1s 8d. per score.
For every drove of calves, sheep, lambs, hogs, or goats – 5d. per score.
All carts or carriages let for hire without the owners name or place of abode on some conspicuous part on the offside of the the cart or carriage to pay double poll. (Parkgate, Dumfries.)

Because this system did not take sufficient cognisance of the local user such as the milk seller, many evaded the toll gate by crossing fields. This undesirable aspect added expense on the poor income of small dairy farmers and hindered some of them from selling milk in the liquid market.

Tolls were abolished by the Roads and Bridges (Scotland) Act, 1878. In 1909 the government created a Road Board with access to a Road Fund financed by the proceeds from motor taxation. The Minister of Transport was constituted in 1919.

Interestingly, it is forecast that Britain will have a network of toll roads by 1998 and that the business would be worth £100m. It is envisaged that micro-chip cards and cameras suspended from overhead gantries will be used, dispensing with a ticket system involving thousands of cashiers in toll booths, thus avoiding traffic congestion. (Sunday Times, 1994.)

As the Turnpike Trusts gathered money for the improvement of roads there was an obvious need for road engineers. 'Cometh the hour, cometh the man.'

Two Scotsmen, sons of the soil, made tremendous contribution to road engineering. John Loudon McAdam (1756–1836) and Thomas Telford (1756–1836.) John McAdam was the son of an impoverished laird, James McAdam, Waterhead, Carsphairn, Kirkcudbrightshire, who like many others of the time suffered from the collapse of the Ayr Bank and was compelled to sell his estate. Thereafter, John McAdam emigrated to America where he was a very successful trader especially during the American War of Independence. (1775–83.) After the war he returned to England and was appointed a victualler to the Admiralty. Later, in 1815 he became Surveyor-General of roads in the south of England around Bristol where he successfully put into practice his theories on road metalling which has since perpetuated his name, before the advent of tar.

The basis of this process, which was to make roads suitable for animals and vehicles, was by using small broken stones instead of the formerly used large rounded pebbles. 'The stones are broken into irregular shaped fragments never exceeding 6ozs. each, which spread over the road in thin layers of three to six inches in depth, are worked together into a solid mass by the traffic passing over them. When once fixed the road becomes a hard crust, impervious to sudden wet and if the water is prevented from settling and if most of the mud is scraped off, it will remain good for a long time.' It seems amazing that it took such a long period of time to evolve such a simple process!

When John McAdam was appointed Surveyor-General of the roads of Britain, he was commonly called the 'Collosus of the Road.' It was said that it was due to Sir John Sinclair's encouragement that made him persist with his experiments in roadmaking, who said after McAdam's undoubted success, 'Give every project of usefulness a fair trial.'

Thomas Telford, a shepherd's son from Dumfriesshire, was said by some to be a rival to John McAdam. Originally a mason, he became a surveyor and a road engineer, latterly in the service of the British Fisheries Society and the Highland Roads and Bridges Commission. He is reputed to have constructed nearly 1,000 miles of roads and over 1,000 bridges, including the Dean Bridge in Edinburgh. He also constructed several east coast harbours, the Caledonian and many other canals. (Marwick, 1964.)

CANALS

Because roads were quite incapable of coping with the transporting of the increasing amount of goods, engineers especially in England, turned their attention to river and canal navigation. In England the mid 19th century was the heyday of the canals. By 1834, England was covered with a network of more than 4,000 miles of canals and navigable rivers. (Ernle, 1961.) Those who dug out the canals were called navigators hence the name 'navvies'.

Canals were of limited application for the most of Scotland. As in England their construction was based on what had been seen on the Continent especially Holland, where canals had been used for industrial transport from the 16th century. The Forth and Clyde canal was the most used. It was authorised by a Canal Act in 1768, although it had been envisaged for almost a century earlier. It was promoted by Lord Dundas on whose estate was the eastern outlet. Operations were suspended for financial reasons between 1775 and 1784. It was completed in 1790 from Bowling on the Clyde to Grangemouth on the Forth and was commercially successful for half a century. A direct link with Edinburgh was provided by the construction of the Union Canal from 1817–1822, which joined it at Falkirk and was much used by passengers and for transporting coal to Edinburgh until superseded by railways.

The Monkland canal, built between 1770 and 1790, was important in the expansion of the Lanarkshire coal and iron industries. There were a number of less successful ventures on the west coast where some of the incomplete ones were diverted for railway use.

In Kirkcudbrightshire, there were a number of entrepreneurial landlords with some ambitious projects who 'hoped to facilitate and render less expensive the conveyancing of manure, lime, coal and all sorts of commodities.'

Much of their endeavour was motivated by the realisation of how good the lime content of marl was in improving soil fertility. There were large quantities available in Carlingwark Loch near Castle Douglas. By draining and excavating c.1765, the areas of the Loch was reduced from 180 to 100 acres.

Alexander Gordon of Culvennan had two short canals made, one the Carlingwark Lane from the Buchan Bridge north of the river Dee to the Dee near Threave Island which was used to take marl up to the Glenkens in barges. The other canal , the Culvennan Cut, was dug round the 'barony isle' in 1780 from the Dee near Footalice of Greenlaw with locks at Culvennan to the river opposite Boatcroft.

Because of the success of these two canals, a very ambitious scheme was thought up under the Glenkens Contract Act 1802, by Alexander Gordon, the Earl of Selkirk and Sir William Douglas, who had his own bank, the Galloway Bank Co. They made an innovative scheme which never got passed the planning stage because the expenditure of £33,382 could not be justified. The proposed scheme was to make a waterway from Kirkcudbright through ten locks to bypass the Tongland rapids and to proceed twenty six miles to Dalry, thence hopefully onto Dalmellington. Ambition at its greatest! (Macleod, 1986. & Lindsay, 1968.)

RAILWAYS.

The English novelist William Thackeray wrote 'We who lived before the railways and survive out of the ancient world are like Father Noah and his family out of the Ark!'

The opening up of the countryside by railways revolutionised transport for all. It gave an opportunity to provide a new quick service especially for perishable goods such as milk and market garden produce. In large towns too, they revolutionised the way of life for many people. They enabled suburbs to be created which made towns healthier and pleasanter. So long as people lived within walking distance of their work, towns remained very crowded and congested. They also were a main-spring in the development of seaside resorts. One has only to think about the many 'watering holes' along the west coast of Scotland.

'Distances shrank as steam speeded transport by land and sea.' There were railways in use over 100 years before the steam locomotive was invented in the first quarter of the 19th century. They were known as waggon-ways. The waggons were horse drawn on wooden rails. They were used to haul coal from pitheads and heavy goods to the nearest water ways. One of the earliest was on Tranent estate near Prestonpans and was in existence in 1722 to carry coal to the port of Cockenzie. When iron became more available and cheaper it was substituted for wood. This provided a smoother carriage and so gave rise to tramroads which carried passengers as well as freight, all drawn by horses. The Kilmarnock to Troon railway not only became the first in Scotland to carry passengers but also was where the first trial of steam locomotive was held which was supplied by George Stevenson in 1816. When steam engines were first in use, they were preceded by a man waving a red flag. He was dispensed with when a bell was mounted on the engine. This was done away with under the Road Traffic Act, 1930.

Initially, there was a fierce rivalry between the owners of the 'iron horses' and the owners of the canal companies. The latter were often blamed for using their monopoly to extract unjustifiable rates. As the railways were extended, local railway companies in turn with an aggressive attitude bought canal companies and either closed them down or raised the freight rates so that they were no longer a threat to the railways. Thus the canal system with a few exceptions eventually succumbed to the superior advantages of rail transport.

The opening of the land to the railways was not done without many problems. The original attitude of some awkward landowners was to resent the intrusion onto their land, but when it was realised that there was compensation available and that improved transport might enhance land values, their attitudes changed. Once access to land was made easier, railways expanded rapidly. In that era it was said that Britain was 'an island of lunatics, all railway mad.'

'After several years of negotiation, compromise and labour difficulties, there was rejoicing all along the line when the Glasgow to Ayr line was formally opened on the 11th August, 1840. Many other branches opened up thereafter, especially from 1860–1880. The Nithsdale route was opened in 1850, the Dumfries to Castle Douglas in 1859. A great deal of discussion took place be fore the latter line was opened. 'Two petitions were presented against the Bill necessary to construct the line, but the objections were met in a conciliary manner.' The line was surveyed in 1853, the Bill received Royal Assent in 1856 and opened in 1859. This was connected to Kirkcudbright in 1864 by a single line. This and many other branch lines were closed under the 'Beeching cuts' in 1965 under the 1955 Modernisation Plan of the railways, when many loss making services ceased, due to fierce competition from road hauliers and private cars.

Branch lines were important lines for the agricultural economy of Galloway. '200 waggons of sheep per day were frequently dispatched to Liverpool during the autumn sales.' All over the country this new form of transport altered methods of marketing and was reflected in the costs. Compared with droving on the roads there was a smaller loss of weight in the animals and less hassle in finding grazing, water and fodder en route. Instead of so many cattle being sold as stores to drovers they could be fattened in their home areas and easily transported to nearby increasing consuming centres.

Places became important as market towns if they had a railhead in a stock rearing area. There was Lairg and Inverness for sheep from north Scottish farms. Likewise there was Lanark, Lockerbie and Castle Douglas for cattle as well as sheep from the southern farms. This hastened the demise of the droving trade and the establishing of auctioneering firms. Railway transporting of milk and dairy produce is considered elsewhere in this book.

An important line opened in 1877 was the one connecting Girvan and Portpatrick, which was then the port for Ireland. This not only gave a large part of the South West access to Glasgow and its environs but also linked Glasgow to the Irish sea routes. This line was continued to Stranraer in 1863. (Smith, D.L. & Donnachie, Ian.) These links were very significant in the development of dairying in the South West. Many farmers today in Galloway talk about how their forefathers 'came through the tunnel' i.e. the Pinwhirry tunnel which is 394 feet above sea level, as they moved from farming in Ayrshire into Galloway.

The mind boggles at the thought of how these first railways were constructed in the mid-nineteenth century. Thousands of workers were employed, excavating cuttings, driving tunnels and building embankments, with tools no bigger than a pick and shovel and every particle of earth and rock had to be carried in a wheelbarrow or a horsecart. Much of the work was done by immigrant and itinerant Irish labour. Many farmworkers were also employed who were displaced from farms when more machinery became used in agriculture.

As time went on various railway companies amalgamated or were absorbed. This ultimately lead to their being five large companies, the Caledonian, the South Western Railways, the London and Northwestern, the North British Railway and the Midland Railway. After about 1923 the two lines which were of special importance to the producers were the London Midland and Scottish Railway and the London and the North Eastern Railway. The latter line was essential for the milk supplies of Edinburgh, because there were few milk producers in the East of Scotland therefore, Edinburgh was not well supplied with milk. This was ameliorated when most of the milk produced in Dumfriesshire was sent early in the morning to the city, organised by Edinburgh and Dumfries Dairy Company. This entailed a long working day for those involved. Milking started at 3a.m. and the milk was delivered to catch the 6.30a.m. train. A not unusual case was a farmer who drove his milk to the station every morning for the forty years that he was on the farm and missed the 6.30a.m. train only once. His reward was the extra penny he received for delivering the milk to the station, which eventually helped to put his sons into farms!

There are other anecdotes about country lore. In the hill areas in Galloway where stations were a distance apart, the trains stopped wherever there was a passenger waiting. It was said that in certain parts the trains travelled slow enough to allow the guard to set snares to catch the rabbits he collected on the way back. The guards were very obliging in that farmers sometimes stopped the trains to get change in order to pay their men.

STEAMSHIPS

For an unknown time trading was carried out round the sea coast. Sailing vessels of all sorts made use of creeks, rivers, safe beaches and small harbours. This was especially true round the Solway seaboard. There were trading links with Ireland, Isle of Man, North West England, Liverpool, the latter being the most important port for access into a populous area. Similarly there were sailing links up the west coast to Glasgow and beyond. It was much easier to communicate from the South West in these directions than overland because there were no suitable roads through vast areas of undrained land.

To make the delivery of goods more available there were many smaller harbours used because they had to be hauled inland by men and horses. Coal and lime were bulky and heavy. Apart from essentials, smuggling for a time was a popular trade. Hence the reason that many of the nearby manses had large cellars! Sailing boats did carry dairy produce. They were shipped 'to the seaport towns in the North of England, where they found a ready market.' (O.S.A. Colvend. By the same token butter was imported into Kells parish to be used in the smearing of sheep. (O.S.A. Kells.)

Before the establishment of auction markets and railways, breeding sheep were driven to the west coast and shipped down to Dumfries and Galloway. Apart from using the well known ports, Portpatrick, Wigtown Kirkcudbright, Dumfries, Palnackie, etc. there were other small harbours used, Stairhaven, Port Logan, Dromore, Wigtown, Creetown, Palnure, Gatehouse, Kirkandrews, (Borgue), Dub o' Hass, (Dalbeattie), Kippford, Rockcliffe Oldland, Glencaple, Carsethorn and others. Many of the latter have fallen into disuse and others maintained for the pleasure of sailing.

There were two well known small steamships which traded round the west coast. The Countess of Selkirk which was built in 1835 sailed regularly between Liverpool, Wigtown and Kirkcudbright, bringing to Galloway lime and coal from Cumberland and 'bone dust' from Liverpool which greatly stimulated the growth of turnips enabling the expansion of the fatstock trade to Liverpool. There was also the Saint Andrew which for a long time sailed between Palnackie, Whitehaven and other intermediate ports. (Frew, 1909.)

'Steam navigation has given a great stimulus to agriculture... Fatstock can now be conveyed in sixteen to eighteen hours to Liverpool, where there is always a ready market. Before this cheap and easy mode of conveyance was practised, Edinburgh and Glasgow were the only markets of which the farmer could avail himself and these were attended with many obvious disadvantages." (N.S.A. Dumfriesshire. 1834.)

By the same token there were disadvantages seen. "The Irish horses and cattle, which formed the staple articles at various markets at Gatehouse, are almost all transported direct in steam-boats from Belfast and other Irish towns to the leading markets in England...It is owing to this cause alone that the markets of Gatehouse, as also of other towns in Galloway, have declined. (N.S.A. Kirkcudbrightshire. 1844.)

Imports have always caused problems for agriculture, largely responsible for its depressions. These gathered momentum after a paddle steamer, the Great Western, crossed the Atlantic from Bristol to New York in April 1838, taking 14 days. Thereafter there was an increasing trade in the other direction. Tons of Canadian and American wheat and cheese were shipped from the prairies. Refrigeration increased the range of products that could be carried by sea. In 1900 New Zealand shipped 4 million frozen lamb and sheep carcases to Britain plus many tons of butter and cheese. Large quantities of Australian wool could be transported without deterioration and Argentina became one of the world's biggest exporters of beef.

The cost of shipping was dramatically reduced when in 1869 the communications with these far off countries were revolutionised by the opening of the Suez Canal. This meant that for the first time overseas farmers could compete on equal terms with those in Great Britain. 'Steam had annihilated distance.'

The advent of the combustion engine and electricity has worked wonders for communications. Their benefits to mankind are all around to see. Clearly this is not the place to discuss their history. A humourist, however, did see a special advantage in the motor car. The arrival of the automobile had some unseen benefits. It is doubtful if its pioneers would foresee that they were promoting a sexual revolution in the farming community. From the 1920's for the first time a young farmer with his girlfriend could drive away from observation into a wood in a few minutes, or find a mate in the next parish. Admittedly, the statistics in the 1890's and 1900s do not show that the absence of motor cars was a problem!

CHAPTER 3

SPREAD OF DAIRYING.

It is the nature of the soil and the climate that determine in great measure the choice between arable and dairy farming, although centres of population, be they cities, towns or villages encouraged the development of dairying localities. Generally speaking grass growing is best in the wetter west and arable farming in the drier east. It is essential to have a suitable climate which ensures good growth of natural grasses and the modern pasture strains now in widespread use. Consider the well known grassland areas of the damp polders of Holland, the vales of Gloucestershire and Somerset, the flats of Cheshire, the meadows of Leicestershire, the 'dripping climate of Ayrshire, Galloway and not forgetting many parts of Ireland.'

A notable Ayrshire improver, Sir Adam Ferguson and some of his contemporaries, planned their farms specially for dairy farming, when they realised that the soil and climate in that area were better suited for grass than cereals.

Liquid milk is of course the first food of all humans. For a long time it was probably not found outside the houses of those who kept dairy cows and even here skimmed milk was drunk more often than whole milk. Many preferred cheap ale from bére. By and large the milk went into a churn or vat and emerged as salted butter or cheese. Butter and cheese along with bacon and veal were not only needed to guard against hunger but also a necessary part of the family economy, to be bartered for the right to stay on the farmtoun in their hovels. This can be seen in early charters and rentals and also in the regulations in the Acts of Parliament of Scotland from the time of David I in 1147 onwards.

Both butter and cheese were used as part of teins or tithes that had to be paid to the church. Cheese being less perishable than butter became more important for trading. It played a part in the national economy. The export of cheese was forbidden by James VI in 1573; in 1661 Charles II, required 2oz. of bullion to be brought to the mint for each 5cwt. of cheese exported. Under William in 1701 and Anne in 1705, the import of Irish, English or foreign butter was forbidden.(Fenton, A. 1976.)

Bartering is the oldest form of trade known to man. It has existed since Ancient and Sumerian times. It is mentioned in Homer and has been around a long time in America. In the past people had to barter because there was no currency to offer for the goods and services they needed.

As far back as the reign of Malcolm II in 1034, the King and his lords had the right to call out all his men to the defence of Scotland and some if not all for foreign service. They also had the right to 'cain' or 'kane' (food rent) from landowners. They could also 'conveth' a night's entertainment when they periodically went round the countryside visiting their tenants. Those who paid their rents in kind were called 'kainers'.This was the forever of the 'bowing' system in farmhouse cheesemaking, which is discussed elsewhere. Payment in kind was not confined to kain butter and kain cheese, there was also kain coals, kain meal, kain wedder sheep, (male) and kain swine.

Burns said in his poem, 'The Twa' Dugs',

> Oor laird gets his racked rents,
> His coal, his kane and his stents.

Stent in this context, was the proportion of pasture land in a common grazing allocated to each tenant or the number of animals allocated for grazing.

The part payment of wages in kind now known as perquisites, are in a lesser degree still given to farmworkers. Formerly they were usually ten stone of oatmeal and ten stone of flour every six months, a quantity of milk varying according to the size of the family and a free house. In addition they were allowed to grow a few drills of potatoes in the field alongside the farmers'.

Till about 1690, nine out of ten people in Scotland dwelt on the land and depended for their living on the productivity of some small pieces of land.Therefore the type of tenant who rented land was varied. Apart from the bone-fide tenant farmers, there were many rural craftsmen within a community who also rented land and divided their time between farming and their trade, such as smiths, masons, wrights, coopers, weavers, shoemakers and tailors. There were also more mobile groups with limited time for farming including fowlers, ferrymen, chapmen, messengers and sailors, etc.They all needed a holding to grow food for their families. (Mitchison, 1970.)

It was when some of these people had surplus milk or dairy produce to sell to the non-farming community that commercialism of dairying began. As the population grew, the greater was the demand for milk and dairy products.As the centres of demand developed there evolved three main methods of dairying depending on the location of the producers.

These were radically changed after the advent of the railways. There was the liquid milk trade, buttermaking and cheesemaking. How dairying became the major farming enterprise in various parishes in Ayrshire can be gleaned from the Old Statistical Accounts.

As already noted, the liquid milk was supplied by the town dairies within the suburban areas, or by a large number of producer retailers living within a six mile radius of centres of population. This was about the distance that milk could be transported by horse and cart. From the New Statistical Accounts of Ayrshire, (1841) John Dow, the parish minister for Largs, points out that: 'The farmers at a distance from the town make cheese with all the whole milk or skim-milk, while those near the town sell all their milk to the inhabitants, or churn all their milk, make butter and supply the town with butter-milk.'

There was a big demand for butter in industrial Glasgow, mining areas of Lanarkshire and Ayrshire and along the 'watering places' on the Clyde. 'In every case the butter is sold fresh, or but very slightly salted, fully salted or keeping butter never made unless for family use or to put past a glut in the market.' (Speir, T.H.A.S.S. 1886.)

This big demand for butter created considerable supplies of buttermilk and skimmed milk. The skim milk was usually fed to pigs whereas the buttermilk was consumed in large quantities by the the working classes in towns. Large quantities of sour milk were used as a bleaching agent in linen manufacture before the technique of applying diluted sulphuric acid was perfected in c.1750. Speir in 1886 writes that, 'It is probable that no road is so thickly crowded with milk carts in Britain, or even the world, as the one leading from East Kilbride through Rutherglen into Glasgow. Before the opening of the railway to East Kilbride from 220 to 300 carts went through Rutherglen into Glasgow every morning in the summer and in the winter from one third to fully more were usual on the road.'

Understandably, dairying in the more remote areas was devoted to cheesemaking because cheese was less perishable and could be transported further. These areas comprised largely of South Ayrshire, Wigtownshire, Kirkcudbrightshire, most of Dumfriesshire and Lanarkshire, the outlying parts of Renfrewshire, Dumbartonshire and Stirlingshire. There were cheesemaking dairies in Argyllshire and on the larger western isles.

From the old Statistical Accounts, (1791–1799) the satisfactory state of the dairy industry at that time can be gauged from three areas in Ayrshire.

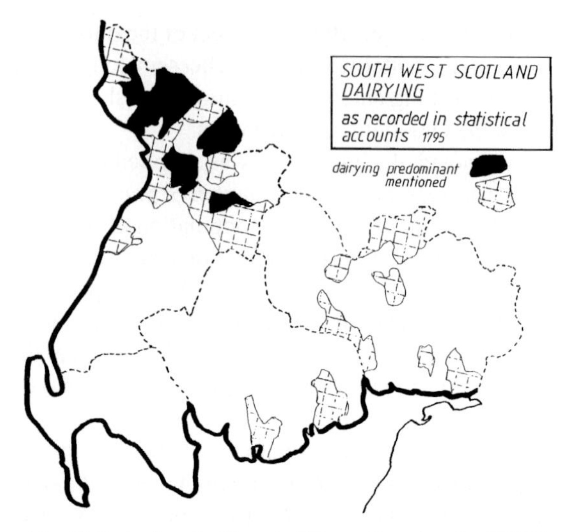

Fig 9 Dairying in South West Scotland, 1795

Fenwick: Butter and cheese have both risen very considerably in value of late and the sales are always good when the trade is good in Glasgow and Paisley.

Beith: It (Dunlop cheese) is a commodity which has been rising in value for a long time past.

Dalry: For some years past the profits of the dairy have been great and it may be said with certainty that the rents of the farms are in general paid from the butter and cheese made.

The spread of dairying into Galloway and Dumfriesshire was gradual till the expansion of the railways from c.1840. The Old Statistical Accounts (1791–1799) and other reports at that time periodically mention the spread of dairying. Mr Fulton was one of the first to change to a different area when he moved from Beith to Carrick in 1790. This was the beginning of quite a rapid spread of dairying into south Ayrshire.

In O.S.A. Mochrum it is reported that: 'Some farmers from a desire to improve their cattle in milking qualities, have more than once introduced the famous "cows of Kyle", but whether it was owing to the difference of pasture, of hard feeding or both, these were found to milk no better than the native breed and being less esteemed in other respects, especially on account of their being horned, very few of them are now to be seen.'

The first dairy in Dumfriesshire was set up at Relief farm in Hoddam parish by a Cheshire man 'who acquired knowledge of dairy work in that country.' (O.S.A. Hoddam.) Robert Burns took Ayrshires with him when he moved from Mossgiel in Ayrshire to Ellisland in Dumfriesshire in 1788. He was reported to have said that 'the black cattle in general are of the Galloway ....is of the opinion that the west country cows give a larger quantity of milk.' Gretna parish is recorded as exporting annually 200 firkins of butter and 50 cwts of Cheshire cheese, as well as £2,500 worth of oats.(O.S.A. Johnstone.)

In 1790 James Ralston from Ayrshire was first to establish a dairy in Wigtownshire at Fineview, Kirkcolm. A number of Ayrshire farmers followed suit. By the 1840s there were thirteen dairies in this parish although the one at Fineview had gone.

From the beginning of the 19th century the spread of dairying was more rapid, especially into south Ayrshire and Wigtownshire. This is very apparent from the parish reports in the New Statistical Accounts, c. 1834 as the following extracts show –

In **Glasserton**: The dairy system is now beginning to be considered more profitable than breeding cattle...and we have in this parish three of four farms stocked with Ayrshire cows.

'In the part of the country above mentioned, (Rhins & Machars in Wigtownshire) the dairy husbandry has been set up by strangers coming from Ayrshire and has since been followed by some of the native inhabitants.

This no doubt is an equivocal symptom of the increased cultivation of the county and by the increased use of manure and of green crop which it occasions, may lead to its further improvement. The superior profits which this system affords, may lead to its continuance and increase, but how far these circumstances may interfere with the favourite employment of rearing and feeding the finest cattle and whether the blood of the native breed (confessedly a most valuable one) may be contaminated by the dairy cows introduced from other counties, are questions that will deserve the most serious consideration.' (Donaldson, Rev. 1816) Machars is from Mahers, a tract of low wet land lying land. Rhins is from Gaelic Rinn, a promonitory or headland. (Mactaggart, 1824.)

There is no doubt there would be quite a controversy when the 'strangers from Ayrshire' moved down into Wigtownshire with their completely different mode of farming. Because cattle were still being driven south in great numbers at good prices the Ayrshires were crossed with a Galloway bull to produce beef crosses. The black is the dominant

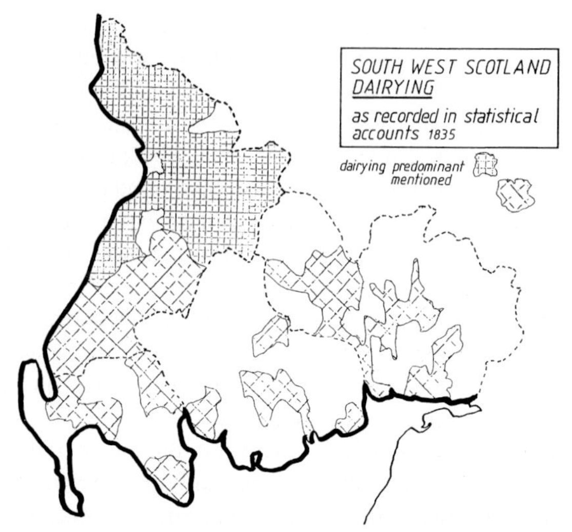

Fig 10 Dairying in South West Scotland, 1835

colour with such a cross, unfortuneately, sometimes a number of the progeny can be red, speckled or spotted which are never popular. Nevertheless, while the enthusiastic pioneers of dairying and their successors for a long time afterwards continued to buy in their replacements from Ayrshire, it is quite possible that Ayrshire bulls would be crossed with Galloway cows as a quick way to get herd replacements.

The movement to enter dairying in Kirkcudbrightshire and Dumfriesshire was not so rapid. In Kirkcudbrightshire the better land was devoted to breeding and to a lesser degree feeding prime beef and also breeding Scotch Halfbred lambs by crossing North Country Cheviot ewes with Border Leicester rams. Fat cattle and sheep were beginning to be shipped to Liverpool.This expanded after the enclosing of land and growing of turnips became more widespread.

Dairying is mentioned only in a few parishes in the New Statistical Accounts c1824.

Balmaghie: Galloway cattle are reared over the whole parish and for them the farmers have a decided preference over all other breeds. There are, however, on some of the farms, a number of Ayrshire cows.

Buittle: The turnip husbandry is greatly extended beyond what it was a few years ago. Feeding of sheep for the last five or six years has, with the exception of 1834, been profitable to the farmer and the facility with, which they are conveyed to the Liverpool market, by means of steam vessels, has contributed to produce this result. The breeding and rearing of cattle is an object of great importance to the farmers, as they generally calculate on realising a considerable part of their profits from this source. On three farms in this parish, the Ayrshire dairy system has been partially adopted with success.

Kirkbean: There are two dairy farms in this parish which keep about 40 dairy cows each. No more of their calves are kept than are required for keeping up the stock. Upon the whole, great attention of late has been paid to the improvement to all kinds of cattle, which are generally in a state highly creditable to their owners.

Tongland: The large cattle are all of the Galloway breed, with the exception of those on three of four farms, where the Ayrshire kind have been introduced, with a view to the dairy system.

The report for Kirkmabreck is puzzling. In the earlier report of 1840, 'pretty extensive dairies, conducted on the Ayrshire plan and that Ayrshire cows are increasing very much,' but in a footnote added in 1844 states, 'Ayrshire are already beginning to decrease.' Possibly some farmers found out they did not have sufficient management skills or good enough land to make a success of this new venture and gave up. A phenomenon not unusual today.

The change from traditional farm systems to dairying in Dumfriesshire was spasmodic. The earliest changes were made at Kirkbank in Johnstone parish, when John Aitken moved from Dalry in Ayrshire and at Hollybush in Cummertrees parish, when William Stewart moved from Fenwick in 1832.(Gillespie, Rev. T.A.S.S. 1868.) At that time the farming economy was again centred round cattle rearing, sheep fattening and a considerable acreage of grain grown for export into England. As elsewhere, there was early dairying near local centres of demand, such as at Moffat when there was an increase in the summer population at the Spa and it was also necessary to supply the mining population of Leadhills and Wanlockhead.

DEPRESSION

There were 22 years of French Wars from 1793–1815. This stimulated new methods and a new spirit into farming, which was encouraged by high prices. In 1780 the price of milk was 2d. per Scotch pint, (ld. per English pint).

By 1808, it was 8d. per pint. Wheat prices rose to £36 per ton, a price which was not exceeded in money terms until 1971 and has never been succeeded in real terms where £36 in 1815 would be about £1,000 in today's money. (Seddon, 1989.) Coincidently, in 1791 Glasgow was a thriving city with a population of 62,000, double what it was in 1755 and by 1821 had increased to 147,000. This, as has been indicated stimulated demands for dairy produce in North Ayrshire and surrounding counties. The extraordinary high price for grain was due to some poor harvests; of the twenty two war harvests in Britain seven were deficient, seven were more deficient and only two were really abundant. (Ernle, Lord. 1961.)

In this era rents rose to their highest level, extravagance was rife, landlords built mansion houses and cottages 'as if prosperity would last indefinitely.' This was the beginning of the 'tied' cottage and bothy system. Money made by farming was reinvested and loans were advanced on stock and crops. Land was cleared, drained, limed and roads constructed. Sadly the years of prosperity came to a quick halt. When there was news of victory at Waterloo, grain prices fell markedly, from 123s. 10d. to 65s.per quarter. The agricultural industry suddenly passed from prosperity to depression.

Britain emerged from the war victorious but exhausted not for the last time. The price of victory was paid by National Debt, excessive taxation, enormous Poor rates, fictitious credit, mass unemployment with discontented labour. A sixth of the male adults had been engaged in the war. Furthermore, industries which were essential during the war became less so, resulting in thousands of spinners, combers, hand-loom weavers with no jobs. This was aggravated by the introduction of machinery into manufacturing processes. There was unrest among both agricultural and industrial workers due to unemployment and desperate poverty from which some died. This lead to riots where crowds roamed the streets and countryside destroying workhouses, threatening employers and landlords, burning ricks and smashing machinery.

Farming was forced to bear a heavy burden of taxation. Tithes were increased by more than a quarter, the county rates for the poor rose seven times, there was a new property tax, increased highway rates, tax on agricultural horses and an iniquitous tax on leather. An income tax was imposed by Prime Minister, William Pitt. When it was abolished in 1816 Parliament voted for the destruction of all records of it.

At first farms met this out of built up capital which was quickly eroded by falling prices of grain and livestock. Farm leases were too long with high rents which meant that confidence between landlords and tenants was destroyed resulting in farms being thrown up. Those who wanted new farms to own rather than rent went overseas.

At this time a shrewd and industrious farmer in the vicinity of Glasgow, was approached by one of his sons seeking his consent to allow him to emigrate to one of the Colonies. The worthy farmer replied briefly and to the point: 'Laddie, if anyone willing to work hard and behave himsel' canna get on and dae weel within seven miles o' Glesca, he'll no' get on onywhere."

Landlords went bankrupt, some due to bank crashes and currency disorders. Expensive habits could no longer be financed nor could agricultural improvements continue. Tenants having lost most of their capital were suspicious of long leases, farmed from year to year on the poverty line.Farmworkers, when deprived of the profits of the animals and poultry they were allowed to keep to supplement their wages, moved into towns and cried for food.

This depression in agriculture lasted twenty years.

Dairy farmers were not so severely effected by the national depression. The farms were generally family farms where hard work, thrift and indulging in some cottage industries, went a long way to counteract the severe adversity. The skill and attention of the womenfolk largely determined the profitabilty of the dairy enterprise. Every process connected with milk, the butter or the cheese, is conducted by women. (Sturrock, 1866.) It was fortunate that there was a continuing upward demand for milk and its products. This encouraged the spread of dairying into the areas where the prices of cattle and grain had dropped to uneconomical levels.

THE GOLDEN AGE

The changing fortunes in agriculture coincided with the beginning of the eventful reign of Queen Victoria in 1837. The impact of the restructuring roads, building bridges and the advent of the steam-locomotive had far reaching effects on commerce, industry in general and agriculture in particular. The greater facility to transport lime, seeds, fertiliser, feeding stuffs, implements, grain, stock, milk and dairy produce had a profound impact on the prosperity of agriculture. This was backed up by the continuing progress of improvements, the benefits of scientific knowledge, which was being spread by better communications, agricultural societies and literature. The production from livestock was increasing by better breeding, feeding and management.

This period till about 1874 has been termed the Golden Age of

Agriculture.

Generally speaking, the size of the British harvest continued to be the chief factor which determined the level of British farm prices. As long as the nation was largely dependent on its homegrown food supplies, the law of supply and demand ensured a rise in price especially in the years of bad harvests. Because of the effects of the depression, the post-Napoleonic Wars, the Government's fiscal policy under the Corn Laws from 1815 onwards protected home grown grain in that no duty free imported grain was allowed into this country so long as the current prices of wheat, barley and oats did not fall below a certain level, e.g. 80s. per quarter for wheat, 40s. per quarter for barley and 27s. per quarter for oats if coming from foreign countries, or, 67s., 33s. and 22s, respectively if coming from the colonies. (Ernle, 1961.) As may be imagined, the policy of the 'dear loaf' as it was called, was greatly resented by the increasing population.

In spite of much opposition from his colleagues who were mainly powerful landlords and who wanted high rents to maintain their properties, Sir Willaim Peel, himself a landowner, repealed the Corn Laws in 1846 to take effect from 1849. This brought down his Government. However, Peel set an example in 1849 by offering his tenants to pay a fifth of their current rents to assist with improvements which he hoped would reduce costs and increase output.

In repealing the Corn Laws the Government also repealed the duties on importing of live animals, meat, hams and substantially reduced those on bacon, dairy produce and eggs. The last remaining food taxes were reduced in 1853 and eliminated in 1860. However, to compensate the government for the resultant loss of revenue, William Peel re-imposed Income Tax at 7d. in the £. This was intended to be a temporary measure!

The Free Traders, as they were called, who succeeded in getting the Corn Laws repealed, insisted that cheaper food was required to reduce the cost of living and thus lower wages which would enable the manufactured goods to be sold abroad. A manufacturing nation prays that 'God speeds the plough in every soil but his own.' The expected dramatic fall in prices did not happen immediately after the repeal of the Corn Laws for a number of reasons. There were poor harvests in the period immediately following.There was extensive European unrest with the Crimean War (1853–56) and the Franco-Prussian War (1870–71), which effectively prevented large scale agricultural imports into Britain. The American War (1861–65) delayed the opening up of the virgin prairies. The population increased during this period by another 6m., a substantial proportion of whom were enjoying rising incomes, thus creating demands for meat, vegetables, milk and dairy products.

The repeal of the Corn Laws heralded the emancipation of the urban dweller. It really was the watershed between country and town. From then on, except in times of war or monetory difficulties, all governments have been determined to keep down the price of food irrespective of the prosperity of the farmers.

It was during this time of prosperity, that farm buildings were built specifically for dairying. In Ayrshire many were built to a type plan which was quite distinctive and is still apparent on many farms today. Generally, they were built in the form of an open square with the dwelling house facing the open side. Immediately adjoining the house and before the days of dairy by-laws, intercommunicating with the house was the dairy, where the cheese was formerly made and later the milk was cooled and put into churns for transport. At right angles to the dairy and again communicating with it was the byre. It was therefore possible to get up in the morning, milk the cows, start the cheese making process and go back into the house for breakfast without going out of doors. On the third side would be the stable. On the larger farms in Galloway, there was often a two storey barn on this side. On the upper floor was installed a threshing mill formerly driven by a water wheel. The grain passed from it into a connecting grain loft while the straw dropped down below into a shed which in turn was connected to a shed to contain the chaff. Before the days of balers all the straw had to be handled loose and the chaff carried in hessian sheets. It was important that these sheds were near the byre doors or there was havoc on a wild winter's morning.

It is a great credit to those who built these steadings that the standard of workmanship can still be admired today. All done by their hands and the sweat of their brows. Some would say today that the buildings were too well built, because it cost so much to alter or demolish them. It is noteworthy that it was almost a hundred years later that large modifications were made to farmsteadings or new buildings erected and that was assisted through Government Grants. Until recent times it was a case of 'make do and mend.'

Thanks to the 'improvement movement' until about the middle of the nineteenth century, the United Kingdom was largely self-sufficient in food and that was with a population which had risen to 20 million, some 75% higher than forty years earlier. (Williams, 1960.) The years 1850–1873 were years of unparalleled progress for the British economy, industrial and agricultural alike. During these years "Great Britain was the forge of the world, the world's carrier, the world's shipbuilder, the world's banker, the world's workshop, the world clearing house, the world's entrepot." (Knowles, L.A.C. 1944.) By 1870 Britain with about one-fifth of the world's population, was producing one third of the world's manufactures and about two-fifths of those which entered into the world's trade.

Throughout these years farming flourished and the railway network throughout the countryside expanded. Cattle droving ceased and urban dairies declined. This gave the necessary motivation for a further expansion of dairying into areas which were formerly predominantly grain growing and cattle rearing, especially in the South West of Scotland. The demand for dairy produce continued to increase in keeping with the expanding population.

At this point in its history a whole new concept was overtaking the agricultural industry. Farming was changing from being a substantially subsistence and extractive process, to one involving the purchase of materials to increase both the quantity and quality of products in response to the rapidly increasing demands of an expanding urban population. Around 1851, the urban population began to exceed the rural, since when it has been rising and their standards and demands have always dominated market trends. An evolution was unfolding.

ANOTHER DEPRESSION

It is often said that all good things come to an end. In farming it can happen at any time. Usually it is caused by two important determinants of profitability, the weather and the price received for products relative to the cost of inputs.

In the 1860's and 1870's the production from the virgin lands of Canada, America and Australasia gathered momentum. The aggregate annual value of imports including live animals for the five years 1866–70 was £77m. The figure rose during the next five years to £108m. and by 1877 to £140m.(Ernle, 1961.) There were also increasing amount of agricultural imports from Russia, Danubian countries, Denmark and surprisingly India, 'all carried to Britain at ever lowering freight rates by the growing number of steamships' (Orwin, 1964.) This had a dramatic effect in reducing the prices of dairy produce, grain, cattle, sheep and wool. It was not until the First World War that the profitability of farming was to become comparable to that of the 1870's and then only for a few years.

The problem of depressed prices was further exacerbated by unbelievably severe weather conditions from 1876–79. Many crops were completely destroyed. During these wet seasons liver rot in sheep wrought havoc with sheep flocks, reducing sheep numbers from 18.4m. to 14.9m. There were also outbreaks of pleuropneumonia and foot and mouth diseases which ravaged the cattle population. To crown all in 1878 the City of Glasgow Bank failed along with others due to deflated currency and heavy national debt, ruining many people. This caused a serious setback to the farming community. Cheese and dairy produce became almost unsaleable. The collapse of the bank produced such a profound feeling of distrust that all trading practically ceased which restricted future developments. At that time one farmer was wont to say that 'high farming should teach agriculturists to live in times of sunshine and prosperity within their means and guard against any lavish expenditure.'

Between 1876 and 1893 prices received for meat and dairy produce fell between 20 and 30 per cent. Grain prices fell 50 per cent and the price of wool halved. For example the average price of wheat fell from 58s. 8d. a quarter in the seventies to 26s. 2d. in the nineties, the lowest recorded figure for 150 years. Many farmers took advantage of the cheaper grain prices and turned to cattle production. 'Up corn down horn, down corn up horn.' However, this natural advantage was lost with the development of refrigeration, which also later had a direct effect on butter and cheese production. Rents fell by 20%, repairs and rebuilding were neglected.

During this period some quarter of a million male workers (i.e. 25 per cent of the total) left agricultural employment. Many did it because farm work was a 'rough, dirty, badly paid job with long hours and few holidays.' (Royal Commission on Labour 1893.) Women too, made efforts to escape from the drudgery of field and labour. 'A young woman will hand over her "kist" (chest or box of clothes) to the porter, get her ticket for Glasgow, pull on her gloves, laugh and talk with her parents and comrades, jump into the train, pay her adieu, wave her handkerchief, sit down oblivious to bandbox and unencumbered with bundles and thank her stars that she is at last leaving the unwomanly job for domestic service and town society.' There have long been discussions on this subject as to whether the pull factors were more important than push factors.

It should be noted for future reference, that this depression was not confined to Britain and while France protected its farmers, Britain adhered rigidly to free trade policy which was considered to confer the greatest benefit on the community as a whole. Denmark was also hard hit, but their resourceful farmers took advantage of the low world of cereals and other feeding stuffs, bought them and converted them into 'the breakfast table commodities', pig meat, eggs and butter for export. While in Denmark the spirit of enterprise, mutual help and cooperation was fostered and developed. In Britain, in spite of the effects of the depression, individual farming was still the order of the day. Our farmers were either too conservative or too independent to copy the example of the Danes.

Fortunately, as previously, the dairy farmers of South West Scotland were not so badly affected by this depression as arable and other stock farmers. More and more of their land was laid down to oats, roots and temporary grass, which provided cheap food for their animals. Where land was too wet or too heavy for ploughing it was put into grass and for those too far from the towns to sell liquid milk, cheese and butter making supplemented by pigs and veal production, were the mainstay of these farms.

Such was the dramatic effect that the depression was having on the country, the Government appointed a number of Royal Commissions – an excuse for inaction. First, the Richmond Commission 1879–82 on Agricultural Distress and then a second one in 1894–8, were appointed to consider agriculture while there was also a Royal Commission on Depression in Trade and Industry appointed in 1886. The second Commission on Agriculture 'found that the depression had eked away all available resources and that landlords and farmers had no further reserves to meet the continued downturn. In the period beween the two commissions the value of farm produce of the nation had about halved, while costs had continued to rise.' John Speir, Newton, Glasgow was appointed an Assistant Commissioner to report on agriculture in the counties of Ayrshire, Dumfriesshire, Kirkcudbrightshire and Wigtownshire. (1894.) This is quite an extensive report giving an insight on the conditions at the time and is referred to here.

He observed that the depression had led to another migration of dairy farmers further into neighbouring counties, particularly into Galloway.

His comments on farming systems for different areas were:–

Ayrshire: 'Apart from a few farms round Ayr, Girvan and West Kilbride, which grow garden crops of potatoes, carrots and other vegetables, every farm in the county may be said to be either a dairy or sheep farm. A very high percentage are breeding stock of the Ayrshire breed.'

Dumfriesshire: 'Dumfries is entered from the north by the valleys of the Nith and the Annan. Dairying is gradually supplanting other systems of farming.'

Kirkcudbrightshire: 'Dairying is spreading very rapidly over Kirkcudbright, which may be said to be the home of the Galloway breed of polled cattle. At present dairying, feeding cattle, hill sheep farming are the principle systems of farming followed.'

Wigtownshire: Very few farmers do any breeding of Ayrshires, the majority confining themselves to the production of milk and cheese. Their dairy replacements are bought from farmers in Ayrshire. The Rhins, the west of the county is almost exclusively devoted to dairying, while the Machars the eastern part contains about equal proportions of dairymen, breeders and feeders of cattle and sheep.'

During the earlier prosperous era leases of farms extended to 15–19 years at which time high rents were paid. As prices dropped these rents were too high for many farmers to maintain their financial position. To overcome this difficulty many landlords gave 10–15% abatement in rent. This action was severely criticised because it was only a temporary measure rather than having a rent review at specified breaks in the lease. Nevertheless, there were some who could not withstand the harder times and either fell behind with their rents or went bankrupt.

Baillie McCreath, a Girvan merchant, said, 'The farmers would go behind each others' backs in bidding for farms. They had no cohesion at all. They make as many laws as they liked, but unless they could restrict the freedom of the subject they would never cure the disease, as land hunger was so intense in Ayrshire. They all knew of a farm just now in which the tenant was giving up because he could not pay the rent, though he had been getting a 15% reduction. No sooner was the farm advertised as being let than there were a lot of competitors offering the old rent for it without the 15% reduction.'

In Ayrshire, there was a surfeit of young farmers desiring farms. This land hunger motivated many to move south especially from north Ayrshire where dairying was long established and benefited from the better large milk market in Glasgow and its environs. The rents were high and rising which encouraged farmers to move where there were cheaper rents and larger farms.

There were other reasons for changes in farm tenancies. The average tenant was in a very subversive position until the passing of the first Agricultural Holdings (Scotland) Act 1883, which gave a tenant statutory right to compensation for his improvements, when at Common Law he had none.

In Common Law, the landlord was the privileged creditor. If a tenant went bankrupt, the landlord had the first claim on the rent owing.

He had also the power to enter the property and to carry off any goods and chattels up to the value of what he was owed. Before the 1883 Act this could be up to six years rent. Under Scots law, the right of hypothec was a survival of the days when the landlord provided stock and seed corn for the tenant then commandeered both, if the tenant became in arrears with his rent. The law of hypothec as applied to agricultural holdings was not finally abolished until 1894.

In the same year the tables turned against the landlords with the introduction of Harcourt Death Duties, which impoverished many of them, thus reducing the availability of much needed fixed capital to impoverished tenants.

In all landlord tenant relationships, the two subjects which have caused many animated discussions are the security of tenure and compensation for tenants' improvements. These have resulted in various amendments to the legislation over the years. The 1883 Agricultural Holdings (Scotland) Act was an attempt to come to terms with these problems. It was originally described as 'a delusion and a snare for the unwary tenants.'

In drawing up longer leases with fixed rents, tenants were given more security of tenure which enabled them to risk their own capital but there were pitfalls. The long leases commonly were for 19 years, which were 'entirely a speculation.' Prior to 1883 there were seldom breaks in the leases. It used to be said that to farm successfully three rents were required – one for the laird, one for expenses and one for the tenant. In times of rising prices with fixed rents they could not be raised to meet the new conditions. On the other hand when prices fell they did not get as much for their improvements as they expected. After 1883 breaks in leases for renegotiations were introduced.

On Eglinton Estate in Ayrshire the rents were still paid half in money and half in grain. The amount paid was based on the friars' prices for the past three years. In some instances cheese prices were used to regulate the rent.

Compared with today's standards there was still some punitive legislation and impossible conditions. In south Ayrshire many leases bound tenants not to claim compensation for improvements under the 1883 Act. and to make sure they did not, they had to agree not to claim unless they applied 70 tons per acre of farmyard manure to green crop, an amount in excess of what the animals on the farm could produce.

In other places, 'The tenant shall not keep any more dogs than are required for farm purposes.' 'For each time any cattle or other stock are found in any plantation he shall pay £1 per head.' 'It is hereby specially provided that should the lessee during the currency of this lease expend on improvements or repairs a further sum than that agreed upon...it shall form a counter claim and deduction from any compensation claimed. 'If the stock carrying capacity of the farm was increased the rent was increased.

This brings to mind the old farming couplet:

Let alone you sit,
Improve and you flit.

A tenant's security of tenure could be at risk if he was interested in politics. For example, the notable and successful farmer George Hope, who farmed Fenton Barns all his life, as did his father and grandfather, in 1873 did not have his lease renewed because eight years earlier he had stood as a Liberal candidate against Lord Elcho who was a friend of his landlord. (Watson & Hobbs. 1937.)

Perhaps it is not relevant here, but it is interesting to note in Speir's report a plea for compensation for the removal of stones should be included in the amendments of the 1883 Holdings Act.

'Over Wigtownshire and Kirkcudbright and more or less over Dumfriesshire and Ayrshire, enormous sums have been expended in clearing the land of large boulder stones. No one who has not seen what has been done can have any idea of the labour which has been expended on suchwork. Not only have sufficient stones been dug out of the land to form walls round the fields but in some cases they are piled in thousands of tons in out of the way places. In one case I found walls from three to five yards wide and five feet high, with new pieces from three to four wide being built alongside those that already exist, for no other purpose than it was the cheapest way of disposing of them. In this case one wall was wide enough to allow a couple of buses to go along the top of it. This was an extreme case, but thousands of a more modified character abound all over the southern counties. It was represented to me that drains in time require renewal and buildings need repairs, yet both of these are called permanent improvements and are acknowledged in the present Act, while the removal of stones weighing from a quarter of a hundredweight to two or three tons is not acknowledged at all, although they are a more permanent improvement than any of those mentioned in the Act. The farmers of the south therefore, ask urgently that such work be acknowledged.

Wigtownshire was greatly affected by the depression as illustrated by the number of farms which changed occupancy. Apart from the issues mentioned, the greater distance from markets was a key factor. 'Some farmers pay a sum equal to one third of their rent for the carriage of their milk alone.' In the Rhins, 83 farms out of 457 changed hands, 25 of which went bankrupt. In the Machars there were 245 changes in 607 farms. In the parishes of Kirkcowan and Penningham, 'every third tenant left his farm without means.' Speir makes the comment, 'The farmers in the Rhins of Wigtownshire are a very highly intelligent class and fairly well supplied with means, yet very few of them are bringing their sons up as farmers and were it not for Ayrshire and other dairymen farms would be hard to let in this district. Farmers seem to think that agriculture is now giving such a small return for the money and energy requisite to carry it on that they considerate it more judicious to advise their sons to try some other line of business.' In effect in the 1890's 30% of the farmers or their descendants in Wigtownshire were from Ayrshire and any farm which became vacant in the counties of Wigtown, Kirkcudbright, or Dumfries were generally taken by dairymen, most of whom came from Ayrshire, 'a veritable congested district, which rears twice as many farmers as there are farms for.' A few came from the counties of Lanark and Renfrew.

At this time in parts of England rents were being adjusted to the times and became sufficiently low to attract quite a number of Scottish farmers to Essex, Hertfordshire and to a lesser degree to Kent and Surrey. 'Scotchmen migrated in numbers from a country where rents were still competitive and brought their knowledge of milk production and their more economical methods.' (Ernle, 1961.) They transported the whole of their live and dead stock to the South by hiring a special train for the purpose. This meant that they were immediately in production by having in place a fully equipped herd of Ayrshire cows. The proximity to London was a great advantage with the vast potential of its liquid milk market and at the same time getting away from the drudgery of making cheese and butter.

It is also interesting to note in Speir's Report that the landlords and factors were of the opinion that the most profitable farm from their point of view was beween 100–300 acres. They nearly all agreed that a better class of tenant farmer was forthcoming, who usually had sufficient capital and they were also business men, 'and who on that account, were more pleasant to do business with, than where either of these qualities were absent. The small farm was considered little better than British slavery.'

Alexander Macdonald, Sub-Editor, North British Agriculturist, Edinburgh wrote an article on "The Agriculture of the County of Renfrew." (T.H.A.S.S. 1887.)

Dairying seems to have been the chief object of the farmers' attention from time immemorial. The cows were speckled or spotted in colour, weighing from 4–5 cwt and their produce was mainly disposed of in Glasgow, Paisley and Greenock in butter and butter milk. There were few cheese dairies. These were devoted to almost solely to the manufacture of Dunlop cheese.

The Alderney breed of cows was introduced in 1780 and crossed with the Dutch and native cattle. They yielded richer cream but a smaller amount of milk than the native cattle and the latter was thus preferred. In some parts of the county the practice of letting the cows for the whole season was adopted, the rate about 1812 being from £13 to £14 per cow. Sixteen or seventeen years previously, however,letting rate was as low as from £6 to £7 each cow. The average of milk was estimated at 7 Scotch pints, about 12 imperial quarts per day and that of butter 4¹/₄ lbs. per week, for six months.

The old system of management differed considerably from that of the present time. The cows were fed in the house during the winter and generally allowed out a few hours "airing" every forenoon, for a drink of water. Farmers seemed careless as to accumulating as much manure on the farm as possible, but no sooner had they become alive to its value than the ancient practice began to die out. The cows rations in the winter consisted chiefly of oat straw with a small allowance of potatoes, boiled with chaff or chopped straw. Hay was usually substituted for straw as the calving approached and the supply of potatoes increased, while a little grain, meal seeds and dust were generally added.

Cows ranged in price from £15 to £21, heifers from £3 to £10 and calves from £1 to £1.5s.; while £10 to £15 was common for a bull. The calves were usually sold to butchers at about £10 per head. But, it is said, that it would be to the advantage of the farmers had they reared more cows than they did. Few cattle were fattened for the butcher.

On the farm of South Halls in the parish of Lochwinnoch the dairy herd included some twenty animals and it is mainly maintained by home breeding. In his report to the Royal Commission in 1880, the tenant John Harvey stated that he obtained 500 hundred gallons of milk from each cow per annum, which was equivalent to £14 per head. His average outlay for food not grown on the farm approached £5 per cow, the material used as a rule was bean and Indian meal.

For the work of twenty cows, he employs two female servants whose united wages, besides board, was £35. When he entered the farm some twenty two years ago, the same class of servant cost only £4 10s each, which represented an advance, notwithstanding the downward tendency of recent years of 50% since 1863. The dairy produce is sent to Glasgow as sweet milk and in the summer of 1880 he received 7d per gallon for it, which was the highest price going. Out of that return he paid ld for railway carriage, with the result that 250 gallons during the summer brought him a clear return of £6.6s. and a like quantity in the winter realised £8 6s 8d. which made the total return per cow up to £14 12s. 8d. The gross sum reccived for milk, amounts to about £290, while he usually disposes of eight cows each year for about £144 and this sum together with about £150 for the timothy hay, represents the entire revenue for the farm. He ploughs as little land as possible, bacause the cost of labour and manure would, in addition to the rent, leave him no profit.

CHAPTER 4

DEVELOPMENT OF THE MILK TRADE

The Scottish dairy farmers survived the depression at the end of the nineteenth century 'by industry, thrift, an excellent rotation system, attention to the breeding and management of livestock, sound labour organisation, skill and pride in farm craft and the combination of agricultural science so far as was then known with practice.' They were assisted by the fact that due to the perishability of their produce there was, as yet little risk of overseas competition and furthermore, the reduction of bread prices, due to cheaper grain being available, allowed more income to be released for urban wage earners to purchase milk, butter and cheese.

In the early days of milk selling, producers were in direct contact with their customers. Apart from the producer-retailers, this contact became less and less tenuous as the years went past, to the extent that today some customers have very little knowledge or understanding as to the source of the milk in the container.

Many urban dairymen when they gave up keeping cows in the town, retained their retailing rounds and bought milk from the countryside which was transported by rail. At the same time those who formerly delivered their milk by horse and cart and new entrants whose farms were contiguous to the railway system also dispatched their milk by train.

Producers had to look for buyers, with no degree of certainty, so that the sale and purchase of milk became very haphazard, especially so since agreements were frequently verbal between individuals and of short duration. This allowed many unscrupulous traders to get into the act, many of whom went bankrupt leaving unsuspecting farmers in the lurch.

During the 1880's, in some neighbourhoods there was a parade of bandsmen with a big drum to let people know that there was a new dairy being set up. Leaflets were distributed stating that the milk was straight from the proprietors own farm and that two newly laid eggs would be given with each pint of milk purchased. A fine trade was done initially and the business was launched, but it was very doubtful whether the entrepreneur's farm ever existed or if he had ever seen one! (Raison. 1933.)

Attempts were made to have contracts, some for a year's duration, but more commonly on a six monthly basis, usually from October – March and from April – September. Unfortunately they were not always foolproof. There were the problems of fluctuating demand and the surplus milk. The demand was always less in very cold weather with hard frost and snow which then seemed to occur more frequently.

The farmer would be telegraphed not to send his milk for a day or two. He then would have to make it into butter or cheese or feed it to livestock. To make sure the farmer did not send the unwanted milk the buyer would keep back the empty cans from the previous day's delivery thus putting the farmer in a spot not knowing whether his cans had gone astray. Not an uncommon happening. Because communications were minimal, he would perhaps borrow cans and send on the milk thinking it was needed, only to discover his cans were sitting empty in the sellers yard.

The aim was to sell an even supply of milk to the buyers all the year round which was hard to maintain in the winter period when cows' yields were low. The feeding regime was not so efficient then. In an attempt to do this, milk was bought from nearby cheesemakers. This was compensated by buyers giving a higher summer price to those who could keep up their supply in the wintertime. This in turn helped the cheesemakers who had difficulty in disposing of the small quantities of milk in the winter which were often too small to justify making into cheese on a daily basis. He was forced to keep several days milk to do this which resulted in a poor quality cheese being made.

There were some other unsatisfactory aspects of the milk trade. If trains were late, a not unusual occurrence even in this day and age, it would not be delivered in the afternoon by which time it would be "off" and unwanted, resulting in a considerable loss in sales. Some buyers insisted that farmers paid a premium of a ½d. per gallon to ensure against the loss of milk souring in transit. Because of irregular deliveries often caused by lateness, milk sent by rail did not command the same price as that supplied direct by producer-retailers. Although the relative value of milk for cheese was as low as 5 – 6d. per gallon, many considered it a better proposition when cartage to the station and railway costs were taken into consideration along with the risk of bad payers in 'the railway milk trade' and losses due to spoiling and spillage.

On the other hand the producer-retailer could command 10d .– 1s. per gallon if he supplied milk all the year round and make deliveries twice or even thrice per day because of the preference for warm milk as it was more likely to be fresher. Before the First World War most of the milk was still being delivered by the farmer to the housewife although the railways were delivering increasing quantities of milk into towns. (Speir. 1886.)

August 15, 1903.
POOR BUT HONEST MILK – Sir, May I congratulate you on the fact that you have at length recognised that nature ignores the milk standard and that milk may be 'poor but honest.' It has been proved that milk, even the mixed milk of large, well fed herds, varies in the most unaccountable way. As much variation as two percent butterfat in every few weeks has been noted...Most customers in town want fresh warm milk at from 7–9 am and from 2–4 p.m. Can anybody tell us how to milk at regular intervals and do this? etc. etc. "M". (Scottish Farmer, 1993.)

Not only did producers gradually lose their direct access to the consumer, but increasingly fewer were equipped to process the seasonal surpluses into products for direct sale. The emergence of the specialist retailer subsequently led to the emergence of a wholesale market, with large businesses exercising a powerful influence and significant control over the milk market in the larger towns and cities. 'They became the controller of the bottleneck of the distribution of a perishable commodity.' They could fix prices both to the farmer and the retailer and many were also engaged in retailing to the consumer to a considerable extent.

It was natural that producers became dissatisfied with this situation and sought ways to counteract this prevailing power by some form of collective action. Up to this point in time the need for rationalisation was not so important when there was little difference between the price received for liquid milk and that for cheese. There was an urgent need for action, when the disparity between the two became wider as farm production increased and surpluses became an ongoing problem. This has since plagued the industry and it motivated the start of cooperative milk marketing.

From about 1890 onwards many wholesalers became processors of milk, with plants for cooling, pasteurising and in some cases bottling milk thus providing consumers with a better quality less perishable product governed by regulations for food and dairies. The Sale of Food and Drugs Act, 1875 gave local authorities powers to prosecute sellers of food which was judged unfit for human consumption or was sold under a description that disguised its real nature. This included water being added to milk. The Sale of Milk Regulations, 1901, set minimum presumptive standards of 3% butterfat and 8.5% solids-not-fat.

'Cooperative capital, cooperative land, cooperative purchase of requisites – still on step to complete our ideal cooperation, cooperative disposal of produce.' (Penbury Agricultural Society, T.H.A.S.S. 1899.)

The first tentative attempts at cooperative milk marketing

established in the 19th century were, ‘At Low Row, Aspatria, Cumberland, Mr Carrick has had a creamery established for some years which draws a considerable quantity of milk from the adjoining part of Dumfries-shire. The first creamery in Wigtownshire was started in 1882 at Dunragit and another in 1882 was set up by Mr Sommervell, Sorn, Mauchline, Ayrshire, on a small scale for the benefit of his tenants.’ (Speir, T.H.A.S.S. 1886.)

Another early attempt at cooperative marketing was made by Lord Rowallan in 1903 when he built a small creamery near Kilmarnock for the collection and the dispatch of milk to Glasgow. In 1906 this was handed over to the local farmers and was known as the Rowallan Cooperative Dairy Association. In times of low demand for milk the surplus was manufactured into cheese and the whey was fed to pigs. Under the auspices of the Scottish Agricultural Organisation Society, which was established in 1905, there were six such dairy cooperatives set up in north Ayrshire before the outbreak of the First World War. After the war the cooperative system spread throughout the South West of Scotland. This is considered in more detail later.

Cooperatives functioned mainly as collecting centres for the dispatch of milk to centres of demand, chiefly Glasgow. They always had difficulties in competing with the producers nearer towns who could supply milk all the year round and thought that they had no need for cooperatives. Nevertheless there was the obvious advantages of bringing together small farmers’ businesses to compete with the ‘Big Battalions’.

Small farms lacked the necessary capital needed to update their equipment and buildings required by new statutory regulations for on-farm processing of milk. This was also a time of growing labour difficulties. With the advent of trains and bicycles the young people who were only earning subsistence wages were being attracted into the towns for more rewarding work with a half day on Saturday and a free Sunday. Many young people emigrated to Canada, Australia and New Zealand. Between 1875 and 1900 the United Kingdom lost a third of its agricultural labour force. A large number of those who emigrated at this time came back in the armed forces. In 1905 nearly 2500 holdings disappeared from the census, most of them being under 50 acres.

Good transport facilities were of fundamental importance. All the north Ayrshire dairy cooperatives were situated near a railway except Fenwick Farmers’ Waterside Creamery. It pioneered steam haulage into the Glasgow district.

FIRST WORLD WAR 1914-1918

During the Napoleonic Wars there were threats of blockading Britain but, because of her superior seapower there was not much dislocation to food supplies. In any case by comparison with the First War period food imports were not so important. This was the first time that food had such a dominant position and its availability could have determined the outcome.

The decline in importance of agriculture was significant in the years before the outbreak of the war. From 1867–9 agriculture supplied a sixth of the nation's food output, a tenth in 1890 and less than a fifteenth by 191–13. It was pushed down by the scale of expansion of the industrial sector and the distributive trades. By this time British farmers were supplying only 13% of the butter, 24% cheese, 25% wheat, about 60% beef, mutton and lamb consumed. (M.A.A.S. Statistics.) Some said that Britain could only supply enough food for the weekends. The meals for the other days had to be imported.

In February 1915, a German blockade began with cruisers, submarines and mines aiming to destroy the British economy. The measure was an attempt to frighten neutral shipping away from Britain with the threat that any vessels moving into British waters was fair game. The British reacted by ordering the Royal navy to seize cargoes of grain and flour heading for Germany and treat them as contraband. This lead to Germany's unrestricted submarine warfare. By the middle of 1915 it became clear that the war was going to be prolonged longer than originally thought. There were large shipping losses which caused alarm and necessitated organising agriculture to greater efforts if defeat through starvation was to be averted. It had been estimated that there was only six weeks' supply of wheat in the country. It was only then that the country jumped out of its lethargy into action on the food front.

It was soon realised that raising agricultural productivity was not going to be easy with the reduced labour force at a time when the outlook for farming was not hopeful.

On 7th August 1914, the day after Lord Kitchener took office as Secretary of State for War he issued his famous call for volunteers. He planned to raise immediately 200,000 men and ultimately not less than one million. He ignored the necessity for the controlled inflow of men who maintained the essential posts in industry, agriculture and communications. He also overlooked the problem of housing, clothing, feeding and training this colossal recruitment. Recruitment offices were choked with men of all classes, ages, shapes, sizes and standards of fitness. They were overtaken by a passionate patriotism. A great many had to be sent home and were told to come back later. 'The patriotic spirit was alive amongst a people whose ancestors had been fated to know more of war than of peace during many generations.'

Surprisingly, military service was not compulsory until January 1916, because it was thought that upwards of half a million men had not volunteered and that the same number of married men were ready to join up but had not yet been accepted. Until then the Government was to recruit single men first. Some members of Parliament threatened to resign if conscription was made compulsory.

Many 'sons of the soil' answered this call. One has only to look at the war memorials all over the countryside to see the dire result. It was the key men of the farms, horsemen and stockmen, that were in demand in the army. Men such as Adam Gray, spent 1915 breaking horses before being drafted to France. The country districts were depleted of tradesmen, blacksmiths and saddlers, resulting in horses having to go unshod and harness and implements going unmended. A great number of horses were commandeered and farm machinery factories turned over to making munitions. It was estimated that in July 1917, 28.2% of the farmworkers were in the army and 36.5% a year later.

In fieldwork the output per man depended on the speed of the horses and the limited number of hours they could work in a day, unlike tractors which never tire. Although by this time there were machines for slicing turnips, chaffing hay, sowing and harvesting of grain etc. the output of farms still depended on the muscles of men and horses. They were needed from the turning of the first furrow to the lifting of the last grain bag on to a waggon for sale, from the first cut of a hayfield, to the hay being forked to the cows in a narrow byre and from milking an ill tempered cow early in the morning to lifting a 17 gallon can full of milk onto a railway waggon. The first tractor to become popular in Britain was the Fordson of which Henry Ford sent over 6,000 for the ploughing up campaign after 1917.

In 1915 the Government appealed for women to sign on for work in trades, industry, armaments and agriculture. Emmiline Pankhurst said, 'Women are only too anxious to be recruited.'

Mrs Fawcett, President of the National Union of the Women's Suffrage Societies said, 'It would raise the standard for women both in work and wages. The war would have a good effect in bringing men and women together and make them rely on mutual friendship and cooperation.' (Chronicle of the 20th Century 1990).

With the formation of the Women's Land Army and the assistance given by a large number of schoolchildren, interned aliens, prisoners of war, soldiers and other volunteers, the farmers were able to meet the targets set for them.

In 1917, the Women's Rural Institute was inaugurated at a meeting in the Goold Hall, St Andrew's Square, Edinburgh, at which Sir Robert Wright,of the Board of Agriculture presided. By 1922 there were 242 Institutes. This organisation played an important role in rebuilding rural life after the traumas of the war.

One of its early leaders was Margaret Shanks, whose father was a member of the well-known Renfrewshire family of Barrhead engineers and took up farming. Margaret was in charge of the land girls in the Glasgow area during the war and became a regular contributor to the Scottish Farmer of which the following is an excerpt.

'She looketh well to the ways of her household and eateth not the bread of idleness. Every new departure and every fresh beginning has, or ought to have, a preface and the words of the Great Preacher has been chosen as appropriate to our domestic economy column. Not that there is any intention of sermonising upon them, but that every good and true housewife may adopt them for her motto and in a strength greater than her own, go forth to meet the daily cares and trials incident to her sphere.'

She also made a comment which would please some chauvinistic men. 'There was no exercise more beneficent in result, than sweeping, dusting, making beds, washing dishes and polishing brass...This with regular exercise out of doors would do more for a woman's complexion than all the pomades that were ever invented!'

In 1918 under the Fourth Reform Act women were allowed to vote 'subject to education and property qualifications.' In 1928 they were given full voting equality with men.

By the summer of 1915 the Government decided to take some positive action by appointing Committees of Enquiry for England, Scotland and Ireland. For Scotland the members were Eugene Wason, M.P. chairman, Charles Douglas, Joseph Duncan, John M. Hannah, Harry Hope, Professor Sommerville, David Wilson, Sir Robert Wright, with William Barber from the Board of Agriculture, acting as secretary.

Their remit was to consider and report on what steps they thought would be necessary by legislation or otherwise to maintain and if possible to increase food production in Scotland. One of their important recommendations was the appointment by the County Councils of District

Agricultural Executive Committees to advise the Board of Agriculture on 'all matters related to the increasing food production and to stimulate local production.' Unlike in England, the powers of compulsion was not given to those local committees but were retained by the Board of Agriculture to act as agents to the Board. The Board's powers were rarely invoked but were there to 'secure equality between the reluctant and the willing cultivator and to deal with the rare cases of refusal to comply with reasonable requests.'

Initially, this committee thought that the proposals for guaranteed prices for cereals were impractical and that the rise in prices since the outbreak of the war would be sufficient to stimulate production on the premise that if you touch a man's pocket, you influence his opinion on action. However, later circumstances forced the introduction of price control.

The Agricultural Executive Committees were mostly farmers and also included representatives from county councils, secondary education committees, agricultural societies and farmworkers' unions.

The duties of these committees varied, – 'granting of licences to sell horses, the issuing of permits to obtain petrol, the certification of farmworkers for exemption from military service and generally the application to agriculture of that whole series of compulsions which became necessary to concentrate all the materials and moral resources of the nation upon the tasks of victory.' (Douglas, 1919.)

The organising of the work seems to have been a bit chaotic. The Executive Committees had the unenviable task of deciding between the needs of the army and the claims of agriculture. The soldiers and prisoners of war were under the jurisdiction of the National Service Department, alien labour under one Government department and volunteer labour under another. The Minister of Food dealt with feeding controls while the Minister of Munitions with fertiliser and machinery.

The Defence of the Realm Act formed the legislative background for agriculture during the later period of the war which straightened many of the earlier anomalies. This was when the effects of food shortages were really being felt and food prices were rising at an uncomfortable rate. The grocery bill of the average household was 25s. per week according to Sir Thomas Clement of the cheese broking firm Andrew Clement and Sons, Glasgow. He became chairman of the Cheese and Butter Imports of the Minister of Food in 1914. By 1915 it had increased to 33s. 9d. Even then experts were arguing that there was no shortage of food, nor likely to be. However, to protect consumer prices, controls had to be introduced.

This heralded a complete change in Government attitude to farming than hitherto. Up until the advent of the War governments had quite deliberately 'abstained from intervention in the field.' From the passing of the 1917 Corn Production Act when guaranteed prices and minimum wages for farmworkers were introduced, successive governments have played an important part in the varying fortunes of British Agriculture.

The weather, of course, took a hand in deciding at what level the grain production would be during the War. 'The five harvests of the War were various in character. A rather late harvesting 1914 was followed by four late slow and difficult years. In 1915 no very serious losses were incurred but in 1916 a harvest almost everywhere, was late and protracted resulting in serious loss in almost every district, especially in the later districts. In 1917 a harvest though late in beginning, was successful in the Eastern and Northern districts, but was disastrous throughout the Western part of the country. The harvest in 1918 beginning rather early in most districts, was also very irregular in its character. Crops on the whole were well secured in some districts but almost continuous rain in the latter part of September and throughout October resulted in much loss especially in the western regions. The losses of crop were seriously aggravated by the labour shortages in 1917 and 1918.' (Douglas, 1919.)

Maximum producer prices fixed for Scottish farm products were- Wheat, 75s.6d. per quarter; barley, 67s. oats 47s. 6d. Potatoes £7, Hay £8 and barley £3. 15s. per ton respectively.

In 1918, the maximum price for farm produced fresh eggs of not less than 1½ozs. each was 5s. per dozen. For small eggs 2s. 8d. per dozen. For fat cattle the price fixed in 1917 was approximately 8s. per stone of 8lbs. not including the offal.

In December 1917, a grading scheme for cattle was introduced under which all fat cattle were to be sold through a public market. The maximum price fixed for Grade I bullocks in 1918 was 77s. per live hundredweight. For sheep in the same year the maximum wholesale price for home killed mutton was 8s. 8d. per stone of 8lbs

These high prices had a knock on effect on the income of the town dairymen who had to buy in all their feed and sell their milk at restricted prices. From September 1917 maximum price for milk was fixed for producers. At the same time the butter price was set at a lower level to discourage its production in favour of liquid milk. For the same reason the sale of cream was prohibited except for individuals and children who had a medical certificate.

MILK PRICES

The Corn Production Act 1917 which was introduced as a wartime measure was confirmed and augmented in the Agricultural Act 1920.

In 1917–18 the maximum prices per gallon fixed to the producer were :–

October 1s. 5d.; November 1s.7d.; December–March 1s. 9d.; April 1s.8d.;

In summer 1918 the prices were May 1s. 2d.; June–July 1s.; August 1s.2d.; September 1s.4d. Later the May price was raised to 1s. 6d. and the June–September prices raised by 4d. per gallon. These prices included the cost of delivery to the buyer's premises or to producer's railway station.

A margin of 2d. per gallon was allowed to creameries for cooling and to provide for accommodation of surplus milk. Wholesalers who delivered exact quantities to retailers' premises plus haulage from the producer or from the country creamery were allowed 3d. per gallon above the creamery margin. The retailers' margin was fixed at 8d. per gallon. (Douglas, 1919.)

Cheese prices were fixed in relation to the price ruling for liquid milk. Butter prices on the other hand were set lower in order to discourage production in favour of securing the maximum supply of liquid milk which was causing some anxiety. The maximum prices set for delivered cheese in 1917 was 132s. per cwt. and butter at 230s. per cwt. In 1918 the prices rose to 168s. and 298s respectively.

The Minister of Food had the unenviable task of restricting prices to a level which would please both the producer and the consumer. 'The prices should be so fixed that they were not so high that the farmer would not profit at the expense of the nation but high enough to be a security and shield so that he could work undisturbed.' The Minister had difficulty in satisfying the strong claims made by both producers and consumers about prices for milk because there were no reliable figures on the subject.

To try to overcome this, the Minister appointed in 1918 a Travelling Commission, 'to investigate the costs of milk production in different parts of the country and make a report recommending prices for the months of May– September 1919.' Luckily, by coincidence or otherwise the deliberations of the Commission differed little from the prices already fixed by the Minister of Food. It did also recommend that prices should be higher for Scotland in certain months 'to make allowance for the later growth of grass in Scotland.'

Because of the desperate need to produce human food rather than animal food from 1914–1918, cattle and sheep numbers were reduced slightly in Scotland. This was dictated by the scarcity and high price of animal feeding. There were also difficulties in getting labour especially on the larger farms, some of whom had to change from arable to beef production. As late as 1918, the casualties in the war were so great that a further 55,000 men were called up from Scottish farms. In spite of it all, the production results were remarkable, considering that the real efforts were not made until well after the war had commenced. By 1918 the production of wheat was 54% higher than in 1916, barley was increased by 17%, oats by 38% and potatoes by 68%

There were many problems caused organising forage for animals needed in the war. Britain alone used 533,000 horses, (314,00 in France), 231,000 mules (81,000 in France,) 9,000 donkeys and 3,000 oxen. The battlefront was augmented by thousands of horses from America and South America which came in a variety of shapes, sizes and breeds. There was an increasing demand from Britain as Belgium and France were ravaged. The prices of hay and straw rocketed. This necessitated the Army Council controlling the price and distribution of hay for the army and civilians alike.

An epitaph was composed to all those who died during the war, 'They did not flinch.' In many respects this could be applied to agriculture as well.

It is a pity that more politicians did not listen to the Earl of Selbourne, who was Chairman of the Special Agricultural Sub-Committee of the Restruction Committee. In 1917 he said that, 'nobody dare, with proper agricultural skill and application of science and wise laws, put a limit on increased production in the future.'

Lord Ernle in recording his account of the food campaign hoped that, 'should similar necessities ever arise in the future, our national action will be guided as well in adoption as in avoidance by the experience gained in 1916–18.'

RATIONALISATION

It has been said that the first serious attempt to rationalise the dairy industry in this country was taken in 1915, when the United Dairies Ltd. was founded as a holding company in London. It has been called 'a war baby' because its formation was motivated by the scarcity of men, horses and transport due to the war.

The companies amalgamated into the United Dairies Ltd. were, the

Dairy Supply Ltd., the oldest London wholesale milk firm, with auxiliary country milk depots and dairy engineering sections; the Great Western and Metropolitan Dairies, Ltd., the largest wholesale milk contractors in London, with its condensaries and creameries in Staffordshire and the Wiltshire United Dairies, Ltd., which included a large condensed milk and creamery business, plus creameries in south west England and two in Normandy.

Each of these three businesses was a product of amalgamation or acquisitions. In 1915 they represented the greater part of the wholesale milk in London. As a result much of the overlapping in the milk trade was eliminated, which released hundreds of men and horses to serve their country in other ways.

The foregoing was taken as a blue print for subsequent developments in the distribution within the liquid milk industry. This was all brought into perspective and highlighted in a report of a government appointed committee on the Production and Distribution of Milk, which became known as the "Astor" Committee, its chairman being Viscount Astor. This was produced in 1920 after three years of deliberations. It was a comprehensive report, dealing with many aspects of the dairy industry, including a review in depth of the laws and regulations governing the sale of milk to the public. This resulted in the passing of a series of Milk and Dairy Acts along with Milk (Special Designation) Orders governing milk production on the farm, animal health, milk quality, etc.

"The researches of the Astor Committee brought to light some of the major defects of the machinery for distributing the country's milk supply, of which one of the most significant was the wasteful competition in the trade supplying the larger cities. Owing to the large firms operating independently, there was a considerable amount of overlapping, both in producing and consuming areas.

Nevertheless, the tendency towards rationalisation was unpopular with some producers and consumers alike, both of whom feared that they might be victims of monopoly control, whether established in the wholesale or retail trades."

Under wartime controls the Minister took over a large number of wholesale firms in order to regulate supplies. This had to be done to ensure a fair share of milk in all areas. These wartime measures helped to consolidate the large wholesalers marketing strength. After decontrol of prices etc. the wholesalers were in a better position to buy milk collectively, while farmers still continued to sell on an individual basis. The bargaining power was in the purchasers' favour which ultimately lead to a trial of strength within the dairy industry when cooperative marketing and milk marketing boards were mooted.

DEPRESSION & COOPERATION.

During the war the agricultural industry was geared up to increasing production which it did with a great measure of success. The nation continued to benefit from this as it readjusted from war to peacetime conditions. There was the rehabilitation of some millions of service men and women and there was the reorganising of munition and other factories used for war production back to peacetime functions. During this time farm prices rose. Generally there was a world food scarcity and many shipping lines were disrupted both contributing to a strong demand for home grown foods.

In the year 1919–1920, the price of oats rose from 50s–65s. per quarter; barley from 70s–125s and wheat from 76s–95s. The price of cattle in Edinburgh rose from 74s 8d per cwt. to an average of 96s 3d. and milk to 4s. per gallon. The price of land and rents also went up. Sitting tenants who had been successful, bought their farms at 20–25 years purchase, depending on their existing leases and the number of years it had to run.

'At the end of the war all classes indulged in a feverish orgy of all those sports and pastimes which had been impossible for four long weary years. Hunting, shooting, fishing and tennis – the majority had no thought of tomorrow. Instead of living for ones farm, the only desire was to get away and pursue pleasure elsewhere. The activities used to be limited to the capacity of the horse and trap as a means of transport. The motor car changed all that.' (A.G. Street, *Farmer's Glory.*)

Suddenly, all this changed, the short honeymoon period of high farming and high prosperity was over. World production of grain and beef had quickly overtaken demand and prices collapsed. Meat, wool eggs, vegetables, butter and cheese poured into this country. Dairy produce imports doubled. Wheat prices halved, oats prices dropped to a third of its former price and wool to a quarter. Retail price of milk dropped to 2s. per gallon. in winter and 1s 8d. in the summer.

Britain was losing its share of world trade, having been the world's number one industrial country. U.S.A., Germany, France and Japan had been industrialising rapidly before the war and were now ready to go after new markets. The price of food was critical in the lowering of labour costs in the economic production of industrial goods. Thus farming was quickly back into another era of cheap food and a Free Trade Policy.

What Earl of Shelbourne said in 1917 was indeed applicable in 1922. 'We are sorry for your difficult circumstances; we are sorry for your ruin but that is nothing to us; we have only one policy and that is the policy of the cheapest article for the consumer.'

For a second occasion in a comparative short time those who lived and worked on the land were quite deliberately abandoned by the State. When the Government saw the high expenditure it would have to pay for implementing the guaranteed prices in face of falling prices, it repealed the Agricultural Act 1920. Agricultural protection was suddenly no more, with no guaranteed prices for grain and no minimum wages for the men working on the land. Many farms were given up and there was another migration of farmers into England, Patersons, Alstons, Mitchells, etc.

When the minimum wage structure was abandoned, farmworkers wages dropped which motivated them in 1923 to a rare strike. This resulted in a wage fixing mechanism being introduced under the Agricultural Wages (Regulation) Act, 1924, whereby County Wages Committees were established. This led to a rise in wages.

In this depressed state of farming liquid milk prices were free from overseas competition unlike butter and cheese whose prices dropped dramatically. This opened the gap between liquid and manufacturing prices which encouraged more farmers to produce milk for the liquid market causing increasingly difficult market conditions. In this scenario a great deal of concentrated thinking focused on cooperation.

As far back as 1894 John Speir wrote in his report for the Royal Commission on Agriculture, 'It would be for the benefit of both landlord and tenant alike if a cooperation for the manufacture of butter and cheese, so successfully carried out for many years in Denmark, Switzerland, Canada and the U.S.A. were more fostered than it has been by the landlords of this country. There are a number of cases where landlords have land within convenient carting distance, close to a railway and an efficient water supply where factories could be efficiently erected. In some cases many old buildings already exist in the shape of meal and other mills. If they were put at the disposal of the tenants and they were to find the utensils many might be started at a very low outlay. Under this system the cost of manufacture is reduced to the lowest limit. While the quality might not be up to the very highest grade as made in some private dairies, it would certainly be higher than the present average. If such a system were gradually adopted, the saving to the landlord would be immense as the numerous dairies on every farm are much more expensive to build and keep up than one sufficiently large to handle all the milk at one centre.'

This immediately poses the question which has been asked for many years. Why did the dairy farmers, especially in Scotland, not act together as early and compatible as some in Holland, Denmark, or even France? A.D. Hall, Secretary to the Board of Agriculture and Fisheries, addressing a Conference on the Improvement of Agriculture in 1917, answered the question, 'Why has Cooperation made such strides in Denmark compared with its progress in this country? "Simply, the Danes are a community receptive to the idea. They worked out for themselves that they were alive to the power that cooperation could give them. They were aware that this mental awakening could bring types of men with flexible active minds who could best turn social and mechanical developments round them for their own use. If we get a new stimulus and mental awakening for our farmers, we shall reconstruct our farming during the difficulties that are coming to us.'

The cooperative movement did start in this country before the First World War with producer and consumer cooperatives. The first Agricultural Cooperative Trading Society to be registered in Scotland was the Farmers' Supply Association Ltd. Leith in 1884, when farmers were experiencing great difficulty in obtaining tested fertilisers. It was 19 years before the next one was formed. In 1903 Tarff Valley Agricultural Cooperative Society was started in Kirkcudbrightshire.

When the advantages of cooperation were gradually being realised, the Scottish Chamber of Agriculture arranged for a Committee to be appointed with the remit, 'To formulate a scheme for extending the benefits of cooperation to Scottish Agriculture, with the power to take such action as might appear expedient for giving the same practical effect.'

The result was the formation of the Scottish Agricultural Organisation Society in 1905, which is now better known by the initial letters of its title, the S.A.O.S. The S.A.O.S. does not itself engage in trade nor does it take any part in politics. Its main function is to assist in the promotion and development of Agricultural Cooperative Societies. As a result of the propaganda carried by the S.A.O.S a considerable number of societies were founded in the early years of its existence.

In 1908 there were c.100 and by 1914 c.200. A few of these developed into large businesses which exist today. The majority faded out for a number of reasons mainly from the hostility of existing merchants to whom many farmers at the time were in debt. Over the years experience in this country has shown that voluntary cooperation is alright in a rising economy but rarely of any use in bad times because they have no resources to withstand adversity. They tend to be massacred by self destruction.

In the more advanced countries in Europe the cooperatives were really formed as a result of adversity and necessity after the revolutions in France in 1830 and 1848. It was a case of 'export or starve'. At a time when the marketing of food, especially dairy produce, was so disorderly, the Danes and others were quick to organise themselves to exploit this market. Exporting was the major motivating factor. Their long disciplined experience stood them in good stead to compete successfully. They had total commitment.

The Danes had two well taken marketing advantages in earlier years. Firstly, after the First World War they were quick to see the benefit to them of having one price for all milk. The milk for the liquid trade was bought on the same basis as that bought for buttermaking which varied according the world markets. There was no price cutting as was happening in the British market. Secondly, there was a far greater emphasis put on the quality of the raw material and the end product.

'The crux of the matter is that the Danish government over many years has not only organised her agriculturists but has insisted upon efficient methods of production, grading and the subordination of individual effort to the controlled teamwork by which the national well-being has been built up.' (Raison, 1933.)

How different the situation was in the U.K. Each farmer preferred to produce what he wanted and to what he thought he was entitled, irrespective of standardisation and quality, to the market on his own doorstep. The average farmer had an aversion to risking his scarce money to employ experts, never thinking that it was possible that they were better equipped to exploit the market than himself. It was the failure of the U.K. farmer to develop producer cooperatives that made him so vulnerable to market forces and to the power of large companies.

CHAPTER 5

MARKETING OF MILK

The chaotic marketing conditions prevailing after the war were similar to those that existed before it. It has been noted that there was a measure of discipline under war emergencies which disappeared. Every dairy farmer had to find a market for his own milk for the whole year. 'Some senior farmers can recall Milk Wednesday in Glasgow when dairy farmers went round the distributors to collect their money, after which many adjourned to Graham's Square next to the cattle market, where about every second door was a public house and many drowned their sorrows. Shades of Tam o' Shanter on market day.' (Urquart, 1979.)

There is an old saying that 'a sheep's worst enemy was another sheep'. In those days a dairy farmer's worst enemy was another dairy farmer. Somehow action was required to solve two problems,- how to control the power of the wholesalers and how to control the increasing amount of milk which was surplus to the liquid milk requirements. The major difficulty was that the population required a regular amount of milk all the year round from cows which gave a seasonal production supplying most of the milk in the summertime.

First efforts to do this was the important early work done by the S.A.O.S who set up a Dairy Scheme to organise the formation of cooperative dairy associations and milk depots. In this it was ably supported by the National Farmers' Union of Scotland after its formation in 1913.

Although the following list is not definitive it shows a number with their approximate years of registration.

Rowallan Cooperative Association	1908
Lugton Cooperative Association	1908
Dunlop Cooperative Dairy Association	1908
Kilmaurs Dairy Association	1909
Stewarton Dairy Association	1910
Fenwick Farmers Cooperative Association	1911
Creamery Association (Thankerton)	1911
Lesmahagow Dairy Farmers' Association	1914
Galston and District Farmers' Cooperation Association	1915
Royal Four Towns Agricultural Cooperative	1918
Dalry Farmers' Dairy Association	1919

Upper Nithsdale Dairy Farmers' Association (Sanquar)	1919
Stewartry Dairy Association (Kirkcudbright)	1919
Craigie and Symington Farmers' Association	1920
Dalbeattie and District Farmers' Association	1920
The Galloway Creamery (Stranraer)	1920
Maybole and District Farmers' Association	1920
Port William Dairy Farmers' Association	1920
South Ayrshire Farmer's Association	1920
Strathendrick Farmers' Dairy Association	1920
Gretna and District Dairy Association	1926

(The title 'Stewartry' which is used here dates from the 14th century, when Archibald the Grim received in perpetual fee all the Crown lands between the Nith and Cree rivers and appointed a Steward to collect his revenues and administer justice throughout the district.)

The Galloway Creamery had stiff opposition from two nearby creameries belonging to the Scottish Wholesale Cooperative Society and United Dairies.

There were also Inverness Dairy Farmers' Association, 1912 and Wick Farmers' Dairy Society, 1925, both were essentially retailers of milk to their respective towns and surrounding areas.

Practically all these associations had depots with plants capable of handling milk, cream and cheese. A few of them made butter. It could be said that the pioneers who formed the first creamery in Ayrshire laid the foundation of milk marketing organisation.

At the instigation of Mr John Young, in 1922, the father of Sir William Young, who became chairman of the Scottish Milk Marketing Board, the Federation of Cooperative Dairy Associations was set up. This was the first tentative step by farmers towards a system of collective bargaining.

Some semblance of order in the market place was established by what became known as the 'Glasgow Agreement'. This was drawn up by the National Farmers' Union representing the non-creamery producers, the Federation of Cooperative Associations, the Glasgow Wholesalers' Association, the Glasgow Cooperative Association and the Glasgow and District Dairymans' Association. 'That the prices should be fixed annually and a differentiation should be made in price for basic supplies surplus to the requirements of the liquid market.'

The basis of the 'Agreement' was that all the milk produced on a farm during November–February was paid for at the 'agreement' price.

To the average monthly supply during these months was added 20% which established a 'basic' quantity, or in modern terms, a 'standard quantity'. If a producer produced more than that quantity over the other 8 months of the year, it was considered to be 'surplus'. This 'surplus' was paid for at the manufacturing price which was computed monthly by taking the average price of Canadian and New Zealand cheese as shown in the provision markets reports less 2d. per gallon. This was a precarious start to the introduction of 'pooling' arrangements for milk pricing which was to have a dominant role for the future of the dairy industry.

The effects of this 'surplus' clause were far reaching and within two years the anomalous position of a surplus of winter milk arose. This had been affected by a change round in calving dates; more cows calving in the autumn. This increased the winter production and so the 'basic' quantity, thereby reducing or avoiding the penalty of the lower price for 'surplus' during the spring and summer months.

This winter surplus was a greater problem than the summer surplus because winter milk was and is more costly to produce than summer milk. At the time summer milk manufacture was uneconomic so naturally winter milk was even more uneconomic.

Although this collective bargaining between the representatives of the producers and the trade usually succeeded in agreeing to a price for milk for a year ahead, it still rested with the individual producer to find a buyer who would accept his supply of milk at the 'agreement ' price. Apart from being economically sound this method had the advantage of simplicity and was linked to cheese prices. Unfortunately, as production expanded and as world values for manufactured dairy produce continued to fall the position of many creameries and farmers' dairy cooperatives became untenable and were forced into liquidation

The position was further aggravated by the fact that there was no control over the sale of milk for manufacture and some of the distributors exploited both producers and consumers by buying milk at the manufacturing price and using it to meet the liquid milk demand. There were about 80 major distributing businesses in Glasgow alone. This led to difficulty in maintaining the 'agreement' price which forced many farmers to sell a greater part of their output at the 'surplus' or manufacturing prices. The liquid market reached such a state of confusion that it culminated in the collapse of this form of collective bargaining in the year 1926–27.

STATHENDRICK FARMERS' DAIRY ASSOCIATION.

Strathendrick Farmers' Dairy Association was a party to the Glasgow Agreement. Records of this Association are available and serve to illustrate both advantages but also the problems of marketing milk in this way. Extracts about the organisation have been gleaned from early Minute Books showing some practical details.

This Association was founded in 1920 and like the others was registered under the Industrial and Provident Societies Act, 1893. The objectives of the Association 'were not primarily to amass profits, but to provide its members with the fullest advantages in the marketing of their milk supplies and in the supplying of their requirements in milk cans, petrol, paraffin, lubricant oils etc. in the most reasonable terms possible.'

The attendance at the first two annual general meetings were not recorded. The producers, called milk suppliers who attended the meeting on 8th October 1923 and sold their milk through the Strathendrick Farmers' Dairy Association were; John Michie, President; Alexander Hosie, Blanavaid; James McAdam, Drumtain; John McQueen, Finnich; Wlliam Murray, Cairnlea; John Patterson, Woodlea; Richard Marshall, Rumans; James Allan, Keirhill; James Orr, Shandon; Walter Bilsan, Badshalloch; Thomas Cumming, Easterhill; M. Mitchell,Jr. Cannoquill; George McLaren, Harvieston; Alexander Ritchie, Hill of Balgair; John Haddow, Broughmore; Alexander Christie, Dalfoil; James Laurie, Balglass; William Caldwell, Hillheads of Glenside; John Stewart, Auchengyle; Thomas Black and Alexander Dykes.

It can be seen from the 1920 Financial Statement that the association made a modest start.

The producers selling their milk through this Association signed an agreement.

'We the undersigned, hereby agree to sell to the Strathendrick Farmers' Dairy Association all the whole milk except what we require for consumption on the farms, to be produced by the cows on our respective farms as noted for the period of one year. We warrant that the milk to be supplied will be of genuine quality, free from adulteration and to the best of our knowledge and belief the cows from which the milk is supplied are free from any disease which makes the sale of the milk illegal.'

The prices ruling under the Glasgow Agreement for the year 1923–24 were:

Milk delivered to	Railway Station	Roadend
1st November – 28th February	1s.5½d	1s.7d.
March	1s.1½d.	1s.3d.
April	1s.½d.	1s.
1st. May – 31st July	9½d	11d.
1st. August – 31st. October	1s.1½d.	1s.3d.

After the prices were agreed it was not always easy for individual companies to get their milk sold. When the Clydebank Cooperative Creamery, which opened on 5th October 1925, were negotiating with Strathendrick Farmers' Dairy Association, they wanted the contract price to be "subject to a cut not exceeding 2d. per gallon any month they found it necessary and that if any milk did not reach the buyer in time for breakfast, the producer was liable to have 3/8d. per gallon deducted from his account on the grounds that the milk was too late to be of any sale value. The Association naturally found this an unsatisfactory arrangement and put an advertisement in the Glasgow Herald – 'Several farmers with milk for sale from 1st. May. Can be delivered 7 days per week in any Glasgow district.'

Groups of producers were allocated to certain buying companies. For example Messrs James Barbour, Hugh Caldwell, William Caldwell and Duncan Fraser sold their milk to Dumbartonshire Dairy Company. Other companies to whom milk was sold by this Association were: Ross's Dairies, Dumbarton Road; Caldwells Dairies; Brisbane & Beatties Dairies, Pollockshaws; James Adams, Springburn; Fred Cunningham, Partrick; and Sloans' Dairies. "Terms: ¼d. per gallon over Buyers' Railway Station prices if delivered by the Association's lorry."

`One way or another the collective arrangements worked for a number of years until the production of milk exceeded the liquid milk requirements then the real problems came to the fore.

When the Dumbarton Dairy was 'flooded with milk' they made a request that Mr Barbour should keep his milk at home for one week and they would bear any loss incurred. Mr Barbour was asked to make his milk into cheese, which was not an easy task to undertake at such short notice. Three months later his milk was again refused and this time the company would not compensate him for the loss incurred when it was made into cheese. A lawsuit ensued and the settlement found in favour of Mr

Barbour and the Association. As a result of this legal decision, the Dumbarton Dairy Company refused to take any of the Association's milk. A deal was subsequently made with the Clydebank Cooperative Society who were able to handle the surplus at 7½d. per gallon through their new creamery built in October 1925.

It was reported at a meeting on 5th November that, 'the milk supplies from Messrs. Allan, Christie, Dalgleish, Marshall and Scott were unsold and that arrangements had been made with Messrs. Brisbane & Beatties's Dairies, Pollockshaws to take these supplies meantime. No price was fixed. Messrs. Allan and Christie were asked to try and dispose of their supplies in the East.'

'A discussion ensued on the advisability of starting a small creamery. It being left to Messrs. Alston and John Patterson to make enquiries on the subject, or whether to make double cream with it.' Capital was subscribed for this purpose. The question of cost held up this development, which led to it being abandoned and the capital invested. At the same time a lorry was purchased to haul the members milk.

By the same token there were other problems. Mr F. Cunningham, Partick, said, 'If the Association consigned any more milk to him after the 31st May he would not lift it from the railway station. The secretary was instructed to call him and make an endeavour to get him to take delivery of the milk and make the best possible arrangement as to price.'

'Because Clydebank Cooperative and Messrs. Brisbane & Beattie had stopped taking spare milk after 1st. June 1927, a hurried arrangement was made with John Allan, Buchclyvie Station for the use of his premises and cheese plant and that an experienced cheesemaker, James Murray be engaged at £4.10s. per week.'

There was no doubt that in spite of many difficulties the Glasgow Agreement was a triumph for collective bargaining and introduced the principle of pool pricing which was built upon in the years ahead. However, the producers were not in control of the surplus production which was paid at the manufacturing price some of which went into the hands of the liquid milk distributors who used it to undercut their competitors.

The creameries too, were in a confused state. Although their Federation was a party to the price fixing arrangements, it also had little control over supplies and were rightly or wrongly accused of pushing some of their supplies on to the liquid market. This became more evident in the years 1926 – 27 when there was a distinct increase in production due to more beef farmers turning to dairying. Faced with an unpredictable surplus and a volatile milk product commodity market, due to imports, wholesalers and creameries were hesitant, indeed opposed to continue to negotiate agreements with Associations, preferring freedom to purchase in an open market. This situation set the alarm bells ringing throughout the industry with the fear of the collapse of collective bargaining which would mean a return to the rat race of individual bargaining.

This course of events made producers realise that the marketing of milk required reorganisation and the outcome was the formation of the Scottish Milk Agency.

THE SCOTTISH MILK AGENCY LTD.

This alarming situation motivated an attempt to do something positive. The matter was taken up by the Scottish Agricultural Organisation Society and the National Farmers' Union of Scotland. They elected a Joint Committee to draft a scheme for a central selling agency. It became known as the Scottish Milk Agency, Ltd. registered under the Industrial and Provident Societies Act 1893 and 1913. It intended to go right to the root of the matter by "securing a market for the milk produced by its members, to regulate the supply of milk to the liquid market and to make provision for the disposal of the supply surplus to the requirements of that market." (H.M.S.O. 'Report of the Committee on Agricultural Cooperation in Scotland" 1930. Cmd.3567). It came into operation on the 1st. November 1927.

The membership of the Agency was open to societies, associations, companies and individual producers who signed its form of contract. Every producer of milk had to take out at least one share from the agency and every corporate member one share for each supplying producer of milk. Initially the Agency had a capital of approximately £1000. A Committee of Management was appointed representing the producers and the farmers' cooperative dairy associations with an independent chairman. At general meetings each corporation had a vote for every supplying producer.

The Committee of Management comprised of –
Chairman, Alexander Murdoch, C.A. Glasgow.
Representing the individual producers were-

Major J. Keith, Pitmedon, Udny.
A.S. Armour, Killocraw, Bellochantuy.
Robert Laird, Lawthorn, Irvine.

David Craig, Newhouse, Crosshouse,
J. Weir, Over Glaisnock, Cumnock
J. Sloan, Dormiston, Tarbolton.
E.J. More, The Ryding, Airdrie.
W. Cassels Jack, Robiesland, Lanark.
G. Lambie, Pilnuir, Newton Mairns.
James Picken, Milton, Kirkcudbright.
R. Grierson, Clendrie, Kirkcolm.
A. Buchanan, Garscadden Mains, Bearsden.

Representing the Farmers'Cooperative Dairy Associations were :–

James Kilpatrick, Craigie Mains, Kilmarnock.
James B. Stevenson, Douganhill, Dalbeattie.
R.T. Dickson, Auldmuir, Dalry.
John Young, Skerrington Mains, Hurlford.
Colonel W. T. R. Houldsworth, Kirkbride, Maybole.
Colin Christison, Barglass, Kirkinner.

While the Milk Agency was a voluntary scheme, its members were required to enter into a three year contract to sell all their liquid to it and not to sell any other liquid milk without its written consent. The Committee, however, agreed not to disturb, without good reason, contracts existing between individual producers and distributors, provided such contracts were registered with the Agency.

Members were required to declare on their contract forms the average daily quantities supplied each month for the previous three years. For these basic quantities with a variation of 10% either way, members were paid the liquid milk price. The Committee of Management had power to pay a lower price for quantities in excess of this limit and to make deductions for shortages. There was no premium for uniform production but members who had an abnormal variation in their monthly deliveries were required to accept a lower price for a proportion of their supplies.

It was decided not to start the Agency unless 60% of the milk produced in the Glasgow and Clyde Valley areas was guaranteed to the Agency. In the first month's operation it was estimated that this proportion of the total was being consigned from 1200 individual producer members and 600 members consigning through 14 creameries.

To meet the expenses of the Agency and to provide funds for compensation, development and reserves a deduction was made, 'not to exceed a 1d. per gallon. All sales by members were registered with the Agency and the latter guaranteed payment for all such registered sales.

All accounts for milk supplied by members, whether as individuals or through corporations was paid to the Agency, which in turn was paid to the members after making the necessary deduction per gallon. The amount of these deductions depended primarily on the liquid and manufacturing prices and on the amount of milk handled by these two classes.

Seven of the Cooperative Associations in Ayrshire became members of the milk Agency. Dunlop, Fenwick and Kilmaurs did not, nor did those in Kirkcudbrightshire and Wigtownshire. Those who were members were under obligation to accept all unsold milk at agreed manufacturing prices. The creameries could manufacture the milk in whatsoever way they pleased but they could not sell it liquid without consent of the Agency. Any profit from the process went to the creamery concerned as did the loss. The Agency in special circumstances made allowances to creameries in respect of losses incurred in manufacturing if it was on the instructions of the Agency. Difficulties arose when distributors did not fulfil their contracts forcing extra liquid milk to be manufactured at a considerable cost to the Agency.

Though the sales of milk were registered with the Agency, contracts continued to be negotiated between producers and distributors. If they were broken the producer would have to find his own buyer or require the Agency to find a market for him and register a contract on his behalf.

At the commencement of the Agency's operations, an agreement was made with the Glasgow and District Dairyman's Association by which producer wholesalers' and retailers' prices were fixed for a year ahead. All prices were uniform for nine months of the year, but lower by 4d. per gallon in the months of May, June and July. The producers' price was fixed for milk delivered to the buyers' railway station or to such point that the cost of transport was approximately the same as to the railway station. Certain premiums and deductions were allowed :–

a) An additional 1d. per gallon for milk delivered at the dairyman's premises before 6.30 a.m.
b) A deduction of 1d. to 1/2d. per gallon where the purchaser collected the milk within 30 miles of Glasgow.
c) Special rates for brine cooled, pasteurised and accommodation milk.
d) In selling its members' milk the Agency was to have regard to special quality, such as butterfat content. (Grigg Commission, 1933)

In the first year the Agency was very successful. This was largely due to severe weather conditions causing a 20% reduction in supplies, compelling many reluctant distributors to sign up on the Agency's terms. It was in a position to say 'not a drop of milk unless you guarantee to take your supplies from us.' There were, however, some large consumer cooperatives who managed to secure sufficient supplies from non-agency producers and retained an independence which eventually undermined the position of the Agency.

Because of this success the Agency purchased on favourable terms the Kyle Creamery in Edinburgh, thus strengthening its position in dealing with surplus milk. It also extended its operations into the Aberdeen area in 1928, achieving 100% support in that area.

Carried away by the euphoria of success, the milk price to the producer was jumped up 3d. per gallon for the four winter months. This was done without consideration of the consequences. Naturally producers made efforts to increase production. With the aid of more motor lorries and an improved railway system more farms who formerly made cheese on the farm came into the liquid milk field. Furthermore, as the returns from other types of farming were poor, non-milk producers were encouraged to come into the dairy industry. All led to an increasing surplus of milk which had to be sold at the lower manufacturing price. It cost the Agency dear, draining the reserves to such an extent that in the following year the price of milk to the producer members was reduced below that of the non-members who did not contribute to the overheads of the Agency.

For example the price for the liquid milk negotiated by the Agency with the trade was about 1s 2d. per gallon. Because an increasing amount had to be manufactured at about 6d. per gallon, the Agency could pay its members only 11d. while some of the non-members managed to get the full liquid price of 1s.2d. per gallon. There were others who got about 1s. This meant that the non-cooperating members became the majority being better off than those supporting the Agency. 'They were reaping where they had not sown.'

By 1930 the stability of the Agency became unsettled with so much surplus milk forcing down the milk to cheese price of 5d. per gallon, which was below the average milk price for cheesemaking in the South West of Scotland. This meant that the creameries had to be compensated, necessitating a levy of 3d. per gallon being imposed. This naturally caused alarm and despondency among the members of the Agency when they saw non-members in the favoured position of receiving inflated prices without paying this levy. With this state of affairs and human nature being what it is, this could not last long. It didn't.

This position was compounded by the actions of the producer-retailers. They were eligible for membership of the Agency on payment of a subscription of 5s. per cow. The Agency undertook to purchase at manufacturing price any milk that was left on their hands. While they agreed with the current prices and appeared to act accordingly, many circumvented this by giving their customers extra measures!

The reaction of the Strathendrick Farmers' Dairy Association to the presence of the Agency is noteworthy as taken from the Minute Books.

When the Agency became a reality, after lots of discussion it agreed that, 'This Association should join the Milk Selling Agency provided the Agency has guaranteed supplies equal to 60% of the estimated requirements of Glasgow and Clydebank Valley area and subject to the voting form of the Corporation being safeguarded and by giving the Corporation members attending an Annual General Meeting an equal number of votes to the number of producers supplying each Corporation. That thenceforth, milk cans have to have names and addresses indented on them and made suitable for sealing.'

However, as market conditions became more difficult the relationship between this Association and the Agency became strained due to a number of factors. For some time the distributors had a distributive margin of 9d. per gallon which they insisted on maintaining. To do this the Agency wanted the producers to drop their prices from 1s.3d. to 1s. per gallon. The Agency also wanted its members to be levied ½d. to a 1d. per gallon to build up a fund in order to enter the wholesale trade in Glasgow. This was also to be used to expand the sales of the contracted milk in England in order to leave the minimum amount of milk to be sold for manufacture.

The matter which really caused dissatisfaction was when the Agency wanted the Association to forego the 10% variation clause which other Dairy Farmers' Associations had. This variation clause, as has been noted, calculated on the output of the winter months, was at times difficult to maintain if there was disease problems or output was affected by bulls breeding unsatisfactorily. The last straw was when changes were made to the constitution and rules of the Agency in such a way that 'Strathendrick was in danger of losing the advantages of its geographical position as a producing area contiguous to the north end of Glasgow.' In effect it was because it was selling all its milk into the liquid market and objected to bearing a proportion of the losses on the surplus.

At a subsequent meeting T.G. Wilson was moved to say that 'an overwhelming case has been made for the Association to withdraw from the Agency and accordingly so move.' This proposal was seconded by James Turner.

When Strathendrick Farmers' Dairy Association withdrew their support from the Agency, a number of deals were made with the trade which were doubtfully any better than those done via the Agency.

Charles Ross of Ross's Dairies agreed to take all the supplies which previously had gone to Sloan's Dairies, John Hamilton and East Kilbride Dairy Farmers, Ltd. amounting to 1320 gallons daily. He agreed to the Association 11d. per gallon beginning on the 20th November 1930 and pay 1d. more up to the end of the year on condition that this penny would be refunded in the summer, provided that the gallonage then received did not exceed that received between 20th November and the end of the year.

The Clydebank Cooperative Society on the otherhand agreed 'to pay 11d. per gallon in the event that this Society deciding to retail milk at 1s.8d. per gallon. Both of these firms agreed to handle a proportion of any surplus at 4d. per gallon but the Clydebank Cooperative would only contract for only 50% of the supplies during the Fair Holiday, July 16th–25th, or take it at the surplus price. 'Any farmer who could dispose of his milk to a better advantage during the Fair Holidays would be at liberty to do so provided he gave one clear day's notice of his intention.'

Interestingly, about this time the Association bought 400 shares at 30s. and 400 6% Cumulative Preferential shares in East Kilbride Dairy Farmers' Company, Ltd.

As a result of some doubtful decisions by the Agency producers became disenchanted with it. At the beginning of the financial year 1931–32 many refused to sign their contracts with the result the Agency ceased to have a meaningful control of the market in the Glasgow area.

The failure of the Agency was due to a number of reasons. There was the apparent inexperience of the management which resulted in an unsound pricing policy. There was the inherent weakness of all loosely formed federations in having no compulsion on farmers who joined together and there was no compulsion on those who did, to observe the contract prices negotiated with the Trade. The Trade on the otherhand found plenty of producers who would sell under the agreed price. This was aided and abetted by producer-retailers who were masters at undercutting prices and fundamental to it all, there was no adequate solution on how to make the best use of the unknown quantity of surplus milk when it became available.

Due to poor communications and no budgeting no one knew how

much milk was available for sale. There was no knowledge as to what was happening to the milk. There were no guarantees that the milk sold at the liquid milk price was actually retailed as such, or by the same token there were no guarantees that milk sold at the the manufacturing price was not sold in the liquid market.

There are certain conditions inherent in the production and distribution of milk which make it peculiarly difficult to deal with the surplus economically. Fresh milk is a very perishable animal product which cannot be turned off at will, therefore, its production is not easily controlled as a factory article. It must be disposed of quickly. The production units are usually small and are scattered over a wide area creating organisational difficulties. The units of production work in highly variable conditions of soil and climate, making differences in unit costs and producing variable amounts throughout the year. On top of all these factors is the influence of imports and various political implications which must not be forgotten.

'An organisation on a purely voluntary basis which leaves a section of producers outside its scope must be continually beset with difficulties arising from the actions of the individual element. Even with an organisation on a statutory basis there remains the vital necessity of a wise and far seeing management, particularly in regard to price policy.' (Grigg Commission, 1933.)

The Scottish Milk Agency, Ltd. was considered the largest experiment of its kind for organising the marketing of an agricultural product that had been attempted in Great Britain and it attracted widespread attention. It was formally wound up at a meeting in Glasgow in 1935 on the motion of Col. (later Sir) W.T.R. Houldsworth. He described it as the first great effort on the part of milk producers to combine to look after there own affairs. It may have failed but not financially, under the chairmanship of Mr Alex Murdoch. In spite of its difficulties, the Agency paid out its shareholders nearly 30s. for each £1 share.

After three years the industry was once again back to a free for all under conditions which were even worse than that which led to the formation of the Agency in 1927. 'Every producer was a bidder for a share of the liquid market.'

'A man might spend days going round milk distributors in Glasgow begging them to take his milk. He was in no position to haggle over the price. The problem was to find a buyer. When every kind of dish on the farm was full of milk, a farmer laid little in store on his right to dispose of his produce in anyway he pleases. It may be amusing but a little tragic that there are those who decry schemes because they threatened to deprive the individual of his liberty.'

In Wigtownshire David McHarg, Robert Grierson and their colleagues had to send their milk as far afield as Dundee, Manchester and Birmingham and at times received no payment for it.

CHAPTER 6

SCOTTISH MILK MARKETING BOARD

The Scottish Farmer in 1954 recalled the setting up of the Milk Marketing Boards by reporting 'these Boards were in a sense the children of adversity and confusion.' they were so necessary for the collection of the county's milk so that producers could gain maximum rewards in the long term, through developing markets for milk and milk products.

We have already seen how confusion had reigned for many years. There was also adversity, adequately summed up by Lord Murray, 'the precipitous halving of prices in 1920–22 was followed by a more general depression until 1926 and then a subsequent three years of relative stability. then in September 1929 came another world slump, beginning in the U.S.A. British farm prices were no exception and in the next three years fell a further 34% until in June 1933 they were back at a level at which they had been before the First World War.

The fall in prices which was almost unparalleled in its severity, caused acute agricultural depression; the industry became increasingly undercapitalised in relation to the agricultural area under crops and grass. Not only did existing buildings, drains, fences, hedges, roadways and equipment deteriorate, but insufficient fresh capital was attracted to make possible extensive and often fundamental changes in farming systems necessitated by the new situation.'

This was the situation facing the advocates for a new system of marketing for milk. The setting up of cooperative marketing organisations Was advocated in 1923 by the Departmental Committee on Distribution and Prices of Agricultural Produce under the chairmanship of Lord Linlithgow (the Linlithgow Committee.) It took the breakdown of previous attempts at collective bargaining to make farmers realise that for organised marketing to succeed, there had to be price discipline. 'the most effective method in converting inertia into progression and in directing the latter along the right lines is that of price' in order that farmers would take themselves out of 'circles of desperation.'

In the South West of Scotland which produced about 60% of the total Scottish production the milk output and price was lower in 1930–31 than in 1924–25. This was partly due to the difficulties and doubts within the dairy industry itself and partly as a result of the depression and unemployment in the economy in general. This caused the demand for agricultural products including milk to fall, thereby increasing the proportion going to the lower priced manufacturing outlet.

After the demise of the Milk Agency there ceased to be a stabilising factor in the milk market. In the early thirties hundreds of farmers were getting as little as 4d. per gallon for their summer milk. In Galloway it was as low as 3d. per gallon. for cheesemakers. What else could they do? There was no other enterprise to which they could turn. For years some were in arrears with their rents. They could not clear their merchants accounts. Many survived by the thrift of their wives and the 'pocket money from poultry and egg sales.'

'Not infrequently adversity tends to breed men of mettle to take up arms on behalf of their weaker brethren.' Fortunately for the Scottish dairy industry there have always been such men around:–

William Aiton, John Speir, John Young, George Buchanan, James Kilpatrick, Andrew Ross, Sir W.T.R. Houldsworth, Alex Murdoch, Sir George Wilson, T.G.Henderson, W.J. Wright, J.G. Inglis, D. Sratton, J.K. Murdoch, Sir David Lowe, Sir William Young and not forgetting those who are still alive!

There is no doubt that the failure of the Milk Agency more than anything else was responsible for the introduction of the first Agricultural Marketing Act in 1931 under which the present Milk Marketing Boards were incorporated. This instilled a new willingness in men of strong character to do something about the sad state of the dairy industry and to encourage the support of the politicians.

A great deal of credit goes to Tom Johnston the then M.P. for West Stirling for furthering the interests of the farmers on the matter of marketing. Having witnessed past failures, he realised that if farmers' cooperative marketing was to survive, producers would have to submit to some degree of discipline. He sounded out his views with the farmers in his locality and found support. It is not often that some radical thinking from a radical man can win support from not so radical farmers! Nevertheless, he prevailed upon Dr Addison, Minister of Agriculture to promote the Agricultural Act which came into effect in August 1931. It vaguely stated 'to regulate the kind and quantity of the commodity to be sold on a particular market.'

This Act was not particularly well received by the leaders of the National Farmers' Union, especially in England, in spite of the desires of the dairy industry. They thought that the sellers would have to submit to too many regulations. They were also suspicious of a Labour Government having compulsory powers over a minority, it being thought that it was the thin edge of the wedge towards nationalisation. There were, rightly,

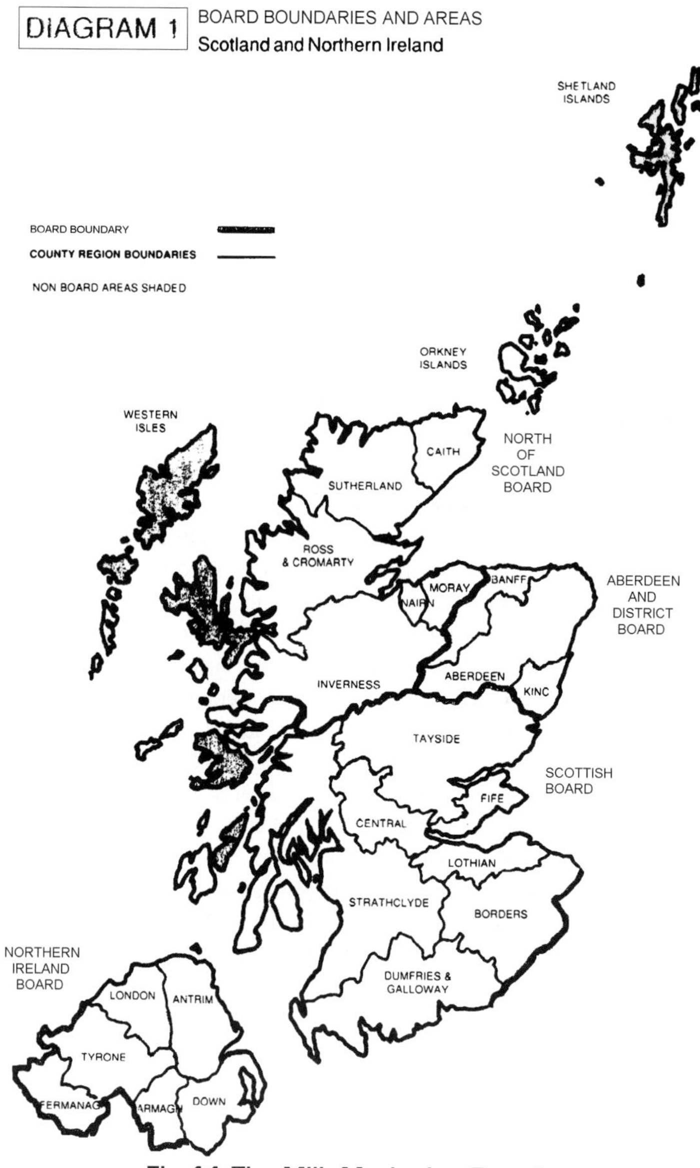

Fig 11 The Milk Marketing Boards

strong reservations about how a scheme set up under this act could operate without control of imports, which had been the cause of many earlier problems.

This doubt was subsequently remedied by a Conservative Government in 1933 by passing another Agricultural Act. This Act was zealously guided through Parliament by Walter Elliot from Lanark who was Minister of Agriculture. It was reckoned to put 'fire in the belly' of the previous Act. Powers were given 'to regulate the volume of imports through quotas or other devices of any commodity that was subject of a Scheme'. Unfortunately some of those powers were nullified by the Ottawa Agreements which allowed the dairy produce of the Dominions easy access to the British market which stoked up problems for the future. These Acts were described as 'enabling acts' under which marketing schemes of various commodities could be instituted. There were schemes for hops, pigs, potatoes and milk.

The role of the Minister of Agriculture was to 'hold the ring' to see that the schemes operated with due regard to the public interest. 'That they are substantially representative of the persons who produce the product in the area to which the scheme is applicable.' Assurances were given that the Act provided a basis whereby farmers can organise their industry to secure better farming, better business and better living. It is only compulsory in that it enabled the majority, of their own free will, to bring the minority to act in the common interest. the essential features of co-operation – the voluntary initiation of action, democratic control, stable treatment of individuals and performance of service on a cost basis have been carefully preserved in the Act. (Plunkett, 1932.)

The setting up of a Marketing Scheme in Scotland benefited from a similar experience in England. There, the Government appointed a Reorganisation Commission for Milk under the chairmanship of Sir Edward Grigg. (Grigg Report 1933). This Commission produced a report outlining a scheme to be recommended to producers. After a lot of consultations and amendments the final scheme differed somewhat from the Grigg Report.

There was no Commission for the Reorganisation for Milk appointed in Scotland as there was in England. Instead a committee under the chairmanship of Major Sprot of Riddell, president of the Scottish Agricultural Organisation Society, was appointed to look into Agricultural co-operation in Scotland. This committee in conjunction with S.A.O.S. acted similarly to the Grigg commission. In effect its objective was to find the most Stable way to set up a Marketing Scheme which would 'compel the minority to co-operate.' The crux of a successful scheme was how to apply the 'pooling principle' and still retain the support of the producers who supplied liquid milk all the year round. ('level producers') After discussions with the Scottish Chamber of Agriculture and the National Farmers' Union, who later amalgamated in 1939 and after many meetings throughout the country, the Sprot Committee recommended that the Government should give consideration to the desirability of protecting cooperative marketing agencies against recalcitrant minorities provided the scheme could prove that it represented not less than 75% of the production of the commodity.

The question of 'level producers' was resolved at a meeting in the conservative club in Glasgow where all opinions of the milk industry were represented by John Young, Skerrington Mains, for Dairy Farmers Cooperatives, Alex Murdoch, Hillside, secretary of East Kilbride Dairy Farmers' Association, for the Glasgow Wholesalers Association and David Stratton, factor to the Weymss Estates in Fife, for the East of Scotland Milk Producers' Federation. It was agreed that 'the scheme was necessary if it gave powers to the Board to compel producers to comply with the Board's price policy.' This decision by those eminent men gave a strong lead for the promotion of a Milk Marketing Scheme for Scotland. Before a scheme could be approved it had to go through a procedure designed to ensure that the effects it would have on producers, distributors and others were fully considered. This necessitated a notice of the submission to be published in the London Gazette or where appropriate in the corresponding Scottish or Irish Gazettes. Thereafter, objections and representations were invited and unless the Minister proposes to modify the scheme to meet the objections, he must arrange an independent Commissioner, normally a barrister, to hold a public enquiry into them and to report.

Once the scheme received Parliamentary approval its main provisions were suspended until a poll of all registered was taken. The scheme lapsed unless at this poll at least half of the registered producers voted and at least two thirds of those voting were in favour. (Winnifrith, M.A.F.F. 1962.)

T.G. Henderson, who came from a farming family in Fyvie, Fife, was the first organiser for the N.F.U. before being appointed secretary to the S.A.O.S. in 1925, which we have seen played a leading part in the setting up of the Milk Agency. He was also very instrumental in the formulation of the Milk Marketing Scheme for Scotland. T.G. Henderson was the driving force at the very centre of the protracted negotiations. He

made an interesting comment on the political scene at the time.
'In 1931 the Labour Government was very dependent on the support of the 40 Liberal members in Parliament. The tactics of the Government and the Opposition were very interesting to watch. The conservatives realised that the legislation of this kind was necessary but they also new that the underlying principle was anything but popular with their following. Their attitude seemed to be to let the Labour party take the responsibility for pushing this controversial measure through Parliament with the help of the Liberals, while they would content themselves at that stage by pressing for amendments to safeguard the various interests concerned so as to ensure that any board that might be set up would have to exercise powers in a moderate and sensible fashion.

The Conservatives were pretty sure that they would be back in office before long when they could make further amendments and in particular provide for control over imports. That in fact was how things turned out for it was a conservative Government which passed the Agricultural Act of 1933 which extended the powers of the 1931 Act mainly to regulate the importation of agricultural products and the sales of home produced agricultural products.

The Labour Government on the other hand were so anxious to place on the Statute Book an Act enabling producers' Marketing Boards to be set up that they were prepared to accept almost any safeguarding provisions in the marketing legislation. Sometimes we used to think that it was overloaded with safeguards.' (Urquart, 1979.) This explains to those who have since studied the Schemes what a fine piece of legislation it has been for the survival of the dairy industry over many years.

Under the same Marketing Acts there were Schemes for hops, potatoes, pigs and bacon.

Just before the Agricultural Act went on to the Statute Book in 1931 there was a conference held which was described as 'perhaps the most representative conference of milk producers ever held in Scotland'. This was a conference held, 'in order that producers of milk may have the opportunity of considering the desirability of attempting the formulation of a scheme for the organising the milk marketing in Scotland.' This conference greatly influenced the promotion of the Scheme.

PUBLIC INQUIRY

The obligatory Public Enquiry into the Scottish Milk Marketing Scheme opened et the Minister of Labour Offices, 103 Waterloo Street, Glasgow, on the 21st November 1932 and continued for six days. It was conducted by Mr Peter Rintoul, C.A. who was accompanied by Mr R.G. Hattle from the Department of Agriculture for Scotland. The 29 promoters for the Scheme were represented by Mr J.L. Clyde who later became Lord Clyde, President of the court of Session for a fee of £100. The promoters had some difficulty in raising this fee.

The objectors on the other hand were represented by Mr A.P. Duffes, K.C. as well as Mr Hill-Watson, Advocate, Mr Donald Mackay and Mr J.M. Croswaite.

It could be said that there were two types of objectors. there were those with vested interests who saw that the Scheme was going to be a major threat to their businesses and really did not want a Scheme at all. On the other hand there were those who were anxious to have a Scheme but were objecting to certain features of it in their apprehension on how it would work in reality.

Such were the feelings at the time that the promoters refused to allow their names to be submitted to the Inquiry in case that were victimised by milk buyers should the farmers vote against the Scheme. Furthermore, among the objectors were well-known men who eventually became members of the Board. Mr T.G. Wilson, later Sir George Wilson, became Chairman. Mr David Marshall, a solicitor from Dunfermline, who acted for the vociferous East of Scotland Milk Producers' Federation also became a member. Many of the so called objectors were in fact supportive of the Scheme but were arguing on behalf of their own vested interests with a view of getting the Scheme amended.

This is not the occasion to give too much detail about a six day public enquiry a summary of which is given in R. Urquart's History of the Scottish Milk Marketing Board. A few comments may suffice.

At the beginning of the Inquiry Mr Clyde explained fully the necessity of having proposals for a Scheme in the light of past experience which hasalready been discussed. Later he indicated that many of the amendments suggested by the various farmer and dairy industry organisations could be incorporated in the Scheme. there were half truths and misinformation which required clarification especially about pooling arrangements and pricing policies.

The creamery cooperatives were very apprehensive about their position. They wanted a guarantee that they could carry on as they were. This of course was premature because a Board was as yet not in existence and did not know what milk was available, yet they were essential to take up the surplus.

Andrew Ross, then president of Kilmaurs Dairy Association said that their creamery was so well recognised and indispensable to its members, that they resolved to oppose the Scheme on the main ground that it gave no guarantee to the creameries of their existence.

Kilmaurs Dairy Farmers Association did not elect to dispose of its assets to the Scottish Milk Marketing Board as many did. This is referred to later. Instead it acquired Fenwick Farmers' Cooperative and became a subsidiary of East Kilbride Dairy Farmers Association Ltd. The latter company had become incorporated in 1920 and took over the Glasgow Dairy Company Ltd in 1928. the Glasgow Dairy Company Ltd was founded in 1878. Mr Ross became a director of East Kilbride Dairy Farmers' Association Ltd at the time of the merger and became chairman on the death of Mr Arthur Gilmour.

Andrew Ross was a man of outstanding integrity and moral worth. He assumed his son-in-law Bill Weir in the partnership of Ross & Weir who built up the internationally known Wheatrigg herd of Ayrshires.

Sir Thomas Clement from United Dairies, a free trader and a loyal supporter of Lord Beaverbrook's 'Empire Preference' was vehemently against the Scheme unless it embraced the whole of Great Britain. He was supported in this idea by the Scottish Cooperative Milk Trade Association.

The idea of having one Board in Great Britain did not go away. In 1935 meetings were held to discuss Amalgamation or Co-ordination of the Scottish and English Boards. Messrs. Bell, Speir and Henderson reported to the Board that the advantages were more apparent than real. There seemed an initial advantage of ld. per gallon. This would be lost if the English Board could not maintain their scale of prices as in their opinion was likely to happen.

The English Board was eight times larger than the Scottish one and had a willingness to amalgamate but they would not bear any part of the cost of dealing with the Scottish surplus which was proportionately substantially greater than the surplus in England. Mr Henderson thereafter wrote that 'When it became clear that under a British Scheme, Scotland would simply be a low priced region, in other words our producers would derive no price advantage, the idea of amalgamating with England was dropped.'

Although over the years there has been a great deal of co-operation between all the Boards, each respecting one another's business, it was not until 1962 that the Federation of U.K. Milk Marketing Boards was founded.

Strathendrick Farmers' Dairy Association may or may not have been typical of organisations which were apprehensive about their involvement with the proposed Board. their members were well advised by Sir George Wilson and also had the advantage of Sir George's brother, Sir John, who was a barrister in London, assisting with their representations and also lobbying M.Ps. in London.

The Association went from a stance whereby Donald Mackay said on its behalf at the Inquiry – 'Your scheme will practically destroy the Society' which after ironing out the difficulties changed to supporting Sir George Wilson's opinion that 'I have arrived at the conclusion that on balance the members stood to gain by voting in favour of the Scheme.'

The assurances which the Association sought and got, swayed the members' opinion in that the Board was willing to use the services of the Dairy Association Cooperative Societies to maintain contact with their registered producers and otherwise facilitate the working of the Scheme especially with regard to collecting and paying for the milk as formerly. 'That any profit arising from the haulage business would supplement the rate of payment received from milk supplies and so offset to some extent at least in the loss that might arise through the operation of the 'flat rate payment.'

In the case of the Edinburgh and Dumfriesshire Dairy things were not so simple. It was 'root and branch' against the Scheme. With most of their supplies being sold in the lucrative Edinburgh liquid market they had no desire to change their position. Similarly the Scottish Cooperative Milk Trade Association who, in spite of their name, were said to have 50% of the liquid milk sales in Scotland, were totally against the Scheme at this stage.

Towards the end of the Inquiry Mr Duffes, K.C. in his summing up declared that they were being asked to support 'an unwanted unworkable and fictitious Scheme, for which few were in favour.'

On the other hand, the promoters contended that the difficulty in marketing milk was not the liquid milk but 'the scramble to avoid cheese milk' and accordingly, the trouble which lay at the bottom of the whole business was the proper disposal of the surplus milk. If that difficulty could be got over plus fixing prices notably as far as producers, distributors and manufacturers were concerned, then the matter would more or less resolve itself. How far have we progressed?

THE BEGINNING

The results of the required poll exceeded expectations much to the relief of the promoters of the Scheme and their associates. 77% of the producers with 78% of the production were in favour of the Scheme. It is a matter of conjecture whether the 'doubters' were influenced by the fact that 96.4% of the English producers voted in favour of their Scheme.

When the result of the poll was published the Scottish Farmer was wont to say 'It is too early to judge whether the marketing schemes are to be efficient or otherwise. They mark an entirely new departure in British agriculture and no doubt experience will bring to light many points that rare adjustment or amendment. Producers hope for the best. Many of them support the scheme from the conviction that organised marketing is necessary for their welfare. Many others, possibly the majority, support it because the Government made it clear that regulation of imports is to be conditional on the organisation of the marketing of home produce.'

The Scheme was legally approved and the Board became operational on the 1st October 1933, However, there was a two month 'suspensory period', making the official starting date the 1st. December, 1933. This was to allow time for members of the Board to be appointed, time to draw up a register of some 8,200 producers, research the amount of milk available and how it was to be moved and particularly to combat with the very difficult task of trying to estimate how much milk the 2,400 producer-retailers were selling.

In England there were 165,000 registered producers and 65,000 producer-retailers.

'It can hardly be to the permanent interest of either farmers or dairymen to continue to fix prices on the basis of opinions naturally biased by the conditions of bargaining, instead of a reasonable approximation of the facts of the situation.' (T. G. Henderson)

In order that the Board could obtain as much information as possible about the disposal of supplies with the minimum of inconvenience to all concerned, each registered producer received a questionnaire with 41 questions. the producers were required to state their lowest daily production in winter and their highest in summer; the manner of road haulage and the distance from Glasgow, Edinburgh or Dundee whichever is nearest to their farm; the distance from the pint of delivery from the farm; the distance from the farm to the point at which the milk is lifted; the amount of haulage charge per gallon and where the milk is carried by rail.

Fig. 12 Earl of Stair
1933-1935

Fig. 13 Sir George Wilson
1935-1950

Fig. 14 Sir James B Douglas
1950-1962

Fig. 15 Sir William Young
1962-1980

Other questions related to the distance of the farm from the nearest creamery, whether the milk cans belonged to the producer or to whom; what water supply and cooling facilities exist on the farm, etc. It would be of interest to know how well this questionnaire would be answered if it were to happen today.

From this position in time it seems inconceivable that all this was expected to be done from an office set up in two bedrooms in the Caledonian Hotel in Edinburgh with T.G. Henderson as Manager and secretary, J.K.Murdoch as Marketing Officer and a small typing staff. 'Those posts were advertised a fortnight ago and the salaries offered were £2000 and £1200 a year. There were several hundreds of applications.' (Scottish Farmer, October 7th 1933.) In that year the wage for an agricultural worker was c.£80.

J.K.' as he was frequently called, like Mr Henderson, was well experienced in the dairy industry and was an ideal enthusiastic, hard working Marketing Officer. He was brought up at Crofthead, Ochiltree, Ayrshire and left Ayr Grammar School at the age of 15. After working on his brother's farm for a year he spent 18 months milk recording then studied cheese and butter making at the Kilmarnock Dairy School. For six months he was assistant to Professor Drummond, principal of the Dairy School and thereafter gained practical experience making cheese and butter at Corra Farm, Castle Douglas, for two years. For three years he was with the United Creameries, Ltd. and for part of the time he had charge of the Colfin Creamery, which he built from the foundation to a concern handling 4000 gallons of milk daily. When the Stewartry Dairy Association was founded in 1921 he was appointed manager and set up the Kirkcudbright Creamery.

In 1933 he was appointed Marketing Officer of the Scottish Milk marketing Board. He actually applied for the managership to which T. G. Henderson was appointed. The Board's Executive Committee were nevertheless sufficiently impressed with J. K they offered him the position of Marketing Officer without interviewing other applicants. Typical of the man in spite of holding out for a higher salary he got the job. At the time he said, 'As with all pioneer schemes there were no precedents. It was all trial and error and one of the biggest difficulties was dealing with the trade buyers in trying to regulate a milk market which was in a terrible state. The trade were in the saddle.'

Until the first annual general meeting of the Board a Provisional Board was appointed. The members were:–

Earl of Stair, chairman; Messrs. Hugh G.Baird, Silvercraigs,

Fig. 16 Mr I. A. McAlpine O.B.E.
Managing Director 1969 - 1985

Fig. 17 Mr T. G. Henderson
Manager and Secretary 1933 - 1958

Fig. 18 Andrew Howie C.B.E.
1982 - 1994

Kirkcudbright; Alexander Batchelor, Craigie Home Farm, Dundee; F.A. Bell Chapelbank, Auchterarder; George Buchanan, Hunterhill, Paisley and Col. T.R. Houldsworth, Kirkbride, Maybole, Ayrshire; W.J.Harvey, Edinburgh; Alexander Newlands and A.S.L. Young.

On the 16th May 1934 the first Annual General Meeting was held in Glasgow at which according to the constitution, a Selection Committee was appointed. the Selection committee comprising of 50 registered producers representative of the whole Board area, was elected each year at the Annual General Meeting. The duty of the Selection committee was to elect the Board members. Candidates for election to the Selection Committee had to be nominated by at least ten registered producers but did not have to be milk producers. Where there was more than f ions a vote was taken which had to take account of proxy votes to be deposited at the head office of the Board not less than 72 hours before the time of the Annual General Meeting.

Interestingly, there was no form of procedure for the conduct of business by the Selection Committee laid down by the Scheme, but they were enjoined 'to make such provision as they deem adequate for the representation on the Board of the registered producers in the various parts of the area of the Scheme.'

The Scheme of the Scottish Milk Marketing Board applied to the counties of Angus, Perth, Clackmannan, Kinross, Fife, Stirling, Dumbarton, Renfrew, Ayr, Bute, Lanark, Dumfries Kirkcudbright, Wigtown, the Lothians, Peebles Selkirk, Roxburgh, several parishes in the county of Argyll, Campbeltown, Southend, and the counties of the cities of Edinburgh, Glasgow and Dundee.

This area was extended in 1950 to include Mid and North Argyle and the islands of Islay, Coll and Gigha.

To make sure that all the area covered by the Scheme was fairly represented on the Selection Committee, the N.F.U. Milk Committee in later years, became unofficially involved by adopting a so called 'gentleman's agreement'. The allocation of producer representatives per the 'gentlemen's agreement' in 1975 was,:–

Dumbarton & Renfrew 3
Argyll 2
Lanark 7
Ayr 11
Bute 2
Dumfries & Stewartry 9
Wigtownshire 5

Lothians 2
Borders 2
Angus 1
Perth 2
Fife & Kinross 2
Stirling & Clackmannan 2

Eight Board members were elected by the producers and two were nominated by the Secretary of State for Scotland. The latter members were appointed because of their experience in commerce, administration, public affairs or were specially conversant with the interests of consumers of milk and milk products. The eight producer elected Board members retired on rotation every four years.

This arrangement foundered between 1980–82 by the alleged abuse of the use of proxies when certain areas nominated an excessive number of candidates which tended to unbalance the principle of having fair area representation. The current procedure came into being when the Scheme was amended in 1982.

In the light of the writer's experience it is doubtful if this amendment was an improvement to the procedure of the Selection Committee.

Those appointed to the Board at the first Annual General Meeting were Messrs. F.A. Bell; George Buchannan; A.G. Shirra Gibb, Wyndhead, Lauder; Col. Houldsworth; John Speir, Newton Farm, Cambuslang; Earl of Stair, David Stratton and T.G. Wilson. Two members were appointed by the Secretary of State. Mr W.J. Harvey, former City Treasurer of Edinburgh and ex-Deacon Convener of Glasgow, John Dallas. Mr Harvey was chairman of the Milk and Health Association which was associated with the official experiments in the testing of milk diets in schoolchildren. Mr John Speir, Chairman of East Kilbride Dairy Farmers Ltd., was the nephew of John Speir who pioneered the system of milk recording.Mr Shirra Gibb was one of the first farmers in Scotland to produce Grade A milk.

Mr T.G. Wilson was the son of Sir David Wilson who was a chairman of directors of The Highland and Agricultural Society of Scotland and of the Board of Governors of the West of Scotland Agricultural College. Sir David carried out fundamental scientific work on the nutritive value of grasses which was summarised by Professor Stephen Watson.

Mr Stratton as has been noted was involved with the East of Scotland Milk Producers Federation at the promoting of the Scheme while he was factor to the Wemyss Estate in Fife. He moved to Kilmarnock to be factor for the Lord Howard de Walden estate which had about a hundred dairy farms on it. He had a very fundamental reason for being on the Board. He said he was interested in the work of the Board 'to see that the producers obtained a good price for their milk, so that they could pay their rents and maintain their farms.'

The Board were given powers to determine the first hand selling price and the minimum retail price of the liquid milk. This protected the wholesalers and retailers from undercutting their respective markets. These powers were withdrawn during the 1939–45 war and were never fully restored.

Joint Committees representing Board, Distributors, Manufacturers, and Haulage Contractors were appointed on an advisory capacity 'to facilitate price determinations and in order to promote harmony in the relations between the Board, distributors of milk, manufacturers of milk products and haulage contractors.' As will be noted later these powers were strengthened in the post-war era.

PROBLEMS

The newly established Board had not its problems to seek. There was still the vociferous minority with their doubts and uneasy feelings about the future working of the Board always ready to criticise. As can be imagined the Board were in a difficult position initially. It was not until it had been in operation for time that the full extent of the problems could some be measured. Estimates on the production of milk were the promoters but they had no reliable data to go on. The proportion of the milk surplus to the rarements of the liquid market turned out to be greater than was anticipated. To make matters worse there was a serious fall in the value of milk for manufacture due to the dumping of imported cheese facilitated by The Ottawa Agreements Act 1932 which allowed free entry for milk products from the Dominions for three years. Imports provided 90% of butter consumed and over 55% of these imports were Empire duty free, while 70% of cheese was imported of which 90% was Empire duty free.

As a result, there was a wide disparity between the prices on the liquid milk market and those on the manufacturing milk market, 14d. per gallon compared with 4.73d. this led to aggravation between producers on the East and West of Scotland. Members of the East of Scotland Milk Producers' Federation were very vociferous in their criticism of the young

Board Meeting in Board Room, Bothwell Street, Glasgow, June 1962. Mr J. W. Clement, Mr W. J. Wright, CBE, Mr D. H. Ross, TD, MA, BL, Mr J. Russell, Sir Alexander Glen, KBE, CB, MC, Auditor, Mr H. McCallum, CA, Assistant Accountant, Mr J. Hamilton, CA, Vice-Chairman, Sir William Young, CBE, JP, Chairman, Sir James B. Douglas, CBE, General Manager, Mr J. G. Inglis, OBE, Miss J. S. B. Hamilton, Secretary, Mr T. W. Gibson, Mr R. H. U. Stevenson, JP, Mr A. R. Semple, OBE, Mr J. M. Whiteford, Marketing Officer, Mr I. A. McAlpine, BSc(Agric), NDA

Fig. 19

Board Meeting in Board Room, Paisley, February 1979. Auditor, Mr W. H. Hunter, CBE, CA, Deputy Managing Director, Mr W. Orr, CA, Mrs T. Beattie, JP, Vice-Chairman, Mr R. A. Lammie, Chairman, Sir William Young, CBE, JP, Managing Director, Mr I. A. McAlpine, BSc(Agric), NDA, Mr E. Sandys, Mr D. Yellowlees, Mr J. A. Minto, JP, Mr J. G. Marshall, Mr W. L. Forrest, Mr W. B. R. Elder, MBE, Mr J. Caldwell

Fig. 20

Board to the extent of accusing the promoters of the Scheme of having misrepresenting the position when explaining the Scheme to producers before the poll. they had a real financial advantage in that all their milk went into the liquid market in stark contrast to the producers in Galloway where most of their milk was made into cheese.

Protest meetings were held and questions were asked in Parliament. There were threats of a breakaway scheme which attracted press headlines. In the Glasgow Herald on 6th September 1934,- 'Scottish Milk Scheme Grievances: Will there be a Breakaway? Lively Edinburgh meeting.' In the Scotsman on the same date: 'Milk Marketing Crisis; East of Scotland Producers not Prepared to Pay , Levy. Breakaway from Scheme Failing Immediate Remedies; Board's New Proposals Inadequate.' Haulage rates, P.R. levies, demands for a premium for level production and the cost of administering the Board were the main grievances. Some of these have never gone away!

The Scottish Board was not alone in being criticised. The English Board came in for some flak from farmers and the press, especially Lord Beaverbrook in his Daily Express, wher it was derogatively, yet colourfully, described, as 'The Mickey Mouse Board'; 'The Milk Muddling Board'; 'The Milk Boar'.

The advent of the Board relieved a large number of producers of their concerns about the cost and haulage of milk but there were those who were not satisfied. Although it cannot be quantified, it is a fair guess that most of the 23% of the producers who voted against the formation of the Board were those who were in a favourable position nearby towns, railway stations and especially producer retailers.

Initially the haulage cost was according to the distance a producer was from the nearest 'haulage centre' which were Glasgow, Edinburgh and Dundee. This did not please the producers in the Central and East of Scotland. The Board after much wrangling ingeniously pacified them by establishing another 12 'haulage centres', the distance from which decided the value of a producer's standard haulage rate which was deducted from the 'Pool' price.

They were really for accounting purposes rather than actual costs of transporting milk. This was significant in the remoter areas such as in Wigtownshire where the maximum rates were paid, yet most of the milk was transported short distances to local creameries. Nevertheless, it assuaged the discontented by reducing their haulage costs and made them more amenable to accepting the 'pool' price principle and other Board decisions.

In December 1934 the haulage rates using the above centres for the purpose of calculating were:–

Not exceeding 5 miles $^{1}/_{2}$ d. per gallon.
Over 5 but not exceeding 10 miles $^{3}/_{4}$ d. per gallon.
Over 10 miles but not exceeding 30 miles 1d. per gallon.
Over 30 miles but not exceeding 40 miles $1^{1}/_{4}$. per gallon.
Over 40 miles $1^{1}/_{2}$ d. per gallon

PRODUCER–RETAILERS

The producer-retailers occupy a special position in the industry with special problems which are distinct from ordinary producers and distributors. Before the inception of the Board producer-retailers were in a relatively advantageous position in having an assured market admittedly not without its problems, however, the cash could always be collected on the spot. their position changed.

From the Board the producer was entitled to the pool price as a producer and as a distributor he was entitled to the distributor's margin which in its earlier years were fixed by the Board. However, he received from his customers the retail price which was greater than the total sum to which he was entitled as a producer and a distributor.

The controversial issue was that producer-retailers had a distinct advantage over their fellow milk producers. In trying to be fair to all the Board imposed a levy on the producer-retailers to pay their share of its administrative costs because they bought and sold milk to the Board to balance the supply and demand of their businesses. It was also to pay a contribution towards the cost of keeping manufacturing milk out of the retail market. On the other hand they sold liquid milk into many places where regular supplies were not available. The levies were an important income for the young Board as there were some 2400 producer-retailers who sold 25% of the liquid milk. They have been a source of controversy since that time.

There were also 'rogue retailers' who bought milk from then unregistered producers and took over a Dairy Shop in Glasgow which was selling about two or three gallons per day. They put up a notice saying 'Cut Price Milk'. In a short time the business was built to 20–25 gallons sold daily, thereupon the business was quickly sold before they could be legally charged.

The producer-retailer levy was at first on a per cow basis about £5 per cow. The Regional Officers visited each to record the number of milk cows. Often a vet had to be called to decide whether the cows should be classified as milk cows or otherwise. the cow levy was quickly abandoned when it was discovered that many of the poorer farmers with about 20 cows were paying a cow levy of £100 when the rent of the farm was only £40–50.

When the levy was changed to a rate per gallon sold retail it rose until it was considered too crippling and many refused to pay. In the first three years there were 1000 prosecutions against those who were in arrears, costing the Board £16000 in litigation fees. Those disgruntled poducer-retailers also objected to the Cooperatives paying their members a dividend on purchases and no levy to the Board.

Ultimately the authority of the Board was challenged in its demands. When a coal merchant, William Innes had not paid his levies the Board seized eight cows and wanted to put them up for sale. This caused an outcry. Farmers and press descended on Tranent on the day of the sale. A 'catalogue' was produced giving 'pedigrees' including Misrepresentation by Statement out of Promoter. Legalised by Parliament out of Error. On a wall, on the farm there was an effigy of Mr Walter Elliot, Minister of Agriculture which was later burned in true modern day style of a demonstration.

Just before the sale Mr W.J. Wright, who later became Vice-Chairman of the Board, representing the East of Scotland Milk Producers' Association addressed a meeting. He pleaded that while there many sympathisers for Mr Innes's stance against the Board he hoped that 'the demonstration would be entirely orderly and peaceful and there would not be the slightest transgression of the law.'

When the sale began the auctioneer was booed and jeered. One Cow was bid for a 1d. and another for 9½d. The sale was abandoned and the cows were led through the streets of Tranent preceded by pipes and drums. During that night the Cows disappeared. The press headlines were 'Cows spirited away'; 'Empty Byres Mystery.. Milk Board Sequel.' Ultimately they were found by the police in various premises and sold at Paisley market for £77 2s.6d.

FERRIER CASE.

The Ferrier court case had a dramatic effect on the future thinking of the Board. It was sued by William Ferrier, Blouse, Jock's Lodge, Edinburgh who was a producer-retailer with a town dairy.

William Ferrier trained as a joiner and after working in South Africa came back to Scotland. Before going into farming he attended

Fig. 21 Mr S. G. Inglis O.B.E.
General Manager S.M.M.B.
1958 - 1969

John Stevenson
Changue, Cumnock

John Whiteford
Nether Southbar, Inchinnaw,
Paisley

Fig. 22 Adam Gray, Mrs A. M. Gilchrist, Fraser Evans, Andrew Howie,
Ian Wilson, Jim Brown, John Duncan, Mrs Evelyn Mundel, Robert Simpson

classes in agricultural economics and veterinary science at the East of Scotland College of Agriculture. In 1925. his herd gained a first class certificate of merit for clean milk production and was one of the first to introduce the bottling of milk in the East of Scotland. He took a keen interest in the formation of the S.M.M.B. and was a witness at the earlier Public Inquiry.

Many producer-retailers were annoyed that the amount of the levy being charged was an increasing burden of crippling proportions. William Ferrier became their spokesman and was well supported. He had been levied at 2d. per gallon when the price was 14½d per gallon this totalled £292 4s. 10d. and he objected. His first court action went against him in the Sheriff Court in 1935 and he lost his appeal to the Court of Session. However, he won his appeal to the House of Lords in 1936.

The Scheme provided in section 24(2) that the Board shall recover from those producers who do not receive payment for their milk through the Board 'such contribution as the Board may from time to time consider necessary to cover the costs of operating the scheme.' Until the decision by the House of Lords, 'costs of operating the scheme' were interpreted as including a sum representing the difference between the actual price received by the Board for milk disposed of by it in the manufacturing milk market and the price which the Board assumed it would have received if such milk had been sold in the liquid market; and the Board had from the beginning calculated its levies on this basis.' (Cutforth Commission).

As a result of this wrong interpretation of the Scheme it was amended, 'resolving the problem by an ingenious compromise' which caused aggro in N.F.U. producer-retailers committees for a long time. The levy was reduced by about half the amount which the Board had been previously charging. Needless to say that this adverse publicity did not endear it to the outspoken critical M.P.s who as always want to make political capital out of such occasions.

Mr F.A. Macquisten, K.C. M.P. for Argyll in 1935 said at a protest meeting in Edinburgh 'There has been no such injustice as The Scottish Milk Marketing Board since the days of bloody Claverhouse and the persecution of the Covenanters. Why should we have Boards coming between the people's food and the people? The Milk Board is the most extraordinary body since the time of Charles II. It is its own court, its own prosecutor, its own judge and puts the fines which it extracts into its own pocket. Stalin has not got on to the Milk Board and as for Mussolini, he is a gentlemen compared with it.' This and the antagonistic Beaverbrook press encouraged the Board's critics.

Fig. 23 BOARD MEMBERS 1983
Gordon Anderson, Mrs Rena Campbell, Henry Christie, Adam Gray, David Yellowlees, Andrew Howie, William Weir, Jim Brown, Jim McIntyre, Jack Brewster

Fig. 24 Board producers discuss topics of common interest as they assemble prior to an AGM.

Initially, the Board did exercise some autocratic powers to which Mr Macquisten alluded. It didnot please wholesalers and retailers. The Board determined the first hand selling price, the distribution margin and the minimum retail price. The ongoing criticism which was highlighted during the various litigations motivated the Government to set up a Reorganisation Commission on Milk Marketing for Great Britain, under the chairmanship of MrA.E. Cutforth. (CutforthCommission, 1936.)

The main value of this detailed 360 page report on the workings of the Milk Marketing Boards was that it recommended that 'the producer boards continue to perform an important integral part of milk marketing organisation....We do not favour any form of direct quantitive control of production or sales.' Its main reccommendation was that a permanent Milk commission should be established as a central authority for the milk industry as a whole 'and as such will advise the Government on questions of milk policy.' It also recommended that there should be only two Boards for Great Britain, one for England and Wales and one for Scotland. The Government did not support either of these reccomendations because of the cited strong opposition from both producers and distributors.

The powers that the Board had at this time were necessary to instill some discipline into the whole industry which to its detriment had so obviously been lacking. As Sir George Wilson said:– 'The main object of the Scheme was to preserve the value of the liquid market as a whole, this is the criteria for profit to the dairy farmer in this country.'

The Board was accused of exacting unduly high prices from the consumer. If the price was too high it was not bought. The prices which the Board negotiated with the trade resulted in the majority of the consumers having to pay more for their milk than in the years immediately preceding the advent of the Scheme, 3d. per pint compared with 2½d. In 1936 the Board proposed to increase consumption by a reduction of ½d. per pint. When referred to a Consultant the decision went against the Board. The Board thereupon invoked its statutory powers and over-ruled the Consultant's decision. The authority to do this was withdrawn during the Second World War and was never restored.

Again as Sir George Wilson said- 'The Scheme was established on the initiative of the producers themselves. They can have it amended, they can have it revoked, it is administered by a Board largely appointed by them who are responsible to them and whom they can individually and severally dismiss. It is therefore a democratic organisation.'

Briefly the main factions of the Board were to organise the collection of milk and arrange its delivery to agreed flyers.

Fig. 25 The Board's Senior Executive Group.
Dr. J. D. W. McQueen, Marketing Director, Mr A. S. McCartney, Director of Creameries, Mr J. S. Pirie, Finance Director, Mr W. Davidson, Board Secretary, Mr I. A. McAlpine, Managing Director.

Fig. 26 A Number of The Board's Department Heads.
Mr G. M. Smith, Technical Director, Mr J. M. Swanney, Director of Cattle Breeding Services, Mr J. D. Hannah, Director of Regions and Farm Services, Mr R. M. Kennedy, Sales Director, Mr D. C. Connell, Director of Computer Services, Mr B. S. Speight, Director of Livestock Advisory Services.

To arrange for manufacture of any surplus milk i.e. in excess of the liquid market.

To collect the payments from buyers, including levies on the producer-retailers.

To pay out the sales proceeds so that each farmer gets the same average or pool price irrespective of the market to which the milk was consigned. In addition, the payments of quality premiums were undertaken.

Many of those factions were taken over by Scottish Milk Ltd. from 1st November 1994.

Throughout the years since the inception of the Scottish Milk Marketing Board on 1st December 1933 till its demise on 1st November 1994, it organised several services for producers and customers, some of which are mentioned in detail later in this book. This involved eleven departments Secreterial Services, Finance, Marketing, Sales Department, Farm Services, Data Processing, Cattle Breeding, Livestock Advisory Services, Creameries, Creamery Sales and Central Laboratory.

As a result of the Ottawa Agreement which allowed large amounts of Empire duty free dairy produce into this country the gap between the price for liquid milk and manufacturing milk widened, 14d. per gallon compared with 4.73d. This encouraged farm cheesemakers to change to this more lucrative market for all their milk which increased the amount to be handled by the Board thus further depleting the pool price.

To prevent prices dropping still further under the Milk Act 1934 the Government payments to the Board payments of a minimum price for milk for manufacture of 5d. per gallon in the summer and 6d. per gallon in the winter. These payments were for two years and were to be repaid later, however, subsequent legislation released the Board from repayment and extended the period of the guarantee atil 30th September 1939. This was the government's first attempt at guaranteeing returns to the milk industry and could be seen as a forerunner of the guaranteed pricing system which was the bedrock of the 1947 Agricultural Act

Prior to 1934 there was quite a large amount of liquid milk sold into England to which the English distributors strongly objected. After a great deal of arguing about the amount of compensation to be paid, it was agreed that the English Board would pay the Scottish Board £100,000 per annum to stop this trade.

About this time the Board was involved in the wholesale liquid milk trade selling to small distributors. This ceased in 1936 until 1984 when it bought over W.W. Stevensons Ltd. in Glasgow, which processed, packaged and distributed large volumes of milk.

Previous experience had shown that to sustain adequate prices for the liquid milk there must be a measure of control of the milk that was surplus. This resulted in probably the most dramatic and entrepreneurial decision, now long forgotten, that the Board ever took in its history. It purchased nineteen creameries. They were valued at £200,000. The Trustee Department of Barclay's Bank loaned the capital at 3% interest over a period of 20 years. The 'Creamery Movement' is discussed later.

In spite of all the initial problems the formation of the Scottish Milk Marketing Board put the whole milk industry on a sound basis. It was a remarkable achievement on how quickly the Board 'got into its stride' and above all how expeditiously the finances were arranged. This assured market brightened the prospects for milk production as witnessed by the production in the Board area increasing from 107.6 million gallons in 1933 to 122.8 million in 1939.

ABERDEEN and NORTH OF SCOTLAND BOARDS.

When the Marketing Acts authorised the setting up of the Milk Marketing Boards it was envisaged that there would be one board for Scotland. At a very early stage in the discussions about the schemes it was quickly realised that the producers were not going to support one that covered the whole of Scotland. The basic reason for this was the dominant position of the producer-retailers.

In the North of Scotland two thirds of the producers were producer-retailers selling about half of the milk. Similarly in the Aberdeen and District area half the producers retailed milk. They had no desire to enter into the pooling and transport arrangements being canvassed. Separate Schemes were initiated for two areas. It was said that at that time the Scottish Cooperative Wholesale Society controlled 50% of the liquid milk sales in Scotland.

The Aberdeen and District Board milk marketing scheme was based on that of the Scottish Milk Marketing Board and the previously existing marketing arrangements of the Aberdeen and District Milk Agency. This Agency was formerly the Aberdeen section of the Scottish Milk Agency and was registered as a separate society in 1931. This covered the counties of Aberdeen and Kincardine. This area was extended to include the county of Banff in 1950.

Initially this Board had an unusual constitution; it consisted of the members of the Committee of Management of the Aberdeen and District

Milk Agency, which was responsible for the promotion of the scheme, together with four persons elected at a general meeting by registered producers who were not members of the Agency. Another two members were coopted after consultation with the Market Supply Committee. The Chairman was appointed by the Board but he did not have to be a member of the Board prior to his appointment, nor be a milk producer.

The North of Scotland Milk Marketing Board, comprised of five registered producers elected at each annual general meeting and two persons coopted after consultation with the Market Supply Committee. The area of this Board extends to the counties of Inverness, Moray, Nairn, Ross, Caithness, Sutherland and Orkney. In 1950 this area was extended to include Moray and Orkney.

The county of Shetland is outside the areas of the Milk Marketing Boards.

THE MILK SCHEME

Apart from Burns there have always been rural poets with the skill to reflect in rhyme the verses of the time and this, no less, by an 'Unknown' in 1934 writing about the S.M.M.B.

When glancin' ower the news the nicht
Ma e'e fell on a wondrous sicht;
I read – O fortune, am I richt,
Or am I dreaming?
I read a ryme ower the licht,
By T.S. Fleming.

That worthy is if I'm no wrang,
Related to the butcher gang,
And they I'm shair, don't care a hang
For us producers;
When they the balance get to bang
We're aye the losers..
He speaks o' fortaes keepin' coos,
In raisin' milk an' scrappin' ploos,
He maun be ravin',
I keena, if they'll like his views,
Even up in Str'aven.

He writes o' what the Scheme will cost,
O'what the workin' man has lost,
A few baubees at most
Is a' we're chargin'.,
Retailers haud the winnin' post,
They've kept their margin.

The scheme, nae doot, has its mistaks;
That is the faut wi' many Acts
But let us get tae candid facts,
And maybe figures,
Afore we mak' unjust attacks
Upon oor neiboors.

We with the question had to grapple;
Dairymen had us by the thrapple;
An' they could squeeze oor Adam's apple
An' that richt thorough;
We fain would seek some savin' chapel
In purgatory.

The pool he likens to a pump;
Producers lyin' in the sump;
As' langs they keepit in a lump,
Nocht could gang wrang;
But when the big hauf took the hump,
It lost the fang.

But fairmers aye were kittle cattle
No aye the best to lead to battle;
As soon's they hear the cannon's rattle
Some soad retreat,
By listenin' tae senseless prattle
That spells defeat.

Noo, hooswives, tak' this guid advice;
Increase your milkman's bill by twice;
By that you will reduce the price
Thae hale year through,
An' help producers oot the vice
They're in the noo.

Yours
UMPIRE, West Lothian (Scottish Farmer 14th March 1934)

The Milk Marketing Boards developed into sophisticated efficient businesses over the sixty two years of their existence; until their demise on 31st October 1995.

They gave producers price stability which is so essential to any business, especially for a perishable commodity such as milk. The supply cannot be turned off at source if the market takes a downturn. The principle of collective bargaining with a degree of commitment and discipline enabled producers, large and small, to receive a fair price and at the same time giving a large number of small buyers and a small number of large buyers a reasonable return. For all parties there was also the advantage of a secure transport system.

As the milk industry comes to terms with the 'non-statutory new world', will it be as successful as the old? 'Those who live longest will see most', and that will be another story!

CHAPTER 7

SECOND WORLD WAR 1939-1945.

During the twenty years between the wars, there was a considerable advancement and extension in the liquid market. The building of creameries nearby railway stations led to the change from farm to creamery cheesemaking. The expansion of the liquid market was greatly aided by the introduction of creamery pasteurisation and refrigeration.

Public Health authorities were giving more attention to milk guided by the first Milk and Dairies Act for Scotland passed in 1914 though not truly operative until after the war when it was modified in 1922 and 1925. These stimulated interest in clean milk methods and influenced keeping qualities.

There were dramatic changes at the farm level. The advent of electricity enabled machine milking to be more widely adopted. The collection of farm supplies by motor lorries made transport more rapid into towns again extending the area for the production of milk for the liquid market.

This was going on at a time when farming generally was in a depleted state due to a long period of low prices. A large number of tenants had no capital and those who had, could not invest it because of stringent leases. On the other hand there were many landlords also without much capital to invest because their tenants could not afford to pay increased rents. This resulted in their land not being farmed in a proper manner.

Many millions of acres reverted to permanent grass. Hedges, fences and dykes were badly kept. Few permanent buildings were built compared with the 1845–75 era and there were masses of rabbits. The impression created at that time about the countryside was that it contained, 'many motely undisciplined farmyard animals, including laying hens of all sizes varieties and tempers, files of ducks waddling to the pond, miscellaneous cats and dogs and a heavy jowled sow vacuuming morsels into her mouth as she swept from the barn to the stackyard and back.!' (A.G. Street, *Hitler's Whistle.*)

Stanley Baker in his book *'Milk to Market'* (1973) has written – 'A sense of betrayal pervaded the farming scene during the 1920s and 1930s arising from the failure of Governments immediately after the First World War to redeem the promises that they had held out as an inducement to farmers to come to the aid of the nation's rescue when food shortage threatened. Successive Governments showed a callous indifference to the plight of British agriculture.'

Sir George Stapleton in his book '*The Way of the Land*' writes:– 'The historian of the future is likely to look on the period between the wars of our time, as one of the bleakest and most barren in the history of western civilisation. It was not a period of surging endeavour, there was no urge to drive forward to a goal clearly seen and fervently desired, for there was no faith and no creative impulse, only mass introspection and mass morbity and an almost incredible muddling of values.'

As mentioned earlier, this depressing state of agriculture was largely caused by the Free Trade Policy of the U.K. Government because it was thought that the country would best prosper by trading high value manufactured products in return for raw materials and goods. This made the country extremely vulnerable to blockading. European countries, on the other hand had adopted a more protectionist policy towards their agriculture so that when Hitler came to power, Germany was less reliant on outside supplies and in effect was more than 80% self sufficient in food.

In the three years preceding the war, British farming supplied a mere 30%, by wholesale value, of the country's annual peacetime food requirements. These proportions varied for the different foods. While home production accounted for 100% of the country's liquid milk, 94% of its potatoes and 50% of its meat, as much as 84% of the country's sugar and oils, 88% of wheat and flour, 91% of butter and 65% of its cheese were imported from overseas. (Hammond, R.J. 'Food', H.M.S.O.)

These salutary facts made the Government realise that in the event of hostilities, food was going to become a 'Munition of War' and be a decisive factor in a situation where Germany had a distinct advantage. Therefore, something had to be done quickly to mitigate this advantage.

In 1937 a Food (Defence Plans) Department was established within the Board of Trade to 'formulate plans for the supply, control distribution and movement of food, including feeding stuffs for livestock, during a period of war, with a view to ensuring that the food supplies of the United Kingdom are maintained and distributed in all eventualities, including an aerial attack.'

In the same year under the Agricultural Development Act, (1937), a Soil Fertility Scheme was introduced to give subsidies for the application of lime and basic slag. A grant of £2 per acre was given for ploughing up pasture which was seven years old or over. By 1945, 6 million acres had been renewed.

In every county in Great Britain a War Agricultural Executive Committee was appointed by the authority of the Emergency Powers

(Defence) Act 1939. They were similar to those which were constituted in 1916 and drew a lot from their experiences. They comprised of local farmers, landlords' and farmhouses' representatives, along with staff from the Department of Agriculture and Agricultural Colleges, who gave the committees a more scientific dimension than previously.

A wide range of powers was given to those committees, although some of them could not be executed without the prior consent of the Minister of Agriculture. They could 'direct the use of any agricultural land, prevent its use for any purposes, terminate the tenancies of land in respect of which such directions were not complied with, especially if not cultivated in accordance with the rules of good husbandry.' Each farm was surveyed to assess its potential capability. In the south of Scotland about two thirds of the arable area had to be ploughed and put through a rotation, which was quite difficult in the 'broken' areas of Galloway. The possibility that this might be done bamboozled many a knowledgeable inspector.

Initially, there was some uncoordinated planning and direction which was often due to outdated maps. A well publicised example was when a farmer was directed to plough part of a main railway line. When he wrote to draw the local committee's attention to this, he said he would do his best but he thought that the embankment was rather steep! Fortunately it was seldom that the powers of compulsion were invoked, not that there were many justifiable complaints. However, due to the wisdom of having a number of farmers of proven ability on the committees, they were usually resolved amicably.

Lord Woolton, Minister of Food in 1942 declared – 'The need for food is so great that farmers must be prepared to deliver the grain to the nation at the expense of their pockets, their land and even their animals.'

For Britain this was the nadir period of the war. Until December 1941 the country was alone. Germany was in possession of a vast area of Europe and in control of the continent from Narvik to Bayonne. 4.5 million tons of British and Allied shipping had been lost in the Atlantic in 1941 and 1942. It was a desperate time.

The agricultural industry responded to this need. The face of the countryside changed responding to the various campaigns and advertisements, such as 'Dig for Victory;' 'Silage saves Ships;' 'Ploughing of Farms is as vital as Arms;' 'Plough now by day and night and beat the weather.' Millions of acres of permanent grass were ploughed up, including golf course. There were about a million allotments scattered over the country and potatoes were grown and pigs kept in Hyde Park, London.

Imports of grain and flour were reduced from 10 million tons to 3 and imports of animal feeding stuffs were reduced from 1.9 million to 11,943 tons between 1938–1943. This was counterbalanced by a phenomenal increase in production – oats by 33%, wheat by 32%, barley by 72% and potatoes by 57%. (Marshall, 1946.) This intensity of production brings to mind Anthony Trollope writing in 1865 – 'The truth is if you farm well, you farm ugly,' meaning perhaps that picturesque nooks and corners have to make way for a planned and profitable strategy.

This remarkable achievement was done by a workforce that was being depleted even before the war began. Between 1921–1938, 25% of the male and female workers had left the land, this included 44% of the male workers under 21. However, compared with the First World War, the labour force was more carefully organised as agricultural work was generally classified as a reserved occupation. This time 12% of the countrymen joined the forces compared with about a third in the previous war.

The farm staffs were prevented from moving out to other industries by the Undertakings (Restrictions of Engagements) Order of June 1940. 'An employer shall not seek to engage any male worker whose normal employment is agriculture, except for work in agriculture.' This was followed by the Standstill Order, the irreverent name for the Essential Workers (Agricultural Scotland) Order which prevented the cessation of a worker's employment by either employer or employee without the approval of the National Services Officer. This caused a bit of concern amongst those who were in the habit of moving about the country-side especially at 'term time', traditionally on the 28th May and 28th November. It caused more concern to the farmer who had an unsatisfac-tory dairyman. Nevertheless it created more stability among the labour force 'to get on with the work.' To ameliorate this situation, a new wages structure was introduced. An average ploughman's minimum wage rose from 34s. 6d. in 1939 to 76s. in 1945.

Sight should not be lost of the older and key men of the remaining labour force. By their dedication and long ours of work they were among the unsung heroes of the war. In trying conditions of shortages and blackouts they had to try to mould the large number of heterogeneous people who wanted and did assist on the farms. Without their help the nation would would have starved. There were volunteers, men, women and children from all walks of life. There were servicemen, prisoners of war and most importantly, the Women's Land Army.

Some farmers did not think that a skilled farmworker should be called up because they thought that it took ten times longer to train a novice into a passable farmworker than it took to turn a raw recruit into a useful fighting man. Certainly, there was an initial hostility by some to the employment of women for the usual chauvinistic reasons, but the Land Girls quickly proved themselves and made a useful contribution to the war effort. These girls must have been tempted to echo Nelson at Trafalgar – 'This is warm work, hardly to last long!

1300 ex-Land Army girls held their first re-union on 2nd November 1974 in Glasgow's Kelvin Hall to which they came from as far afield as Banff, Selkirk, Holland and Canada.

It was fortunate that more farm machinery became available. This enabled work to be done long after horses were tired. In some places there were long debates for and against the use of tractors. Some thought they would destroy the structure of the soil and that for many jobs they could not replace the horse. Others pointed out that the tractor did not eat anything when it was idle. Nevertheless, to assist with staff shortages, the Agricultural Executive Committees organised a tractor service with fleets of ploughs, balers, binders and threshing mills etc. acting as 'Flying Squads.'

At a critical time during the war when shipping losses were at their highest, Winston Churchill made an appeal and gave an assurance to the U.S.A. in a phrase which is now part of our common language- 'Give us the tools and we will finish the job.' This led to the Lease-Lend arrangements with America under which some 4000 tractors and 170 combine harvesters were imported. These were vital in the action being taken to avoid the severe food crisis. Among the tractors imported were Ford-Fergusons, the precursors of the Standard-Fergusons, familiarly called 'the wee Grey Fergies'. These were to sweep the country in the post-war years with their hydraulics, 3-point linkage and a system of machinery to suit. This 3-point linkage on which the machinery could be mounted plus the manoeuvrability of those small tractors, made the demise of horse work on the farm inevitable.

In any crisis there is the problem of priorities. In the quest for more homegrown food to feed the nation, it was fundamental that the production of grain took precedence over livestock production. At that time 100 acres of land devoted to beef and mutton production could maintain only 9 persons for a year, whereas the same area devoted to wheat, could maintain 210 and for potatoes 420. By the same token, land devoted to milk production has a greater output than that producing beef or sheep. (Marshall, 1946.)

The farmer at the beginning of the war could be forgiven for comparing himself with Kipling's Tommy Atkins, –

'It's Tommy this an' Tommy that, an' "Chuck him out the brute!"
But it's "Saviour of 'is country" when the guns begin to shoot.'

From necessity food had to be rationed. This was a tremendous undertaking. When the threat of war loomed ration books were printed in 1939 and the actual rationing of food began in 1940. Each person was entitled to ¼lb. of butter and bacon, ½lb. cheese, 1lb. sugar per week.

There were allowances of 3lbs. sugar and 2lbs. of oranges for those wanting to make marmalade if the receipts were sent to the Local Food Office. Beekeepers also received extra sugar. Meat rationing was based initially on price so that the cheaper the meat the more was obtained. When margarine and shortening were rationed, the total rationing became ½lb. per head per week at which time the butter available was reduced to 2ozs. per head per week.

For many necessities a points system was used based on one used in Germany. Each item had a value and purchases could be made up to a maximum number of points. The points value of each item rose and fell according to its scarcity. Among the items thus valued were canned meats, fruits, vegetables, breakfast cereals, biscuits, condensed milk and clothes. Although every effort was made to make rationing as equitable as possible, in time of scarcity it was inevitable that there was favouritism, queues, under counter sales and black marketeering.

Thanks to the valiant efforts to increase home grown foods the two 'filler foods', bread and potatoes, were not rationed during the war but were later, in 1946 when there was a world scarcity of wheat. In 1947 there was one of the worst winters ever recorded which delayed spring planting by nearly two months. This was followed by flooding and a drought. Potatoes were rationed and bread also, to 9 ounces a day.

Milk was rationed until 1951, butter, margarine, cheese and meat until 1954. Cheesemaking was restricted to the Cheddar variety to maintain an easy-to-handle uniformity of the product during the rationing period. After 1954 regional cheesemaking was allowed and its production grew steadily.

A Rationing Scheme for animal feeding had to be introduced on 1st February 1941. Coupons for animal rations were available from the Department of Agriculture though it was the Agricultural Executive Committees who considered and recommended individual applications for supplementary rations.

In this scheme dairy farmers were allocated a higher proportion of available supplies because of the higher nutritional properties of milk. This did not endear them to their colleagues in other sections of the animal industry. The rations for dairy cows were based on milk sales. It was expected that home grown foods would produce a maintenance ration plus 1 gallon of milk per cow per day. The coupons were issued according to the monthly milk sales less the quantity assumed to be produced from homegrown foods.

This principle did not produce the amount of milk required, because the quality of the homegrown foods, especially grass, was not good enough. The milk output in the South West of Scotland dropped from 93,829,000 gallons in 1938–39 to 86,940,000 gallons in 1942–43. This led Sir George Stapleton, the first director of the Welsh Plant Breeding Station, Aberystwyth to say,:– 'Abundant, cheap supplies of imported foodstuffs were the foundation of farming practices and many a sailor was lost during the war because the value of grass was not appreciated.'

It could be said that this was more applicable to England rather than Scotland. At the beginning of the war temporary grass in Scotland made up 32% of crops and grass acreage compared with 10% in England. Ley farming (taking the plough round the farm) had been practised in Scotland since the 18th century. (Chapter 2.) It was a much more widely adopted practice in Scotland than in England. It revolved round a rotation of grain, roots, grain, followed by 4 – 6 years of grass. By sowing improved varieties of cereals and grasses, the yields of the arable land and pastures increased. In essence a fertility cycle developed – More grass, more stock, more stock, more dung, more dung, more grass. This also resulted in a higher output of root crops. In the root break protein producing crops were encouraged such as peas, beans, kale, vetches and tares. This all led to an increase in milk production, but not without frustrations.

The Scottish Farmer reported in July 1940: "DAD'S ARMY" DEPREDATIONS – 'Farmers' little expected that a considerable part of their strenuous efforts to grow more food were to be nullified by the ruthless and stupidly directed operations of our own home defence service. Without any warning, heavily laden lorries invaded our fields of growing crops last Sunday. Immediately about 200 men set to work trampling in all directions through standing wheat, lying barley, early potatoes, sugar beet and everything that came in their way. Damage to some of the crops is lamentable.'

In milk production an increase in output was sought to be more level throughout the year, demanding an increase in winter milk production. However, costs from the latter were high and margins insufficient. The 'margins' between prices and costs in the winters of 1939–40 and 1940–41 were lower than in 1938–39 and much lower in the summer periods.

This point was made in a letter from the Chairman of the English Milk Marketing Board to the Minister of Food during the winter of 1940–41.

'The milk producers' financial position at the end of the first year of the war is worse than in the preceding year. The average gross increase in income per cow for the year has been £2 over the pre-war year but the increased cost of production per cow for food, wages, transport, etc., has exceeded this sum by at least another £1 per cow.'

These facts were eventually appreciated by the Minister of Agriculture when he spoke in Exeter in February in 1942.

'I have never minced words with you and I tell you frankly that we are facing one of the gravest situations in the whole of this war to date...nothing can make the prospect of our food situation next winter anything but graver than it was this winter. The men in the fighting line and in the factories and the women and the children need every drop of milk you can produce. It may mean life or death. Every gallon counts.' (Murray, 1955.)

During the war years the Government determined all policy matters concerning milk. In August 1940, an Order in Council adding Part 1 X (Milk Marketing) to the Defence (Agricultural and Fisheries) Regulations provided that: 'Notwithstanding anything and any enactment or any enactment in any Milk Marketing Scheme, a Milk Marketing Board shall, in exercising their powers under any such Scheme and in particular their powers to prescribe their prices, premiums and allowances payable to producers of milk, comply with such directions as may be given by the Minister of Food for the purpose and maintaining the supply of milk and regulating the distribution and utilization of milk. The Minister of Food may by Order, confer further powers and further duties on any Milk Marketing Board and may by Order relax any obligation or limitation imposed on any such Board by any enactment or by any Milk Marketing Scheme.'

When war broke out the Scottish Board and other Boards were well established. It was fortunate that they had been established long enough to instil confidence in the industry, otherwise if the conditions of 1930–33 had been allowed to continue for a few more years milk would have been even in shorter supply than it turned out to be when the testing time came.

In 1939 milk production was 6% higher than when the Scheme started.

When war broke out it was first suggested that the organisation that the producers had set up should not be taken over by the Government but that the Boards themselves should be put as it were, in cold storage. Fortunately, wiser counsels prevailed and the Boards continued in operation. The Scottish Milk Marketing Boards became agents to the Minister of Food and were 'the ideal instrument to facilitate the transition of the dairy industry onto a wartime footing' and this mission was accomplished with great skill and success.

Many of the current Board officials were appointed to committees associated with the control of the milk supply during the 'emergency period'. Mr T.G. Henderson became Milk Production Officer for Scotland, Mr J.K. Murdoch, Deputy Director of Milk Supplies (Scotland), Mr W.R. Alexander, chief Grader of Butter and Cheese in Scotland. The War Executive Committees established Milk Production Sub-Committees to exercise closer supervision over dairy farmers in the production of milk supplies and its cleanliness. They were also urged to encourage non-milk producers to commence milk production.

The great pressure on milk supplies necessitated its rationing in 1941. Milk had to be imported from England and Northern Ireland. The situation was further aggravated by the expansion of the Milk in Schools Scheme started in 1934 into a National Milk Scheme in 1940. The latter was the forerunner of the post war National Welfare Scheme. As Minister of Food Lord Woolton declared: 'I am determined to use the power I possess to stamp out the diseases that arose from malnutrition especially among children, such as rickets.' This echoed Winston Churchill: 'There is no better national investment than putting milk into babies.'

In spite of the problems and hazards of war, every endeavour was made to cater for the 'vulnerable sections' of the community; nursing and expecting mothers and their young children. This section of the community were assured of a pint of milk per day at a special rate or free according to their means at a time when the rest of the nation might be getting 1/4 pint at the full price. They were also entitled to the special allowances of oranges, fruit juices, cod liver oil and dried eggs. This was most beneficial to the poorer areas where wages were low and food supplies inadequate. Many of these people were getting a balanced diet for the first time.

This 'vulnerable section' took up 60% of the milk output, which meant that the allocation of milk to canteens, restaurants, works and offices was very restricted.

The Minister of Food assumed control over the movement and distribution of milk by rationalising transport and retail deliveries to ensure that the restricted supplies were delivered with the minimum use of fuel and labour. The permanent imposition of Double Summertime with long periods of 'blackout' restrictions did not make life easy for those involved.

During the hiatus of reconciling supply and distribution, there were many misunderstandings and some aggravation between the S.M.M.B. and the Ministry especially with the implementation of the Milk Supply Order (1941). The true supply position was vague, often misleading figures were bandied about causing distribution problems. With calm deliberation all was finally resolved.

To arrest the decline in milk production and if possible to increase it, the incentive of guaranteed prices for all milk sold off the farms was offered. As always, farmers will quickly change their production methods with the encouragement of money! The aim of the new price structure was to maintain an adequate supply of milk all the year round, to satisfy the liquid demand and have a minimum surplus of 20%.

To facilitate this, a winter bonus was paid at an enhanced rate per gallon for the milk produced in the months of November, December and January. The Government set a maximum price that the consumer could be charged and also fixed the distributive margins of the wholesaler and the retailer.

Dairy farming practices did change to produce the much needed milk. Calving patterns were altered to have more milk produced in the winter, improved feeding techniques were adopted and up to date advice was well received from College and other advisers. Thus in spite of wartime difficulties milk production rose above the pre-war level by 1945. The cash incentive helped. Producer prices rose from 15.04d. per gallon in 1939 to 25.71d. in 1945.

It has been said that only two things in farming remain static throughout history, the land and the duty of mankind to farm it so that its productive powers remain unchanged. However, the products of the land and the tools by which the land is farmed change and will always change in accordance with the needs of mankind and the changes brought by man's progress in science and invention. The agricultural industry during the Second World War certainly illustrated this. This era was a historical watershed in agriculture. It provided the final impetus that was to propel it into a scientific age.

The Minister of Agriculture in May 1945 rightly said to the farming community: 'You have played an essential part in achieving victory and have every right to be proud.'

CHAPTER 8

POST-WAR ERA

After the war there was a great deal of speculation about the future of agriculture and whether nationalisation, tariffs, or a free trade policy would be best for the country. Was there going to be a boom or a slump? The most of Europe was starving. This country was short of food and was so broke that it could not afford to buy food from abroad. Even the weather was unkind. In early 1947 there was one of the worst snow storms on record which was a hard blow for an exhausted country to take after six years of 'Dig for Victory Campaign'. Twenty-five per cent of the national sheep flock was killed, spring plantings were delayed for two months, because of floods from thawing snow and ice, plus heavy rains.

The National Farmers' Unions' were asking about what help would be given to a worthwhile young man without capital to enable him to become a farmer, to further the production of food. The protagonists said that he should get the same amount of State help that was being given to any other young man without capital who wanted to become a shipbuilder, manufacturer, hotel proprietor, etc. 'Blessed is he who expects nothing, for he will not be disappointed.' 9th Beatitude.

To assist in this, the S.M.M.B. advertised in the Scottish Farmer in 1946: 'The Board is prepared to help young people desirous of taking up dairy farming as a career to find suitable farms on which to take initial training and to assist those who show the necessary aptitude to take a course at the Dairy School.' Very few farmers' sons then took a degree or diploma course. Immediately after the war, many young men were attracted off the farms by the lure of big wages in industries whose unions were to hold the country to ransom for many years afterwards.

Fortunately, compared with previous post-war eras, there was neither a boom nor a slump. This was largely due to the passing of the Agricultural Act in 1947. It has been said that it was a 'Revolutionary Act' which was to be the sheet anchor of modern farming. This was probably the time when Government became involved with the fortunes of the agricultural industry to an extent unknown before in this country in peacetime.

The preamble to the Act stated that the objective of the Government policy was to 'promote a stable and efficient industry capable of producing such part of the nation's food as in the national interest it is desirable to produce in the United Kingdom and to produce it at minimum prices consistently with proper remuneration and living conditions for the farmers and workers in agriculture and with an adequate return on capital.'

To achieve the laudable aims of the 1947 Act, there were a number of criteria layed down by the first post-war Labour Government.

The agricultural Executives Committees for each county which had been re-instituted under wartime measures were established on a permanent basis. They were charged with 'the duty of promoting agricultural development and efficiency to whom the Minister of Agriculture could delegate any of his functions relating to agriculture.' This was for the prime purpose of assisting in the necessary expansion of food production.

Mr Attlee, the Prime Minister in 1947, called the U.K. farming industry to increase their output by £100 million or by 20% over the next five years which represented some 50% above pre-war level. This was achieved in three years. In 1952 the Conservative Government asked for this to be increased to 'at least 60% above the pre-war level', which was achieved.

A comprehensive system of guaranteed prices for all the principle agricultural products except for wool was introduced. Wool was added in 1950. While there were controls and food rationing, the Minister of Food purchased these agricultural products. In 1954 this ceased except for milk which was derationed in 1950. Thereafter, The Minister of Food was merged with the Minister of Agriculture and an ingenious system of deficiency payments was introduced.

The deficiency payment system was based on the principle that the farmer sold his products on the free market for the best price he could get and the Government then, if necessary, made a payment to all producers of an amount sufficient to bring their average return up to the guaranteed or standard price. The efficient farmer selling a good quality product got the benefit of his acumen, while the less efficient still got the average price.

Another criterion introduced was that the Government was obliged to review each year with the farmers' representatives 'the conditions and prosperity of the industry and decide the action required relative to the level of guaranteed prices and production grants, always taking into account the interests of the consumers and taxpayers.' This was done at Annual Reviews which had been instigated during the war in 1944. At these, there was a great deal of political shadow boxing and verbal wrangling. Usually an agreement was reached though on a number of occasions the agreements were imposed. Of the twenty Annual Reviews held between 1949 and 1972 – the last review before the United Kingdom joined the E.E.C., fourteen were 'agreed', nine were 'disagreed' and on one occasion, the Council of the N.F.U. decided merely to 'note' the decisions.

The confidence given by the criteria of the 1947 Act enabled the industry to go ahead and fulfil the demands of the Government to produce as much food as possible, to overcome the post-war shortages and assist with the balance of payment problems.

The Milk Marketing Boards played little part in the fixing of the guaranteed price, though in 1946 the Scottish Milk Marketing Board initiated in 1946 a milk costing scheme, undertaken on behalf of the Scottish Agricultural Colleges to provide information for price negotiations; a mandatory costing system later also applied to other commodities. The Boards were, however, in regular contact with the Minister of Agriculture and the Department of Agriculture for Scotland and conferred with the National Farmers' Union informing of the producers' views. It was the joint efforts of the U.K. National Farmers' Unions who were actually responsible for the final negotiations with the Government in all price fixing matters.

At that time there was still a feeling of mistrust about the Boards' marketing powers and they were subject to a lot of criticism by certain sectors. This led to a series of Committees of Investigation. Since the First World War no commodity has been subjected to so many reports. All have been 'consigned to a dusty top shelf of the Ministry's archives from which they are only rescued by historians.'

Report of the Committee on the Production and Distribution of Milk. 1917. Chairman, Viscount Astor.

Report on the Marketing of Milk and Milk Products. 1923. Chairman Lord Lithgow.

Report of the Reorganisation Commission for Milk. 1933. Chairman Sir Edward Grigg.

Report of the Commission for Milk for Great Britain. 1935. Chairman A.E. Cutforth.

Report of the Committee appointed to Review the Working of the Agricultural Marketing Acts. 1947. Chairman Lord Lucas.

Report of the Committee on Milk Distribution. 1948. Chairman Lord Williamson.

The consensus of the Grigg and Lucas Reports admitted the benefits of the Boards to the milk industry and recommended the appointment of a Milk Commission which would be independent of the vested interests of producers and the milk trade. Fortunately for the Boards, the Government of the day did not take up these recommendations. Instead amendments to the Scheme were made under the 1949 Agricultural Marketing Act, which modified the Boards powers and made them more accountable to consumers thus allaying the fears of 'the other interests.'

It was established that the appointment of up to a fifth of the members of the Boards' was to be done by the Government. There were also amendments to allow services to producers to be developed. The Boards were held responsible during the war to attain the Government's objective for milk production. 'It was essential that farmers should be encouraged, the need to produce being in the context of the time more important than the costs of production.' These responsibilities were well carried out in peacetime. Milk producers responded to the Government's exhortations by producing the volume of milk which was sought in two years instead of five as planned by the Government.

The problem of the milk shortage was attacked at the source, on the farm. Improvements in dairy farm management were initiated relating to feeding and to improved breeding of dairy cows linked with milk recording. There was a tremendous upsurge in mechanisation and the use of chemicals. Encouragement was given to the compositional and hygienic qualities etc. The Boards had an important role in several of these changes and developments.

Having had their position clearly established by the 1949 Agricultural Marketing Act, the Boards instigated demands for the restoration of their former powers. None materialised until the demise of the Minister of Food in 1954.

Milk price guarantees had to be treated on a different basis from other commodities because milk was sold for alternative markets. The 'necessary surplus' required was considered to be about 20% above the more remunerative liquid requirements in order to iron out the lower winter production with the increased summer production.

The cost of maintaining the milk guarantees became very high. When milk production increased dramatically up to 1954, the cost became politically unbearable. In 1954, when the Minister of Food gave up its trading activities and merged with the Minister of Agriculture, it was decided that each year after the Annual Review, a guaranteed price for milk would be given to each Milk Marketing Board for a specific quantity of milk known as 'standard quantity'. For any milk produced over this quantity, the price paid for it, would be the average obtained for that

Fig. 27 In 1954, after fifteen years of "emergency" wartime control by the Ministry of Food, the Board's marketing powers were restored.

volume which was sold for manufacture. (Shades of the Glasgow Agreement in 1923). This principle rewarded each Board in their effort to sell more liquid milk. Thus the stage was set for the stimulation of consumption that was recommended twenty years before by William Boyd-Orr and others. The standard quantity concept continued to the end of 1977.

Although there were no deficiency payments on manufactured milk as such, the Government encouraged the Boards to get as good a price as possible for it. They did this by estimating each year the average price the Boards were likely to obtain for milk sold for manufacture. If the Boards succeeded in getting a higher price than the average they retained half the benefit and the Exchequer retained the other half by way of reducing the guarantee payment. Conversely if the actual price was below the estimate, the Government made up half the difference. The overall target for this new price structure for milk was to gradually raise the price so that the full cost of the guarantee was eventually paid by the consumer. This was achieved by 1962.

The Minister of Agriculture continued to fix the maximum retail price for liquid milk and the distributive margin based on the information on costs collected from the industry. This protected the consumer from exploitation from either the Boards or the Trade.

THE JOINT COMMITTEE

Although the Scottish Milk Marketing Board had extensive powers over the sale of milk under the 1933 Scheme the buyers' interests were only partially protected by the 'Joint Committee'. The Scheme states that 'in order to promote harmony in the relations between the Board, distributors of milk, manufacturers of milk products and haulage contractors, the Board shall invite such associations representing these interests as may be known to the Board to appoint representatives to joint committees to which the Board will also appoint representatives'. The role of a joint committee was not defined and therefore, at that time it was to all intents and purposes, purely for consultation if and when the committee members chose to meet.

The amendments made to the Scheme in 1956 considerably increased and defined the roles of the joint committees. They decreed that the Board had to consult the joint committee before determining milk prices, allowances and buyers' premiums. In the event of a disagreement an independent consultant was appointed. The consultant's opinion was not legally binding but was generally treated as if it were, since to ignore it would have raised fundamental questions about the nature of the Scheme. This was not so in 1935–6. When the Board tried to test the effect of a lower summer milk price on the level of liquid sales, it proposed a reduction of ½d. per pint for two months by reducing the distributors' margin, using the Permanent Joint Committee procedure. The distributors naturally opposed this proposal and the matter was referred to a Consultant. The latter found against the Board which was ignored.

In 1979 the Scheme was further amended to take account of E.E.C. requirements, changing the role of the Joint Committee from one of consultation only, to one of negotiation and determination involving –

1) The description of the milk to be sold by the Board.

2) The delivery of milk to be sold by the Board.

3) 'The price of milk to be sold by the Board shall be at the same price for all buyers who intend it to be used for the same purpose.'

4) The establishing of scales and terms of any allowances and premiums paid to buyers and to whom they should be paid.

5) To make milk allocation arrangements.

A Joint Committee consisted of an equal number of representatives from the Board and the Trade, each side having only one vote. The chairman could be independent of the parties but usually alternated between the two parties. To reach an agreement both votes had to be cast the same way otherwise an arbiter had to be appointed by mutual agreement and failing that by the Secretary of State for Scotland.

The relinquishing of the trading activities of the Government and the relaxing of some controls brought producers and Boards more into contact with the market place and the trade.

MILK FUND

The administration of the monies received and paid was done via the 'Milk Fund' system. This had to be self financing. Into this U.K. Milk Fund was paid the guaranteed price for the standard quantity milk for each Board and the average manufacturing price obtained in the open market. These two sums were called the 'entitlement income'. Out of this fund was paid the guaranteed price to producers and the cost of distribution. If there was not enough money coming into the fund to pay both of these items, the retail price was raised although it was possible to run a deficit for a limited period. Before the individual producer's price could be finalised, deductions were made for the cost of compositional premiums, sales promotions, advertising and administration costs, etc. of the Boards.

As milk production increased there were not enough outlets in spite of the industry's efforts to increase liquid milk consumption. As the supply exceeded the demand more milk was being manufactured which had a serious effect in diluting the pool price. The position was continually aggravated as producers strove to increase their production just to maintain their overall income.

The Annual Review in 1954 gave the first warning about this growing difficulty. Exhortations were made to encourage producers to go back into other enterprises such as beef and sheep production. Government action was initiated in a White Paper published in November 1956, later in the 1957 Agricultural Act 'to dampen down' production in order to limit the Exchequer support and yet at the same time to retain farmers' support to produce more efficiently. This latter expression was to irritate farmers for many years ahead.

Towards this end, a Farm Improvement Scheme was introduced in 1957 which provided for grants of a third of the cost of new long term improvements. The Minister of Agriculture said: 'We are trying to carry out 20th century farming with the 19th or 18th or in some cases 17th century fixed equipment.' Financial aid for this scheme was extended in 1963. This helped very materially to enable the industry to remedy a situation which had become progressively worse as a result of the inter-war depression, the difficulties of building during the war and the capital and other restrictions which operated in the immediate post war years.

The warning about the overproduction of milk became louder. In the 1958 Annual Review, which was the second one to be imposed, it was stated: 'That the production of milk continued to increase and is now substantially above current requirements, with undesirable consequences at home and abroad particularly within the Commonwealth.... If output is to be reduced which in the view of the Government would be in the interest not only of the nation but of the industry itself, the high cost production must be discouraged.' In another 'imposed' Review in 1960 '....production in this country of milk for manufacture in excess of the reserve required for the liquid milk market is not economic at anything like the present costs of production and reduces the average return to the producers.'

So great was the concern about controlling the milk production, that in 1961, when the Government made an increase in the guaranteed price of milk, 'it was conditional upon the adoption of a system of production quotas by the industry.' i.e. the current standard quantity principle was to be applied to the individual producer. It was thought that this would protect the weaker producers but would be a severe handicap to the many producers who could profitably and efficiently expand their output at rather lower prices. The Government intention was to bring to the attention of the individual producer the folly of producing too much milk at the uneconomic manufacturing price which was further diluting the pool price.

The concept of quotas was rejected by the National Farmers' Union and the Milk Marketing Boards but agreed to find an acceptable alternative scheme which they failed to do.

The thinking about quotas was instigated when the U.K. Government was making overtures to join the E.C.C. where farmers' incomes were mainly from the market rather than from a support system. It was seen that the food supplies would be greatly augmented from the E.C.C. and at the same time the U.K. manufacturing industry would benefit from the large available consumer market in Western Europe.

In 1963 this thinking had to be modified when General de Gaulle pronounced the fatal 'Non' to the U.K.'s membership to the E.C.C. Christopher Soames, the Minister of Agriculture at the time, a fervent marketeer, had to make an about turn on his thoughts on quotas when he said: '...that unless it became essential, it would not be right for the Government to impose an unnecessary degree of rigidity and it is not good for the dairy industry to have unnecessary rigidity.'

Much of this rigidity was already being imposed by a serious of 'price squeezes' emanating from several Annual Reviews, illustrated by the fact that between 1962–72, six Reviews were 'imposed' and one was 'noted'. The prices were restricted allegedly to make farming more efficient. The Government insisted that it gained more of its income from the contentious 'efficiency factor'. Certainly many made use of the improvement grants which were available to improve efficiency.

As far as milk was concerned, the objective of the Government was to use it as an anti-inflationary measure by keeping the price of it down to the consumer. In so doing this had a deleterious effect on dairy farmers incomes. The figures calculated for the 1964 Annual Review showed that real farm incomes in 1963/64 were 10% below that of 1952/53. This was further aggravated by the problem of scarcity and cost of good labour. The cost of dairy labour accounted for 20% of the total cost of milk production which was fundamental to the profitability of the enterprise.

It was then that economies of scale began to be seriously considered in farm planning. To gain such benefits necessitated considerable alterations to farm buildings and equipment. This was the period when outdated byres were converted to cow cubicles, milk parlours were added and silage making became the mainstay of the winter feeding programme. Many found the capital cost of these improvements too great and left the industry. Bankers' attitude towards lending to farmers was very blinkered, not so enlightened as it is today! For many the decision was expand or get out.

During the decade of the nineteen sixties the number of producers in the S.M.M.B. area dropped about a third from 7040 to 4710. Those who remained expanded their herds. In 1960, 44% of the dairy cows were in herds of over 50 cows, by 1968 this had increased to 64%.

The reduction in dairy cow numbers had a knock on effect in reducing beef output, because some 70% of the country's beef then came from the dairy herd. At the same time there were other indications of a future beef shortage. The world population was increasing and many more people were wanting 'body building foods'. Beef supplies coming into this country were becoming uncertain because of the irregularity of quantities from overseas. Argentinian supplies were halved. Imports from other suppliers such as Ireland and Europe were variable causing peaks and troughs which created market distortions. The U.K. was the main import market, really it was a residual market and consequently experienced the full impact of the fluctuations of the world supplies.

Some economists were wont to say that there would be a shortage of beef for the foreseeable future. 'Who's there in the name of Beezbub? Here's a farmer who hanged himself in the expectation of plenty.' '350 years ago by the mouth of a drunken sailor in Macbeth, nailed the eternal problem of food supply. Scarcity spells hardship and starvation for the people; plenty spells ruin for the farmer'. The problem becomes how to provide abundance in a free market without prices falling to a ruinous level.

To head off any fear of disaster a Selective Expansion Programme was set out in the National Plan in 1965. The basic objectives of this was to 'save imports of food that would otherwise be necessary to meet increasing demand and release manpower to other sections of the economy, which necessitates a further relative expansion of agriculture that is based upon the rate of increase in the industry's productivity.' (Annual Review and Determination of Guarantees 1966.)

To realise these objectives encouragement was given to both the dairy and beef industries. An expanded dairy herd was needed for extra beef production so the Standard Quantity was increased. To stimulate beef production from beef and dairy herds the guaranteed price for fat cattle was considerably raised. A beef cow subsidy was introduced 'to encourage beef production in areas which did not qualify for the hill cow subsidy.'

When the Conservatives returned to power in 1970, they were committed to taking the country into the E.C.C. and all their thinking about agriculture was with that end in view. 'The Government's declared aim is to adapt the present system of agricultural support from deficiency system to one relying increasingly on import levy arrangements under which the farmer will get his return increasingly from the market.' (Annual Review, 1971.)

This entailed the biggest changes in agriculture since the establishment of the 1947 Agricultural Act. The guaranteed prices scheme and the cheap food policy were gradually being phased out. It subsequently meant that farmers' income was to be derived from higher retail prices backed by import levies. The levy schemes introduced were for beef, veal, mutton, lamb, pig meat, sugar and milk products other than butter and cheese. There was some modification to the existing scheme for cereals. Till that time the Community's custom had been to protect the farmers from the world competition and to allow the prices to rise to a level that kept most of them in business.

When Jim Prior, Minister of Agriculture, made the announcement for change, fixed minimum import prices were set for milk powders, cream and condensed milk. This was an extension of previously made arrangements on import controls.

Until 1962, New Zealand and to lesser extent Australia, had always relied mainly on free entry of butter into the U.K. as it was the sheet anchor of their dairy industry policy. It has already been seen that this very often caused difficulties for the marketing of the home supplies. From 1962 individual country quotas were agreed for butter at the beginning of each year.

From 1st July 1964, arrangements were made with the principle overseas cereal suppliers, including U.S.A., Canada, Australia and Argentina, to ensure that cereals , cereal products and by-products were not imported below pre-determined minimum prices. Standard Quantities were introduced for wheat and barley at levels commensurate with increasing demand to provide producers with the opportunity to secure a fair share in the growth of the market.

From April 1969, New Zealand, Australia and the Republic of Ireland agreed to cooperate in a scheme of voluntary restraint in deliveries of cheddar type cheese to the U.K. They were later followed by Canada, Holland, Denmark, France and South Africa. (Economic Aspects of the Dairy Manufacturing Industry, Agricultural Adjustment Unit Newcastle. Bulletin no. 12. 1970)

The main objectives set out in the Treaty of Rome, which was signed in March 1957, were in principle not so far divorced from those included in the 1947 Agricultural Act. There was to be increased agricultural productivity, the assurances of a fair standard of living for the farmers, the establishment of agricultural markets, the guarantee of regular supplies of food and the maintenance of a reasonable price of food.

At the time of entry into the E.E.C. there were many doubts as to the overall benefit that joining the E.E.C. would have for the dairy industry. The Common Agricultural Policy seemed to be failing economically because of massive injections of capital for farm reform programmes and the high cost of supporting the intervention system. One of the founding presidents of the Common Market Commission, Herr Hallstein said that: 'We are not in business we are in politics!'

There were grave concerns as to how the dairy industry would cope with about 600 regulations and directives to which it was going to be subjected. The system ensured that all the E.E.C. countries were free to trade with one another and yet all combined against the outsider, at the same time seeking to have common prices within the community.

The six founder member states, France, Germany, Holland, Belgium,

Italy and Luxembourg, set their institutional prices at relatively high levels in order to encourage food production after the devastation of World War II, especially to encourage the German grain farmer and keep the small producers in business. On reflection the setting of the early intervention prices so high led to high cost farming which has since caused many problems. At the time the French and German had all the 'political clout'. However, it must not be forgotten that there was still an inbuilt fear of starvation uppermost in the minds of the early policy makers especially in the face of the 'Cold War.' Some of those who were involved in those negotiations had been among the 8–9 million refugees starving in West Germany.

The U.K., the Irish Republic and Denmark became members of the Community in January 1973. The Treaty of Accession provided for a transitional period of five years during which these countries had to bring their institutional prices up to the level of the original 'Six'. Denmark decided to adopt the Community prices from the date of joining and did not have the transitional period.

In this current era of milk quotas it is worth reflecting that during this transitional period in 1975, the Government issued a White Paper, 'Food from our own Resources' seeking considerable expansion in milk production.

'There is scope during the period to 1980 for increased output of milk in this country with only a moderate increase in the acreage devoted to dairying. The favourable climate for the growth of grass makes this country particularly suited to milk production....With the wider application of better methods of grassland production and the more general use of well-known and tried conservation techniques for grass, a higher density of dairy cows could be supported without increasing the imported feed required per cow.

....While continuing to meet the demand for liquid milk increased home production would supply more butter, cheese and other milk products including skimmed milk powder which can be a valuable protein food for developing countries. There would be a bigger turnover in our processing plants and more value added within the U.K. The major milk product manufacturers have already invested in extra plant, particular for cheesemaking and it would be advantageous to use this as economically as possible.' Never since 1947 had a Government committed itself to such an expansion of the industry.

The response to these exhortations by the milk industry was dramatic, which led many to say that the milk industry eventually became crucified by its own success. In the Scottish Board area in 1934/5 8,166 producers produced 109 million gallons, by 1977/8, 3,243 producers had an output of 238 million gallons.

Also during the transitional period, according to international policy, the support for capital and other improvements as well as support for agriculture in special areas had to be harmonised. This was when the position of the Milk Marketing Boards came under severe scrutiny by the E.E.C. authorities. Many demanded the dismantling of the boards because of their statutory powers. To rebut this, the authorities asked for evidence that dairy farmers wished to retain their organisations. This required a secret postal ballot signifying the support of at least 80% of the producers in each area who owned at least 50% of the cows

The National Farmers' Unions were very active in canvassing to ensure a high poll. The voting took place in October and November 1978, resulting in an overwhelming support. 98.7% of the producers representing 98.5% of the cows in the S.M.M.B. area voting in favour of the retention of the Board.

Mr Henry Christie, from Wigtownshire, who was Vice-President and Convener of the Milk Committee of the Scottish Union vigorously led the campaign and said afterwards: 'The result of the poll has demonstrated in unequivocal terms that while the Boards have statutory powers, they have the wholehearted voluntary support of their producers and this should put them beyond the challenge from the E.E.C. and make them safe for the foreseeable future.'

It was not until 1st January 1978 that the U.K. achieved full membership of the E.E.C. thus safeguarding the country against the insecurity about which Sir Winston Churchill once remarked that '50 million people all dwelling on a small island growing enough food for only shall we say 30 million....is a spectacular example of insecurity which history has not often seen before.'

At the time of joining the E.E.C. it was 90% self sufficient in food compared with about 50% in the U.K. which made the U.K. isolated in an uncertain world, with everyone wanting to 'dump food'.

Self-sufficiency percentages.

	E.E.C.	U.K.
Milk	100	100
Cheese	103	43
Butter	117	12
Grain	91	60
Beef and Veal	89	72
Mutton and Lamb	85	36
Pig Meat	100	69

(Scottish N.F.U.)

About 80% of the U.K. milk price was guaranteed by the standard quantity principle, whereas 10%, namely for butter and skim powder was subject to intervention buying.

As has been noted, a large proportion of the dairy imports were from the Commonwealth especially from New Zealand. The E.E.C. dairy industry saw this as their market and tried to oust the Commonwealth suppliers. Because New Zealand was so dependent on the U.K. market, a special dispensation was made. This caused a great deal of wrangling so much so that many thought that the negotiations for entry were going to founder on the price of butter. Eventually New Zealand got special access for its dairy products into the E.E.C market and undertook to deliver only fixed amounts.

The proportion of milk sold in liquid form in the E.E.C. was low with about 77% of their milk being sold for manufacture compared with 23% in the U.K. therefore, it was in the country's interest to manufacture more and save imports.

Most of the dairy industry's failures have been due to two long standing diseases – cheap foreign competition and failure to adapt to new market conditions. How was it going to cope with the future? Was there going to be any white gold?

Sir Richard Trehane, Chairman of the English Milk Marketing Board, said at the time that: 'With the end of the cheap milk dairy imports and the dawn of a new importance to be given to agriculture's role in the balance of payments saving, have brought about a situation in which the case for expansion has never been clearer.'

Another expansion programme for milk production was set in train when again farmers lived up to expectations, resulting in the paradox that the more successful they became the more they were criticised. This expansion came to a sudden halt with the introduction of milk quotas in 1984.

The shine is going off the 'white gold' if it was ever there, as the food processors and supermarkets take over from the Government in dominating agriculture. That is another story. History stops when the memory takes over!

CHAPTER 9

'THE MILKING'

The movement of milk from the cow to the consumer takes a convoluted route. The introduction of the milking machine and the subsequent changes in transportation has made it now a very sophisticated and efficient process. Before the advent of the milking machine there was nothing sophisticated about getting milk out of a cow twice a day by hand milking. It was a drudge if there ever was one. The liveliehood of many depended on the success of what may appear to many as a rather simple routine. A writer of bygone days was correct when he said that, 'No operation on the farm requires more knack and concentration of attention and nervous energy, if it is to be effectively and skilfully accomplished than the art of milking.'

The process gave a much needed extra income to the poorly paid farm workers as most of the hand milkers were their wives and daughters. The dairyman who was in charge, often had a large family which was a boon for the supply of cheap labour. They usually milked 8–10 cows morning and evening, starting usually at 5 a.m. On some of the larger farms in Wigtownshire the milkers had to milk about 20 cows twice a day.

In 1875 they were paid 1/6d to 2/6d per week and in addition were expected to work in the fields in a busy time. Normal milking times were 6am and 6pm. If the milk had to be supplied to nearby towns milking began at 3am.

The dairyman in charge was the 'stripper' and in a small herd carried the milk to the dairy. He went round the cows after the milkers checking that they had been properly milked. He 'stripped out' the cows. This prevented any laxity especially by learners at an unsociable hour in the morning. The "stripped milk" was of the highest quality which was very important in the making of home made butter and cheese.

For the learner it was a moderate job sitting there precariously on a stool early in the morning with aching fingers and wrists, being occasionally walloped round the face with a 'skittery' tail. Even on the rawest of winter mornings, relief for those burning muscles was obtained by holding them under an ice cold water tap.

Ian Camber Thomson writing in the Scottish Farmer in 1992 catches the atmosphere about handmilking in his youth. 'I was always fascinated by the way the boss ate his porridge. Aunt Kit would serve this in soup plates, but by the boss's plate she would set a bowl of milk. There was a rythm about the way he scooped a spoonful and sloughed it through the milk on the way to his open mouth.

I was watching him finish off the performance by tipping the dregs left in the bowl down his throat and I was thinking of a dredger I had once seen working on the Clyde, when he put the bowl down with a thump and spoke, 'You should learn to hand milk he said emphatically. 'It'll always stand you in good stead.' ' But you machine milk', I protested. 'All except one, she wont let her milk down to the machine.' 'But she kicks.' Did you ever see her kick me?'

True, I had seen him milk her and she seemed quiet enough but I had heard stories. 'You can strap her legs.' The boss was prepared to be magnanimous. There was no escape I had to agree and before I could stop myself I had blurted out. ' If you milk her without a strap so will I.'

It was too late to retract. He was leaning over to clap me on the shoulder. 'I like a lad with a bit of spirit and I am glad you are stopping on. Tomorrow morning then after you are done in the stable. 'The cow looked like any other cow, quietly eating hay. She looked round as I placed my stool and sat down. The eyes were large, placid and undemanding. She went back to eating hay. I gripped the pail between my knees and reached for the teats. Suddenly,viciously and quite deliberately she kicked me and my bucket and stool into the grip and went back to eating hay.

I lay among the cow muck bruised and shaken. The boss seemed to find my predicament hilariously funny and was doubled up with tears streaming down his face. Finally he recovered to say. 'Well maybe I'd better milk her this morning.' This seemed to set him off again, or it was perhaps the sight of my dung plastered overalls.

'You had better stay and watch me', he said. 'I'll just get a clean pail.' I could hear his trumpeting laughter echoing round the hollow acoustics of the dairy as he barged about among the empty cans and utensils. He appeared carrying a bucket and stool. 'This stool is not that dirty', I suggested. 'I shall need that too', he said mysteriously.

The laughter had stopped but he was still jovial as he walked up beside the cow, slapping her heartily on the rump. She lifted a foot but did not kick. The boss sat down confidently, the pail between his ample thighs, the spare stool by his right hand. 'Right lass,' he bellowed reaching for the teats. The cow stopped eating hay, looked round quickly, then stood eyes front. I had a distinct feeling that she had flicked a glance at the extra stool.

Soon the boss was handing me a foaming pail of rich milk. He stood up and passed to me his milking stool, then with his other stool still in his possession he advanced to fondle the cow round the head. 'Well done old girl, we understand each other,' he boomed. I had the distinct impression there was something of a deterrent about that extra stool.

'All done by kindness,' he said gravely as we went off for our breakfast. 'You can strap her tomorrow.' 'I will,' I said. 'And I will have two milking stools.' We had nearly reached the house door when he turned to me and said seriously, 'A bit of advice.' 'Yes?' I queried. 'Take your overalls before you go in. You're covered in shit.' And this set him off laughing again.

Milking, the drudge it was and still is to some, had its more pleasant moments as taken from Crocket's *Raiderland* 'After tea,or the homely plate of porridge, follows the time for cow milking. Shy lads look into the byre door. The bolder stand each at the cow's tail of his chosen as she milks. There is much confidential talk abroad, the 'luggies' drown it. 'I will see you later,' is the burden of many a soft sung song and the place where is well understood by both (often the hayshed) And a beautiful romance blossomed.

Not so romantic is the scene depicted by in Webster's *General View of Agriculture in Galloway* in 1794.

'Once calves are old enough to go outside, they are put in an enclosure by themselves as near as possible to which for the convenience of milking, the cows are kept. When the maids go to perform this operation, which is done at stated periods, the cows and calves are brought together. The calf is placed at one side of the cow and the maid goes with a pail to the other and thus the operation of milking and suckling goes on at the same time. This, however, is sometimes suddenly interrupted from the cow' partiality to the calf, announced with a blow of her foot which overturns the maid and the pail.

The farmers who have not an enclosure convenient for their calves and they are not the least numerous allow their cows and calves to go together, the latter having previously a kind of muzzle put round their noses, on the upper part of which sharp pieces of iron three inches of iron are fastened, this by pinching the cow, prevents the calf from getting any milk until the maid arrives, when the muzzle is removed and the operation goes on as before.'

There is something 'special' about letting cows out of a byre after milking which caught the imagination of S.R.Crockett again from his book *Raiderland.*

'Open the gate, cried Jess from the byre door to the lounging 'odd' lad. He heard by the clanking and jangling of the neck chains of Hornie and Speckly and the rest as they fell from their necks loosened by Jess's hand. The sound grew fainter and fainter as Jess proceeded to the top of the byre where Marley stood sober and sedate and chewed her evening cud. Marley did not like Jess, therefore Meg always milked her. She would not for some special reason of her own 'let down her milk' if Jess so much as laid a finger on her. She usually shook her head vigorously and pushed heavily against Jess as she came nearer. 'Haud up there, ye thrawn randy!' said Jess in byre tones and so very sulkily Marley moved out. As she went out of the byre door Jess laid her switch smartly across Marley's loins, much to the loss of dignity of that stately animal, who taking a hasty step slipped on the threshold and then overtook her neighbours with a slow resentment gathering in her matronly breast.'

In reality, great emphasis was and still is put on the quiet handling of cows. If they were hurried before milking or upset by noise or a bad tempered milker it was reckoned that the consistency of the milk and cream would be altered which had a deleterious effect on the quality and quantity of the cheese and butter made on the farm. This was so important to the meagre liveliehood of those concerned. To emphasise the need for quietness at milking time some farmers had certain rules such as F.R. Evans at Penkiln in Wigtownshire who had a whistle blown. There were more lighthearted moments, a cheeky youngster in the byre could unexpectedly be sprayed in the face with a well directed jet of milk from a proficient hand milking mother. Many a baby was fed by the hand of a milking mother at the end of the byre.

So much importance was rightly attached to having proficiency in handmilking that it warranted official advice from Ministry of Agriculture and Fisheries and Colleges to ensure correct procedures were adopted. In the Ministry's leaflet on *'Selection and Milking of Dairy Cattle'*,(1925), 'The essentials of good hand milking are that it should be performed, (1) Quietly: that is to say that the milk should be drawn in a manner that will cause no discomfort to the cow; (2) Quickly: if performed quickly, more milk is obtained, for rapid milking appears to be beneficial in increasing the flow. A comparison of the results obtained by good and inferior milkers made this point very clear. A good milker is able to milk 7–10 cows in an hour, the common indication of good milking being the production of plenty of froth or 'head' of the milk in the pail; (3) Thoroughly: the last milk being the richest should always be withdrawn.

To encourage efficiency in handmilking, competitions were held in various parts of the country, including the prestigious London Dairy Show. The points upon which the competitions were judged were:

Manner of approaching the cow, 10; Control of cow and pail, 10; Grip etc. of milker, 20; Cleanliness, 20; Clean stripping, 20; Style and expedition, 20; Total 100 points.

It was always recognised that 'women on the whole were better milkers than men.' There was a prestige associated with a proficient milker. Sometimes it was overbearing. Mrs Hogg from Upper Senwick, Borgue, was an example. She had five daughters all skilled milkers and under her control. A 'byre boy' was employed to assist with the heavier work on the farm who became a better milker than Mrs Hogg. When she felt that her superiority was being undermined she insisted that her husband Alex should sack the young man.

THE PROGRESS OF THE MILKING MACHINE

John McCulloch, Agnew Crescent,Stranraer wrote in the T.H.A.S.S.1875 in an article, *'On Dairy Management as pursued in Galloway!'* 'Milking machines have been tried but being defective in many ways their use has been entirely given up. This unfortunate experience in Galloway happened in many parts of the country. In the 1879 Journal of the Royal Agricultural Society of England, the judges report on the trial of dairy implements at Bristol show in 1878 said, 'The judges greatly regret that there was no entry for the best milking machine. He who successfully solves the difficulty will reap a rich reward. The want of such a machine is the one missing link in dairy management. Greater mechanical difficulties have been overcome and one hopes that before many years, to see the milking machine difficulty practically solved.'

The prize for that class was £50. How much is that at today's value? For years experts said that if nothing was done to mechanise this demanding job, the forecasted scarcity of labour especially women, would see the end of dairy farming.

There was no lack of ideas over the years in an effort to eliminate the demanding twice daily chore. There are American records as far back as 1819. The first attempts to emulate hand milking, a feather and later a metal tube was inserted into the milk duct of the udder. Resulting from this hideous idea, Blurton in 1836 patented a cannula machine with a pail suspended from the cow. In spite of the damage that must have been done to the udder this machine was in use for a number of years before being given up as impractical!

Greater attention was next paid to mechanising pressure on the teats similar to hand milking. An American engineer made the first of this

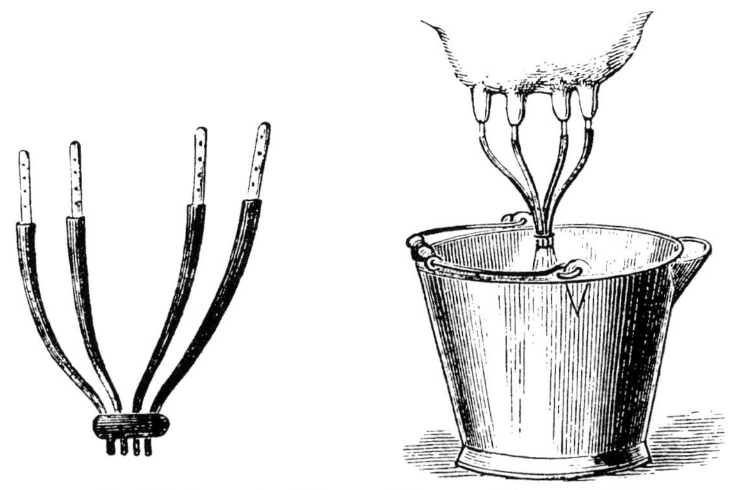

Fig. 28 An early siphon milking machine c.1820

type which was copied in various forms in America, Germany, Sweden and Denmark. There were many examples of mechanically ingenuity using plates, bars, rollers or belts, mechanically, hydraulically or pneumatically operated, commonly called 'lactators'. They all proved to be too complicated for everyday use and they were also very unhygienic. It was, thus,generally agreed that using mechanical pressure alone was unlikely to become a successful substitute for the action of the human hand in the milking of cows.

This lead to closer studies being made on how to emulate mechanically a calf suckling where there is a combination of both suction and pressure used. It is alleged that two British inventors Hodges and Brockenden in 1851 were the first to introduce the principle of vacuum and varying pressures. Colvin in the U.S.A progressed this idea in 1860 by including a form of teat cup. Colvin's hand operated vacuum-milker comprised of a metal bucket with four teatcups and two handles which were moved to and fro to operate the diaphram of the vacuum pump.

The previous failures to have an easily cleaned machine were partially overcome by a 'more hygienic construction' patented by Louis Grasset a French tinman in 1863.

From this period onwards the history of the milking centred for a time on the south of Scotland. Credit for the evolution of the modern milking machine can justifiably be ascribed to a number of Scottish inventors.

One of the first attempts at making a milking machine was done by a plumber, William Murchland, 13, Bank Street, Kilmarnock. He made an ingenious machine by creating a vacuum using a water column and gravitation.

The redoubtable John Speir, Newton Farm, Glasgow, had been toying with the idea on how to make a milking machine between 1875–1881, about the same time as William Murchland. John Speir cooperated with William Murchland on his farm 'to improve his milking apparatus'. This was eventually patented in 1889. By means of a hand operated vacuum pump a continuous suction was provided which 'when operated by a boy could maintain the necessary vacuum for three girls to operate 2 or 3 units each.' The bucket was suspended by straps from the cow and connected to a stall cock by a rubber hose. The teat cups were made from cows' horns each fitted with a rubber mouth piece.

There was, also, a similar machine set up at Haining Mains. John Speir in the T.H.A.S.S.1892, summed up his 'Season's Experience of a Mechanical Apparatus, 'The apparatus as first sent out, although milking fairly well, did not milk sufficiently clean to satisfy the average farmer. At first also, cows which were hand-stripped after being milked mechanically, kept up an unusual quantity of their milk, showing that they preferred hand-milking.

With the latest improvements, hand milking does not interfere with mechanical milking, the cows taking alike to both systems. Where hand-milking is in anyway difficult to accomplish, mechanical milking may be tried without any anxiety as to the result. If at all possible, some mechanical power should be used, as gravitation water, a hydraulic ram, waterwheel, hot-air engine, gas-engine, electricity, steam-engine, or with an American set of driving gear.'

THE WALLACE MILK MACHINE

Stewart Nicholson (1865–1956) was the son of William Nicholson solicitor-sheriff clerk in Kirkcudbright. Although he began work in his father's office, he always wanted to farm. After a time, he prevailed upon his father to rent a field at Castledykes near Kirkcudbright in which he kept bullocks. His enthusiasm to succeed was illustrated by his method of fattening cattle. He made bannocks of barley meal and fed them along with hay. He later farmed the local church glebe.

To become proficient in practical farming, he worked for a short period as a horseman at the Drum farm, Beeswing, Dumfries and thereafter,

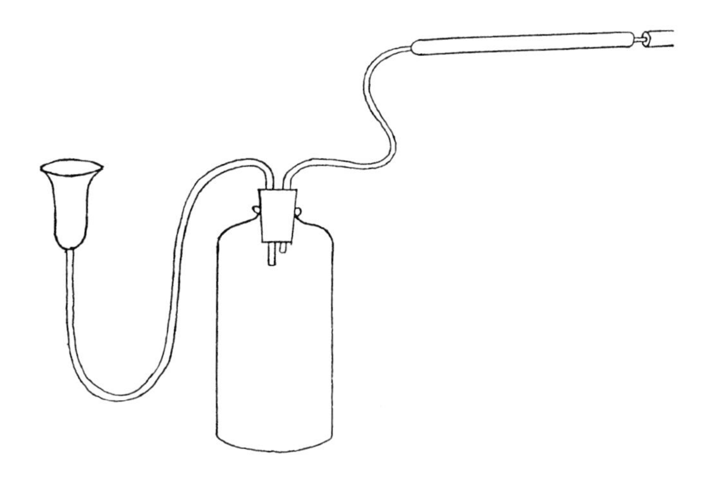

Fig. 29 Stewart Nicholson's drawing of his first Milking Machine, 1890

as an assistant dairyman under John Currie at Kirkeoch, near Kirkcudbright, which was a well known cheese making farm.

It was here that Stewart Nicholson came face to face with the problems of milking cows. He was responsible for the management of the dairy cows which entailed the supplying and supervising a team of hand milkers, usually women. These 'ladies' while they enjoyed the gossip, did not always work in harmony. If one of them left or was sacked for inefficiency, there were complaints because the others had to milk the extra cows. Sometimes where milkers were scarce on a farm, the farmer was obliged to take on an inferior ploughman because he could supply more than one milker.

At times they made the byre resound as they screetched at each other. It was not always words of abuse they hurled. 'I have seen many a can of milk thrown during a fracas. It meant that I had to be in the byre at 5 a.m. and 5 p.m. to keep the peace. I began thinking this was an awful tie when I should be doing something else and wondering if there was no other means of getting the milking done. In Kirkeoch byre one day the idea came into my head – Copy the suckling calf – just like that!'

This was the idea that was to revolutionise the dairy industry. It was also an example of what was written about that time in Hoard's Dairyman, U.S.A. 'A man can fill his mind with useful knowledge by seizing every opportunity to observe the great facts of Nature about him and forcing his mind to think upon those facts.' In 1886 his father, William Nicholson, obtained for him the tenancy of Bombie farm on St Mary's Isle Estate, Kirkcudbright, from Lady Isabella Hope. In those days many landlords chose suitable tenants to ensure a high standard of farming. Mr Nicholson's aunt gave him 100 sovereigns to assist him in buying cows. Once established he pursued his ideas about how milking cows might be done by suction. He experimented initially with a bicycle pump with its valve reversed, so that it sucked and he attached it by a tube to a square sweety jar. When the air was drawn out of it, the jar shattered. He subsequently used a round jar.

To put his ideas into practice, in 1888/89 he said, 'I had a machine made in Edinburgh, it was only a toy, to find if it was possible to draw milk from a teat. When tried on the first teat, the milk rushed into the glass bottle and the quarter was left dry in 2 minutes. When tried on the other teats it would not milk at all. The rubber cup became too soft with the warm milk, but I was convinced that a cow could be milked by a machine so I worked away.'

Mr Nicholson immediately realised that he had to have something more rigid than rubber for a teat cup. The North British Rubber Company came to his assistance and supplied a harder type of rubber. He then experimented with tin torches and bits of exhaust pipe lined with rubber which were shaped to form a teat cup by a Kirkcudbright tin smith, Mr Ramage. This was reminiscent of the old jingle.

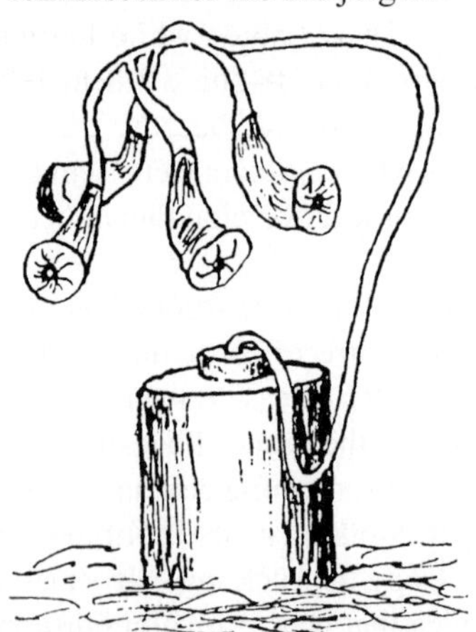

Fig. 30 The Nicholson and Gray Milking Machine

'The Milking'

Mary had a mechanical cow,
She milked it with a spanner,
The milk came out in shilling tins,
And we sell it for a tanner.

Mr Nicholson became convinced that he was on the right track but he was in a dilemma on how to develop his idea further. He was best man to Thomas Clement (later Sir Thomas Clement), who was a partner in the well known butter and cheese selling firm andrew Clement and Sons, Glasgow and he advised Mr Nicholson to consult John Gray, a young dairy implement maker who, although a young man, enjoyed a high reputation for dairy engineering. They formed a partnership in an invention, which was patented as 'A Milking and Quantity Registering Machine' in 1890. John Gray produced teat cups originally made from semi-transparent cows' horns, bored through the centre and fitted with rubber rings to hold them on the teats. Flexible rubber pipes were connected to an airtight 'luggie of white metal' which had a graduated glass up the outside. This enabled the milker to see at a glance the amount of milk produced by each cow. An air pump driven by hand or power created a vacuum.

The experiments with the first prototype were carried out at Bombie Glen by the courtesy of Mr Bickerstaff. This was because Bombie was a cheesemaking farm and all the cows calved in February in order to produce cheap milk from the spring grass thus there were no suitable cows available. Like the Murchland machine, this was also based on continuous suction, which tended to draw the teat too far into the cup causing congestion in the teat with milk and blood. Nevertheless, from press reports the Milking and Quantity Registering Machine was widely acclaimed.

Portable machines with pump, pail and attachments were advertised for 15–20 cow dairies (to milk four cows at a time), at 27s. 6d. per cow installation; fixed machines hand or power, for 30–40 cows (to milk 5-6 cows at a time), 22s. 6d. per cow; and power only, 80–100 cows (milking up to 10 cows at a time), 19s. per cow.

On February 18th 1891, the *North British Agriculturist* reported, 'A new and most important invention, which promises to effect a complete revolution in dairy practice of the country or rather of the world, is presently receiving its finishing touches at the hands of the inventor. This invention is the milking machine invented by Stewart Nicholson, Bombie, Kirkcudbright, whose efforts to bring his invention as near perfection as possible have been most ably supported by his coadjutor and joint patentee, John Gray, the well known implement maker from Stranraer. The extreme simplicity and thorough efficiency of the machine have been enthusiastically spoken of by all the dairy farmers who have witnessed its operation during the past fortnight or so it has been open to inspection at the farm of Bombie.

It is interesting to note the names of the farmers of the locality who took the early opportunity to visit Bombie to judge for themselves the capabilities of the new outstanding invention.

Messrs Kerr, Kirkchrist; Hood, Balgreddan; Williamson, Sypland; Rigg, High Banks; William Montgomery, Banks; Houston, Overlaw; Shennan, Balig; Mitchell, Barcheskie; Wilson, Netherlaw; John Montgomery, Compstonend; Adam Gray, Ingleston, Borgue; William Hood, Chapelton of Borgue; William Gilmour, Balmangan; John Currie, Kirkeoch; and David Wallace, Auchenbrain, Ayrshire.

The *Kirkcudbright Advertiser* on May 15th, 1891, noted that 'It would appear from reports published on all hands, that this the new milking machine as the Americans would put it 'had come to stay'. The machine has been inspected in operation at Bombie by hundreds of farmers and dairymen and one and all have pronounced it a complete success. A machine has already been erected at Low Banks, Kirkcudbright and another at Auchenbrain, Ayrshire and we understand that both of them are giving unbounded satisfaction. Its fame has wafted across the seas, an order having been received from New South Wales and another from Sweden. Machines are also being put in at Howell and Dunragit Creamery and a number of orders are on hand from Derbyshire, Dumfriesshire, Wigtownshire, Fifeshire and various places.

Fig. 31 The first Power Milking Machine installed at Bombie, Kircudbright

This acclaimed machine went on to be exhibited in 1891 at the Highland Show at Stirling and at the Royal Show Doncaster where it won a silver medal. There it was demonstrated to the then Prince of Wales, (later King Edward VII). In the same year, it won a medal at the London Dairy Show. After these successes, it was reported in the English papers. 'The mode of operation with this new machine is briefly this:– Cows horns with india-rubber cushions are fixed on the teats of the cows; flexible pipes from these pass into another pipe, which is connected to an airtight milking pail. An air-pump driven by hand or power, creates a vacuum and the milk is thus drawn from the cow into the bucket the passage of the milk being seen through a narrow window. When the milk is extracted from the udder the tubes fall off and then the operator passes one tube from teat to teat in order to thoroughly strip the cow, which is most important, as the richest of the milk comes at the close.

'I have seen experiments made on cows, which were unused to the novel style of milking and they were not so unruly as might have been expected. About one and a half gallons of milk were taken from a cow in six minutes and it is stated that on a farm where the implement can be tested the operation can be performed in five minutes and the cows are perfectly docile. With one of these machines, a man can attend to the milking of ten cows and an engine of one and a half horse power is sufficient to drive the air-pump. By hand power four can be milked at one time. If this machine should prove to be effectual, it will be invaluable in large dairies as it is difficult nowadays to get handmilkers.'

The successes at shows were not always easily won. Initially, there was a strong feeling against the introduction of milking machines, which was sometimes apparent when they went on demonstration at shows. In order to discredit them, the organisers made available known kicking cows, to show their discomfiture with the machine. To illustrate that the cows would not let down their milk properly, in another part of the show they were suckled with calves before being brought onto the demonstration area.

When the first milking machine in Fifeshire was installed by Mr R.M.Wilson at Brucefield, Dunfermline, The *Dunfermline Journal* reported on the 27th June, 1891: 'For each cow there is a contrivance to which are attached four polished cow's horns. At the widest end of the horn there is placed an indiarubber rim sufficiently large to receive the teat to which it is held by suction. The pointed end of the horn is fixed to an indiarubber pipe which, by means of a sort of pneumatic tube, is connected with the machine provided to create the vacuum. Single and double pails are provided and there is an admirable arrangement by which, when one cow has given all its milk, the action of the machine on that particular cow is stopped without interfering with its companion. The cows, it is said, take kindly to the process and are even quieter than when they were milked by hand.'

There were other quotes from the press. From the *Scotsman*: 'After noting that something like a revolution had been effected in the manufacture of butter, the article goes on : 'As Ruth and the gleaners have been driven from the harvest field by the reaping and binding machine, so the milkmaid seems in danger of being supplanted by mechanical appliances. Cream separators and mechanical buttermakers are now essential requisites in well equipped dairies and the human hand need not necessarily be employed in the working of butter or indeed ever be brought into contact with it.'

From the *Irish Times:* 'No longer will the toff straight from the town be able to ask the pretty maid where she is going. Rude and brutal science is gradually doing away with all our old institutions. Labour saving machines are now as necessary as five o'clock tea. To come to the point, our cows can now be milked by machinery. The apparatus is extremely simple. An air pump from a small engine exhausts the air from a cistern,from which pipes are conveyed to different parts of the cowhouse and connected with airtight receptacles for the milk by movable indiarubber tubes...The inventors of this cast iron lady are Messrs Nicholson and Gray of Stranraer.'

The well known American dairy journal, *Hoard's Dairyman*, carried a more detailed article, 'While the modern appliances for the manipulation of milk after being drawn from the cow leave nothing to be desired, the merit of inventing a machine which should efficiently draw the milk from the cow has up till very recently, eluded all the efforts of the inventor. The want of such a machine has been very severely felt in dairy districts. It had become increasingly difficult in recent times to secure a sufficient number of milkers. Many of the milkers whom the dairy farmer found himself forced to employ were far from being satisfactory and the dirty matter from the udders of the cows and the hands of the milkers in far too many cases was allowed to pollute the milk and injure the quality of the cheese and butter made from it. A machine therefore, should do for the milking of the cows what the separator has done for the separating of the milk from the cream. It is the invention that the dairy farmer has up till now sighed for in vain.

Fortunately, this great aspiration of the dairy farmer has at last been realised by the invention of the milking machine which, in point of simplicity, efficiency and cheapness, is all the most exacting critic could wish...The new milking machine is the joint production of Mr Stewart Nicholson of Bombie, Kirkcudbright and Mr John Gray, the well known dairy implement maker at Stranraer...The idea which has been finally ultimated in this machine, was originally conceived by Mr Nicholson and worked out in conjunction with Mr Gray, who produced all the appliances required for working out the idea to its successful issue. The patent for the machine has been taken out in the joint names of these two gentlemen and the working of the machine at Bombie farm has been witnessed by hundreds of deeply interested dairy farmers, all of whom have enthusiastically hailed it as a certain deliverer of the dairy industry from the thraldom of hand milking.

The machine itself is a marvel of simplicity. There is first of all an air pump as the dynamo, which generates the suction force. Then along the stalls of the byre there is a channel cut, in which there is a metal tube communicating with the air pump and this channel is covered with wood. At the outside of each travis, or stall division there is a "switch" by which a branch tube of indiarubber is brought within the range of the force transmitted through the tube in the channel. The switch is a very ingenious part and by merely being pressed down for half an inch, the branch is turned "on", while by the switch being raised half an inch, the current is turned "off" the branch tube. The branch tube at its other extremity subdivides into four branches, each of which is tipped with a section of a cow's horn, the further end of which have each a lip of indiarubber. These four horns with the indiarubber "lips" are placed over the teats of the cow and adhere closely to the udder by the suction communicated from the air pump along the channel and branch tubes and the milk in this way is rapidly drawn from the udder. The machine also follows the natural method of the calf in drawing the milk from the udder, for every stroke of the pump is followed by a distinct pulsation of lesser force at the furthest end of the branch tubes.

In the invention, as worked out some time ago, the metal tube along the channel underneath the cows was lined with glass and all the milk from the cows was drawn into a central reservoir close beside the air pump, the glass tube being cleaned after each milking by the suction of water along its whole course. Since then an alternative method has been introduced in order to have any cow or cows milk drawn into a separate vessel. By this modification of the original plan, the indiarubber which is put on the switch enters at the one side of a close metal 'luggie' and another branch tube, starting from the other side of the 'luggie' is connected with the udder by the teat cups. In this way the air is sucked out of the "luggie" and as "Nature abhors a vacuum," the milk in the udder is drawn into the luggie to fill the vacuum.

In this connection, it has to be noted that Mr Gray has produced a "luggie" of white strong metal and glass, which is graduated to show the amount milk in it, so that the milker can see the amount of milk drawn from each cow. The cow by this machine can be milked quite clean in from three to five minutes and as one milker can easily attend to the milking of two cows at one time, it is at once apparent that when the dairy farms are all equipped with this machine the difficulty of the dairy farmers with regard to handmilking will be at an end.

We may also note that the cost of the machine will, in an ordinary dairy, only amount to about £1 per cow and less in a large dairy, or little more that a farmer would have to pay for hand milking in the course of a single year and as the machine is so simple and its working parts are not of a kind that will wear much by the work, the essential parts of the machine will easily last a lifetime with little or almost no cost for tear and wear.'

The place of the early milking machine in the dairy industry is summed up by Robert M'Cracken in an article on Dairying written in the *Farming World* in 1891. It was he, who along with Andrew Clement set up one of the first cheesemaking creamery at Dunragit Creamery, in Wigtownshire about 1880.

'After thirty years or more of repeated unsuccessful attempts to bring out a milking machine, the problem has at length been solved. Soon the art of milking will no longer be necessary and all the sentiment with which the milkmaid has become enveloped, will be a matter of ancient history and the poet will loose a theme of inspiration. Surely now will be the golden age of dairying, when all the dairy farmers' troubles will cease.

The milking apparatus will certainly prove a great boon to farmers. By its aid, the hands that do the ordinary work of feeding and attending the cows will be able to attend the milking thus dispensing with the necessity of employing any extra hands for this special work and not only this, but I believe that the milking apparatus will in many cases prove superior to hand milking. Where there is a large herd and six, eight, or ten milkers have to be employed, some of them are sure to be inefficient or to have temperaments which are incompatable with their vocation. In either case the cows suffer and consequently the milk supplies diminish. The machine will always be in the same mood and will never quarrel with the cow, which, while the milk is drawn from her, will stand chewing her cud and enjoying the operation. The milking being thoroughly and efficiently done, we will have fewer bad vessels and the pain and annoyance caused by sore teats will be very much diminshed when the tugging, squeezing process ceases.

The trouble of obtaining satisfactory milkers being thus obviated, farmers will be able to select men suitable for their requirements, instead of having as has often been the case, to take men who could supply milkers, whether they themselves were suitable or not. The ploughmen's wives will not be taken from their homes late and early just at the time when they should be at home preparing morning and evening meals for their families. While the British dairy farmer will benefit by the milking apparatus, we must not overlook the effect it will produce on the continent of America and in our colonies where one of the principal factors in the restricting the area of dairy farming has been in getting the cows milked. The first American modern milking machine was developed in New York by Mr R. Burrell. With the adoption of the milking apparatus in these countries, we must expect an immense expansion in the area devoted to dairying, conseqently increased amounts of dairy produce, rendering the struggle for supremacy here more intense.

Any farmer who adopts this appliance and the instantaneous butter maker will, with the aid of a small engine or other power, be in a very independent position. All he will require to do will be to adjust the milking apparatus to the cow's teats, when the whole process of milking, transferring the milk to the dairy, separating and buttermaking will go on automatically. As soon as the milking is completed the butter will be ready for the market and that almost without the intervention of the human hand. In one department of dairying foreign competition has not yet to any extent entered. In supplying our teeming population with good, wholesome milk, we have a wide field, if carefully cultivated and properly developed. Careful cultivation of this trade is more necessary than some people realise. The methods of sale and distribution of milk, though greatly improved of late years, are still open to objection, as is evinced by the fever scare which is periodically revived in each of our large cities. While in many cases these alarms are groundless, being to a large extent the creation of the fertile imagination of faddists, yet there have been cases where fever has been spread broadcast by a contaminated milk supply. The continual recurrence of scares of these is detrimental to the interests of both the farmer and of the public, as it has a tendency to restrict the use of milk, than which nothing in the way of food can be more beneficial to the rising generation. If in the city, a larger proportion of the earnings of the working classes could be spent in the supplying of their children with milk, we would see fewer of these sadly deformed people, whom we meet at every turn and who are the object of remark by every stranger who visits our shores.'

Thomas Clement realised the potential of the work that both Murchland and Nicholson were doing and tried to advise them about their specifications in order to have their prototypes patented without confliction. In this he was unsuccessful, their disagreements about patents had eventually to be settled in the Court of Session.

To Stewart Nicholson's credit, he knew that his machine was not good enough. He knew that because of the constant suction that there was too much damage being done to the cows' udders especially those of the high yielding cows which he insisted in using as they took longer to milk. This did not help labour relations. James Milroy, who subsequently received an M.B.E. for his prowess at cheesemaking, worked at Bombie for only a year because he could not earn sufficient money to pay his 'rent' according to his 'Bowing' contract due to contaminated milk from damaged udders. So in spite of all the acclaims, the future of this machine was limited.

'After winning the prizes at the big shows and still thinking that the machine was not good enough, I parted with my share to Mr Gray.'

In effect they greed to split up for two reasons. Firstly Gray, unlike Mr Nicholson, wanted to continue with their machine as it was and did not want to put any more time and money into its further developement. Secondly, when the machine was patented it was actuallly in MrGray's name only and Mr Nicholson lost his court case when he tried to claim his share.

This did not deter Mr Nicholson. 'After a time I had my greatest success when I found how to get pulsation by using a metal pipe outside the cup of two tubes with a two way cock operated by hand.' The two way cock by shutting and opening created a vacuum on one side and air pressure on the other, resulting in intermittent pulsation. Unfortunately, Gray had died by this time, so he asked a Mr J. Cummings in Edinburgh to develope his idea. Mr J. Cummings craftily tried to patent it, but Mr Nicholson forestalled this in a resultant court case.

Mr Nicholson had previously tried on several occasions to get Mr Robert Wallace from Castle Douglas to join him in the developement of his machine. He refused until he heard about the pulsator. With the agreement of Mr Nicholson he thereupon patented the new type machine as the Wallace Milking Machine in 1894. Mr Nicholson did not want his name used because of his previous involment with Mr Gray. He thought that it might hinder the sales. Nevertheless, Mr Nicholson continued to assist Mr Wallce in sorting out the teething troubles. Initially, they had difficulty with the strength of the metal in the teat cups. If they fell off, they were squashed if a cow tramped on them, making them useless. Thomas Clement assisted them by putting them in touch with Mr Firth, one of the inventors of stainless steel, who remedied the problem.

At this point the unsung heroes in the development of milking machines should be mentioned. These were the men who went round the farms who tried out the various patents on unsuspecting cows. Many of cows did not take kindly to the idea, kicking out with great gusto at times resulting in black eyes and even an odd broken leg!

Because they were such friends, Mr Nicholson did not bother to have any commercial agreenment with Mr Wallace so that when the Wallace Milking Machine went on to be financially successful Mr Nicholson was left unrewarded. This was in spite of the efforts of his solicitor, uncle Willie, to extract some compensation from Mr Wallace. Thus ended a close boyhood friendship.

It can be said that Mr Nicholson for one reason or another did not make money out of his inventions as did many other inventors even today. However, he held no recriminations, he was always happy in the thought that the fruition of his ideas revolutionised the dairy industry.

The Wallace Milking Machine had the unique feature of having a pulsator on each teat cup. Mr Wallace claimed that this gave it a commercial advantage as it milked the cows quicker and cleaner. Time and experience proved him wrong. An unacceptable level of mastitis appeared in dairy herds due largely to the fierce action of the pulsator being positioned too close to the teats and furthermore there was always a difficulty in ensuring that all four pulsators were operating correctly at the same time. The big twin cylinder vacuum pump eventually proved to be a hindrance.

The pulsating device proved much less harmful on the cow than the continuous suction. It really was a major breakthrough in the evolvement of the milking machine. The intermittent action came as close as was possible at the time to emulating a calf sucking its mother. This was once thought impossible.

The pulsator is often referred to as the heart of the milking machine. It is activated by pressure difference i.e. between atmospheric pressure and partial vacuum. The pressure on the milk in the udder is atmospheric. During the working of a milking machine the udder communicates with a reduced pressure, therefore the milk is caused to flow to a sphere of low pressure in the milk bucket.

Stewart Nicholson's son, James, inherited his father's interest in milking machines. He freely admits today that he never liked the Wallace teat cup, so with his father's encouragement he continued to experiment until he made one he thought suitable to have patented. In his efforts to simulate a calf sucking he would lie on his back in the byre studying one in action. Initially, James Nicholson assembled the new teat cups on his farm at Bombie which sold well because they proved to be much less hurtful to the teats of the cow. On this model the pulsator was situated on the lid of the milk bucket.

Once he had patented the new teat cup, James Nicholson offered it to J.& R Wallace who refused it, because they thought it was no better than their existing one. Other milking machine makers later became interested. It was Manus who positively wanted the the new cup but only if James Nicholson would go to Sweden to have it patented and made there. This he refused to do and the patent was subsequently sold in England to Fullwood and Bland.

THISTLE MILKING MACHINE

The invention of the first pulsator is often credited to Dr Alex Shiels, a medical practitioner with a flair for engineering. He really built on the experience of Nicholson and Gray. Thomas Clement, the entrepreneur that he was, immediately saw the potential of this and encouraged by his father Andrew, in 1895 formed a company known as The Thistle Mechanical Milking Co. Ltd. with a capital of £60,000. They launched two types of machine both made by the other directors, Messrs. Shiels, Elliot, Nelson and Kennedy. One machine was steam powered and the other horse geared. The Thistle Milking Machine, which was first exhibited at the Royal Show at Darlington in 1895 was powered by steam.

Because of the increasing interest in milking machines in 1897 the Highland and Agricultural Society conducted a trial on some of the recently installed machines. A premium of £50 was offered to the one that was considered to have the most potential. This is well reported in the 1898 volume of the *Transactions of the Highland and Agricultural Society*, pp. 166–181.

This was an extensive trial adjudicated by seven judges, who visited seven farms, studying seven machines. Three were the Murchland's

Offices for Patents, Designs & Trade Marks.
GLASGOW, EDINBURGH AND LONDON.

CONSULTING ENGINEERS AND BRITISH & FOREIGN PATENT AGENTS.

TELEPHONE Nº 829.
TELEGRAPHIC AND CABLE ADDRESS: "INVENTIONS," GLASGOW.

CENTRAL OFFICE. 96 Buchanan Street,
Glasgow, 22nd Nov. 1890

John Gray Esq
Ironmonger
Stranraer.

Dear Sir

We duly received yours of 18th inst and as requested have read over and considered the specification of W Murchland's Patent No 15210 Sept 27 1889 for "Improvements in apparatus for milking cows". Taking into consideration what has been put into use and patented prior to the date of Murchland's said Patent, we are of opinion that the improvements protected by you and Mr Nicholson under Provisional application No 13559 Aug 2 1890 do not interfere or conflict with this Patent, and that you can obtain a Patent for your specialities and combination. We enclose copy specification of Murchland's Patent, so that you may see for yourself the extent of his claims.

We are
Yours very truly,
W. R. M. Thomson & Co

1 Encl.

Fig. 32 Letter from Patent Office regarding validity of the Nicholson & Gray milking machine.

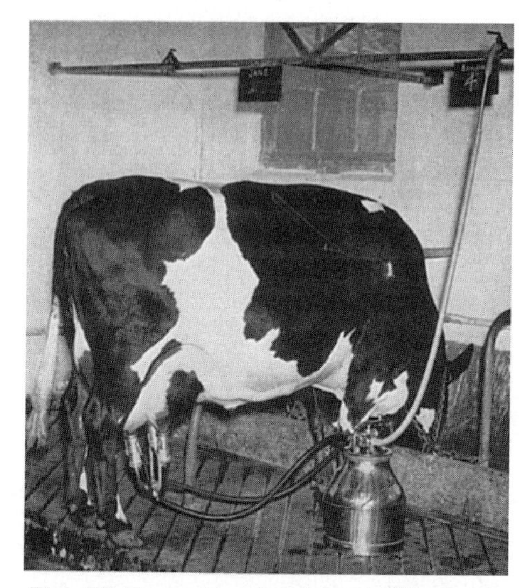

Fig. 33 Typical bucket-type milking unit

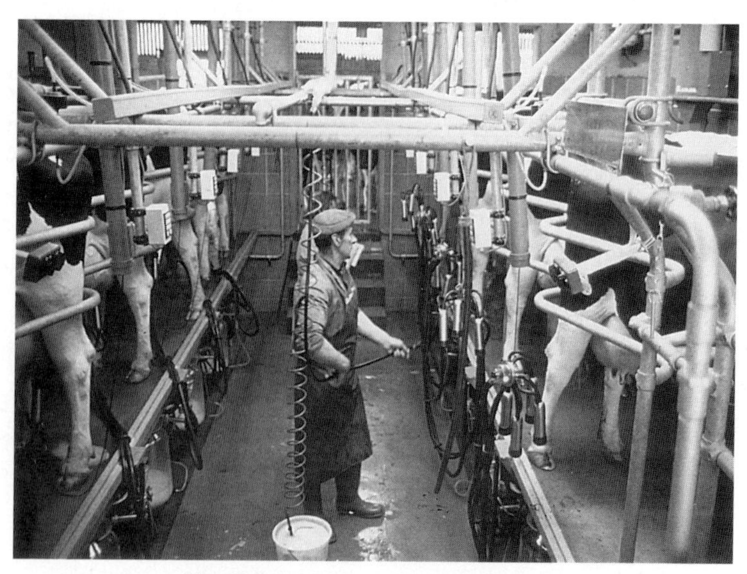

Fig. 34 A Modern Milking Parlour

Milking Machine. Four were the Thistle Mechanical Milking Machines, two of which were steam powered and two were horse-geared.

The panel of judges were :-

Alexander Cross, Knockdon; John Speir, Newton, Cambuslang; John Gilchrist, Orbiston Mains, Bellshill; W.H.Ralston, Culmore, Stranraer; John Drysdale, Fairfield, Kippen; J.R.Campbell, B. Sc. Glasgow; and James D. Park, engineer for the Society.

The committee decided that the trial should be held towards the end of May when the weather would be warmer and 'the keeping of the milk would be subjected to a severer test than if the trial was carried out earlier in the spring. It was also agreed that in order to have the keeping qualities of the milk thoroughly tested, arrangements should be made to have sealed samples of the milk drawn at the different farms both by hand and machine. They were to be forwarded to the Dairy School at Kilmarnock and Mr Drummond be invited to take charge of these samples and report upon them.

Heed was given to special points, many of which are still applicable today.

1) The efficiency and cleanliness given in the performance and operation of milking.

2) The effect of the milking machine on the teats and the udder of the cow.

3) The effect of the milk product itself, as far as the keeping quality was concerned.

4) The facility and ease with which the machine could be thoroughly and effectively cleaned.

5) The power required to work the machine.

6) Its adaptability to the requirements and arrangements of ordinary dairy farms.

The farms visited were :–

Messrs. Burns, Crofthead, Darvel; McFadyen, Staffler, Kilmarnock; T.C.Nelson, Low Carntytne, Parkhead, Glasgow; Tyre Templeton, Gatehead; Templeton, Midton, Kilmarnock; R.Riddet, Cubeside, Dalry; Moffat, Gateside, Sanquar.

The Murchland was favoured, because the milk produced by it had the same keeping quality as that of the hand milked, which was about two days. The milk from the other machines soured in 12–14 hours.......

This defeat mitigated the failure of the Thistle Company. It went bankrupt largely because of the high installation costs on the farms. The Thistle machine cost about five times more than the Murchland. There were also some practical faults. The vacuum could not be maintained satisfactorily due to too much air loss within the system and the milk was frequently contaminated because it was difficult to keep the pipes clean.

It was not until 1905 when J & R Wallace in Castle Douglas produced milking machines for £10 that they really became commercially viable.

When the Thistle Mechanical Milking Machine foundered, one of its directors, Mr Kennedy, in partnership with Mr Lawrence, a Glasgow engineer, produced the Lawrence Kennedy Milking Machine in 1897. They retained the Shiel's principle of the intermittent pulsation. This machine was much more efficient by having the pulsator positioned on the lid of the milk bucket.

This was further modified when Alex Gillies, a dairyman in Terang, Australia, invented a double chambered teat cup to operate on vacuum alone. This was applied to the Lawrence-Kennedy machine and became universally known as the L.K.G. Milking Machine. In it, the pulsator applied a sqeeze to the teat by varying the pressure in the annular chamber instead of interrupting the vacuum applied to the teat.

Thus, after many years of trials and errors, this was the first to embody all the principles of the milking machine as we know it today. At last a humane method of milking cows had evolved.

Thereafter, for a number of years, the L.K.G. and the Wallace vied for their share of the milking machine market. By this time many dairy engineers were applying themselves to mechanical milking using the same foregoing principles, especially in overseas countries such as America and Australia where labour difficulties were even more acute than in this country. In this country the machines which became popular were Alfa-Laval, Gascoigne, Fulwood, Simplex, etc. Mechanical methods of milking cows were first used to a significant extent during the 1914-18 war, more because of the labour shortage than the efficiency of the machines. When labour became more abundant, many of the machines fell into disuse. It could be said that the use of milking machines had a 'stuttery' start. Some used them only when they were in a hurry and because of that they were never properly cleaned between 'hurries', the subsequent dirty milk was often blamed on the machines. 'Milking by hand, was still the most burdensome of regular jobs involved in the production of milk.'

In 1924, the West of Scotland Agricultural College initiated experiments of three year duration, to compare the relative efficiency of a) hand and machine milking and b) the different types of machines. By

Fig. 35 BLK Milking Machine in operation

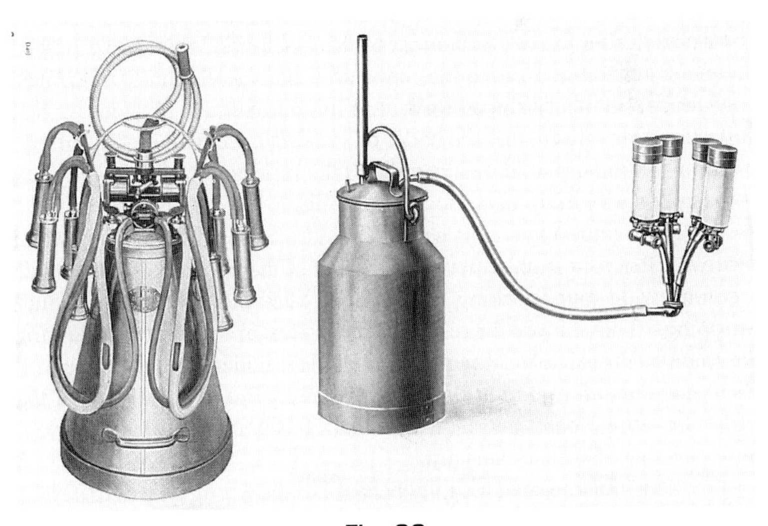

Fig. 36
(a) Laurence-Kennedy Milking Machine with pulsator on top of can
(b) Wallace Milking Machine with atmospheric motor at the end of each cup

1929, 13% of milk recorded herds in Scotland were machine milked and an additional 12% of recorded owners had already discarded milking machines. College studies on the cleaning and care of machines helped to increase confidence and mechanical milking. However, few machines were installed until the 1930s, when elctricity became more available. These installations accelerated at the outbreak of the Second World War, again due to the labour shortage. If it had not been for this, milk supplies during the war would have contracted rather than expanded. In Scotland there were 5650 machines in use in 1942 compared with 22,168 in 1948. (Agricultural Returns.)

By 1944, only about a third of the cows in the U.K. were milked by machine when the average size of the dairy herds in England was 15 and in Scotland 34. The high capital cost for small herds meant a slow uptake of machines even when it was reckoned that after the war, there was a saving of £2–3 per cow. At that time this was about half a man's weekly wage. In places there were the traditional fears of unemployment as workers were being replaced by machines.

There still lingered for a long time, the doubts about the effects the machines would have on cows. There was the fear of the unknown. There were the bad memories of the teething troubles and damaged cows that had abounded during the developement of the machines, which were passed down the generations. For a long time after the installation of machines, cows were still hand stripped for fear of inflammation in the udders. It is still often not realised, that the udder of a cow is never completely empty. It being a living organ, it makes milk all the time and the let down reflex is the cow's way of agreeing to release milk.

These lingering doubts were cleared from the minds of many when Professor Petersen from America as a guest of the *Farmers Weekly* made a countrywide tour lecturing in 1947 and showing a film, 'No Hand-Stripping.' This showed the results of the Professor's research explaining the complex process of let down of milk from the udder and gave some well tried guidelines for good milking. Sir Thomas Baxter, chairman of the Milk Marketing Board, said at the time that, 'It was an epoch-making event in the history of British dairying.'

Many machines were faulty because of the wrong type of materials used. It was after the war that these became more reliable. Many of them were invented to meet the demands of the war, with cheap stainless steel, synthetic rubber and toughened glass. These made the machines more reliable with more emphasis accorded to the comfort of the cow. This was supported by a greater scientific understanding of how the cow physiologically produced the milk especially the complexities of the udder and its reflexes.

The efficiency of later milking machines was greatly improved by the introduction of the magnetic pulsator, which controlled and regulated a uniform number of pulsations on all the units in operation in a byre. This had the effect of reducing the time spent on the milking operation by 20-30% without the milk yield suffering. Changes in any efficient industry are on going. Milking machines are becoming more and more complex and manufacturers are constantly trying to improve their products in either design requirements, use of new materials, or in the application of new ideas and progressions of logical thought. It seems a far cry from milking cows with a few women to the modern milking parlour!

It has been well illustrated in the foregoing that cows' udders can easily be severely damaged by the improper use of the milking machines even modern machines. To obviate this, the Scottish Milk Marketing Board introduced a now well supported milking machine testing scheme whereby regular farm visits are made by Board staff checking and advising the dairy farmers on the efficiency of their machines. For after all, they are the vital link in the production chain and as they are used some 1460 hours in the year like cars or tractors they require proper servicing.

Good luck to the Hoof and the Sows,
Good luck to the Flock and the Fleece,
Good luck to the milking of the Cows,
May they ever have plenty of Peace.

(Sturrock, 1866.)

Fig. 37 A modern byre showing round byre milker which is connected to farm tank. c 1967

Fig. 38 Each day, in all weathers millions of gallons of milk were collected and transported to market from the dairy farmers.

CHAPTER 10

THE MOVEMENT OF MILK
"The milk must get there."

The importance of railways to the dairy industry cannot be over emphasised. They enabled many of the more outlying farms to be drawn into the liquid milk trade. The country milk trade sprang in one bound into prominence and has since gone on increasing.' The railways enabled the evening milk of the country byre to be on the urban doorstep the next morning.

At one time most of the milk was transported by this means which required special organisation in the handling of it. Trains were programmed to reach central stations at hours appropriate to the custom of delivering milk for breakfast.

Before the coming of the railways, the cooling of milk was haphazard. The practice for many years was to set the evening milk to cool in water overnight in tin basins or 'bynes'. The morning milk was despatched uncooled to the town dairy or nearby creamery. In many places the milk had to be delivered twice a day. A number of the town dairies were former premises of old 'town herds.' This cooling method was improved upon with the innovation of the Lawrence refrigerator about 1870. This entailed running milk in a thin stream over the outside surface of zigzag tubes which were internally cooled with a constant flow of cold water.

Although the haulage of milk was greatly facilitated by using oaken 'butts' they were most unhygienic. They caused a lot of problems in keeping milk fresh, not the least problem being to know who was responsible for the milk if it was sour when it arrived to the first buyer. Too often they were left standing for hours on station platforms or in open trucks and were frequently amongst all kinds of other foods. At times they were engulfed and could be contaminated by the smoke from 'puffing engines'.

On arrival at the station in the town early in the morning, the milk churns were opened and the amount of milk they contained noted by the buyers. This was divided between retailers or roundsmen who loaded onto their carts for delivery. It was measured out by a 'dipper' into the consumers' jugs in the streets which were contaminated with dust, dirt, manure and flies; the potential for contamination was considerable, so that the consumer not infrequently obtained an unhygienic commodity.

These problems were compounded by the increased demand for milk that doubled between 1890-1920. Incidentally it doubled again between 1920–1950, but fortunately hygienic conditions were then much better.

Progress, however, was made when the leaky unhygienic milk butts were replaced by standard sized steel cans by 1910. They were first made in 1880. The railway companies initially insisted that they should be conical necked with a 17 gallon capacity. They cost £2.10s. each. It was alleged that this would give them a lower centre of gravity to make them more easily 'rolled' and handled by the railway workers compared with the later adopted 10 gallon cans which were favoured on the farms. The latter were naturally more easily lifted on and off lorries and more easily stored.

There were many arguments about the compulsory sealing of cans. The producer who owned the cans wanted to have them sealed to prevent contamination, adulteration and stealing as he was held responsible for the quality and condition of the milk up to the first buyer's station. The railway companies, who were responsible for the haulage, wanted access to the cans on arrival at the station to allow their 'can sniffers' to operate. They were employed by the railway companies and also by creameries when necessary. They assessed the acceptability of the milk by smelling it whenever the lid was removed. The odour retained at the top of the can was very evident. It has been known that when some cans were rejected and returned to the farm in question, it was mixed with the following day's milk and sent back.

Nothing was done legally to prevent adulteration until the introduction of the Adulteration of Food and Drink Act of 1860. This was supposed to make adulteration illegal, but few local authorities exercised their powers, especially in the rural areas because those who were appointed to administer it were often the persons who were themselves, the offenders. It was in the interest of many 'to let sleeping dogs lie.' There were more compulsory powers under the Adulteration of Food and Drink Act of 1872. There were also railway regulations introduced with regard to the conveyancing of milk by rail in locked and sealed cans.

The Railway Companies' contract said, 'The officials of the Company shall have the power to open any cans in transit in order to ascertain if the quantity of milk therein agrees with the quantity declared.' After a great deal of wrangling the authorities under the Milk and Dairies Order 1926, laid down in the regulations governing the Conveyancing and Distribution of Milk Churns, subject to certain qualifications. 'No person shall open any churn, vessel, or any other receptacle containing

Fig. 39 Horse-drawn milk float c. 1903

Fig. 40 Milk arriving in churns at the creamery

milk or transfer milk from one receptacle to another in any railway van or on any railway station.' This resulted in the companies accepting sealed churns provided the tare weight or gallonage was stamped clearly on the outside.

Most of the country creameries to which farm milk was hauled by horse and cart, later by tractor and ultimately by motor lorry were situated near a main railway line so that it could be more easily despatched to the city markets. In the larger cities, such as London, Glasgow and Edinburgh etc. there were special platforms set aside for the milk traffic. Some of the milk sent to these platforms was known as 'accommodation milk'. It was consigned speculatively to a railway company or to a wholesaler for sale to any trade buyer. In addition to the local supplies, Glasgow buyers drew milk from Kirkcudbright and Wigtownshire. The Edinburgh supplies being sourced from Dumfriesshire have already been mentioned.

When the railway system came to be more used about 1881, the urban market was paying approximately 1s per gallon. From this, the cost of rail and haulage to the station was deducted, giving an approximate return of 8d per gallon. This compared with 3–4d per gallon commonly received by makers of butter and cheese of average quality. This saved farming families the drudgery of churning and cheesemaking and the income was more regular throughout the year, without the customary delay of months while the cheese was maturing .

When the railways were expanding, there were many complaints about the inequality of the rates being charged. It was not an uncommon occurrence to find farmers during their slack seasons of the year taking their produce by horse and cart to a station five or six miles more distant from where it was produced and the railway company hauling it past the very place it had left, because the farmer could get a lower rate from the more distant station than the nearer one. There were other anomalies. The rate from Glasgow to West Kilbride was 8s per ton for potatoes, carrots, grain etc. while to Largs which was five miles farther than from Glasgow, the rate was 6s. per ton for the same goods. At a time when there were large numbers of cattle and sheep being hauled to the northern parts of England, the variation in rates was significant. For example, the distance from Dumfries to Manchester is somewhat less than from Dumfries to Liverpool, yet the rate per waggon of cattle was 7s more for the shorter distance. The single run from Liverpool to Dumfries for a waggon of sheep was 60s. but if the waggon went on to Stranraer the charge was only 5s. more whereas the charge from Dumfries to Stranraer was 31s 6d.

The handling, washing and storing of churns caused problems, especially for creameries and town dairies. It was difficult to get them properly cleaned by hand washing. This was really only effectively done when carried out by automatic washers. The storing and despatching ready for refilling without fresh contamination, was always a hazard. The churns which were sent back to farms were at less risk as they were much fewer in number and could be well washed and steam sterilised in the farm dairy between milking times.

The haulage of milk by rail became more economical and convenient. Deterioration was greatly reduced when large insulated glass lined tanks of 3000 gallon capacity were introduced onto the railways, each replacing 300 cans. It was the use of the motor lorry which completely altered the haulage of milk. It made the movement of milk more flexible and smaller units were able to work effectively. It greatly relieved the farmer of the unproductive daily or twice daily chore of sending his milk to the nearest station or creamery. However, the milk often had to be taken to 'the road end' to await collection because of unsuitable access into some farms or the poor state of many farm roads. In the meantime it could be sitting in the summer sun with deleterious effects. There was no putting a horse in a cart when every animal and pair of hands were required in the hayfield and there were no more worries about the non-arrival of milk churns. It also very importantly gave a new initiative to both farmers and buyers regarding future transport possibilities. Like the railways, it extended even further the area from which milk could be hauled. In fact milk could be hauled easily from anywhere.

Fig. 41 Churns being loaded on to a milk train, mid 19th century

White Gold?

It was a natural progression in the haulage of milk that like the railways, bulk tanks should be put on wheels. This had its infancy in earlier years when farmers in Lanarkshire made their milk into butter and sent this with the buttermilk for sale to the wholesalers and shops in Glasgow. The buttermilk was contained in 50 gallon wooden barrels lashed to or built on farm carts. 'The early morning procession of the horse drawn vehicles coming 20 miles or so into Glasgow with some of the drivers fast asleep must have been a sight to behold. It is immortalised by a local song written by one of the carters and still to be heard, 'Driving into Glasgow in the Soor Milk Cairt.'

Weel, I am a country chappie
Workin' at Bildoon,
A wee bit fairm at Eaglesham
That fine auld fashioned toon,
I gaen wi' milk each mornin'
Sae early efter three,
We tak' the road richt cheerily
The auld grey horse and me.

The ither mornin' early
As the birlin we did pass,
I chanced to get acquainted
Wi' a winsom country lass,
Says I my bonnie lassy
If ye' are goin' the airt,
I'll drive ye' doon tae Glesga
In ma' soor milk cairt.

Wae her cheeks as red as roses
Her ee'n sae bonnie blue,
Glancin' and entrancin'
She thrilled me throo' and throo',
She fairly won my fancy
She stole awa' ma hert,
Drivin' doon tae Glesga'
In ma soor milk cairt.

We cracked awa quite cheerily
As side by side we sat,
An' wi' a blush she telt me
Her name was Maggie Watt,
When passin' bye the water spit
Wae the cairt sounds loud and clear,
A slipt ma' airm aroon her waist
An' spat love in her ear.

Ye' hae heard o' lords an' ladies
Makin' love in shady bowers,
And who they woo'ed an' wun
Among the roses an' flowers,
I'll ne'er forget the mornin'
Wee cupid flung his dert,
And made me pop the question
In the soor milk cairt.

She's never had a hurlin'
In a carriage a' her days,
When I proposed to get
A coach and pair o' greys,
Na' na' says she,
Ye ken the sillar's scarce,
I'd rether hae the jogglin'
In the soor milk cairt

Wae her cheeks as red as roses
Her ee'n sae bonnie blue,
Glancin' an' entrancin'
She thrilled me throo' an' throo,'
She fairly wun ma' fancy
She stole awa ma hert,
When drivin' tae Glesga
In ma soor milk cairt.

When bulk tankers first appeared for a time it lead to an intense competition between the railway companies and the road hauliers. At first the road vehicles were limited in their range of travel because and they could not cope with wet, fog and snow over long distance runs. Ultimately the demise of the railway haulage of milk was inevitable as vehicles and roads improved and road haulage became more flexible, more direct and cheaper. The advent of the diesel engine in mid 1930s enabled a 2300 gallon tanker to compete on equal terms with the railway, although tanker breakdowns were a common risk.

BULK MILK COLLECTION

Because the milk haulage from farm to town dairies and creameries was the highest single operational cost incurred in the handling of milk, the Scottish Milk Marketing Board was constantly aware that the operation must be done as efficiently as possible. It was logical to think that after seeing the material benefit of bulk haulage from creameries to buyers in towns and cities, the next step should be to introduce a scheme whereby milk should be collected from each individual farm by tankers.

This idea was developed, following a visit to the U.S.A. and New Zealand by Sir William Young, Vice-Chairman of the Scottish Milk Marketing Board. The S.M.M.B. bravely introduced a pilot scheme which was the first in the U.K. It cooperated with the A.P.V. Co. to produce two sizes of farm refrigerated tanks, a 300 gallon and 180 gallon, from which the milk would be removed daily. These were supplied to a group of farmers who made a minimum load at no charge. At the end of the experiment these were sold to the group at a written down price.

Fig. 42 The Board pioneered bulk milk collection from farms in Kirkcudbright in 1954 – first collection at Drum Farm, Kirkgunzeon by haulier T. P. Niven, Palnackie.
Brian Pattie, Dr Jeannie Wilson, John Niven, Mrs Jessie Murphie, Jim McClure & Jim Niven.

In 1954, the first farm to have its milk lifted by tanker was the Drum, Beeswing, Dumfriesshire belonging to Dr. Jeannie Wilson, the mother of Ian, a current Director of Scottish Pride Co. Ltd. The experiment covered 23 farms within a ten mile radius of Kirkcudbright Creamery, including that belonging to Sir James Douglas, Barstibly, Board Chairman at the time. This was a fairly dense collection area, which enabled the true cost of tanker collection to be at least two thirds of the cost of lorry collection. The original tanker was a seven ton Bedford chassis fitted with a 1500 gallon single compartment stainless steel tank. The milk was pumped from the farm tank into the tanker by an A.P.V. electric pump plugged in at each farm.

As the field for collection became wider, 2300 gallon tanker vehicles came into use. When more evidence became available to show that further economies could be made by rationalisation, 3400 gallon tankers were used where access to farms were convenient.

At the outset, there was the usual apprehension about a radical change. There was some concern as to how the hygienic standard of the milk was to be maintained at a high level, because chemical sterilisation at that time was not allowed in Scotland, although it was in England. The law was quickly changed to allow the use of hypochlorites for the sterilising of bulk tanks and the teat cups of milking machines. There was a lot of anxiety about the possibility of milk being discharged into the bulk tank from cows suffering from disease, such as mastitis or brucellosis, or having been treated with antibiotics. However, regular bacteriological examinations carried out by the Milk Utilisation Department at the West of Scotland Agricultural College, dispelled the original fears about any deterioration in milk quality. In reality the hygienic quality of milk gradually improved.

Naturally from the farmer's point of view, the first consideration before adopting this dramatic change were the costs and the advantages. The economic aspects of this new bulk collection scheme was thoroughly investigated by the Economic Department of the West of Scotland Agricultural College. The biggest boon was dispensing with the handling and washing of numerous milk churns. Chemical sterilising eliminated the requirement of steam and the expensive coal-fired boiler. There was the advantage that milk in the bulk could be measured at the farm so farmers could check for themselves the quantity sold. With can collection there were milk losses due to spillage or milk being left in the bottom of the churns after emptying. This was avoided with bulk collection.

There were large economies made at creameries. The milk

received at the creamery was pumped direct into holding tanks. The can receiving and washing unit was redundant with immense saving in labour and steam requirements and free space became available for other uses. Refrigeration costs were reduced because the milk was received at around 40°F. and maintained in the holding tanks.

The investigation clearly proved the advantages both to the farmer and the creameries as well as the overall savings in haulage.

The capital cost of the bulk tank on the farm was the stumbling point to many, especially for the smaller dairies. Premiums were paid to encourage their installation. The S.M.M.B. paid 1d. per gallon for five years to those producing 100 gallons or less and 1d. per gallon for four years for those over 100 gallons. Both groups received ¼d per gallon premium after the initial period. Furthermore in 1963, the S.M.M.B. and the Aberdeen and District M.M.B. introduced a personal loan scheme to cover the capital cost with repayment through the milk cheque spread over four years.

Fig. 43 Tanker driver's strike, 1979
Discussing the implications Messrs. Andrew Muir; Jim M'Crae; William Barrowman; Adam Gray & Tom Gillespie.

Most farms were equipped with bulk tanks after ten years and by 1976 100% of the milk in the S.M.M.B. milk was collected by 185 bulk tankers from 3431 producers, 40% of which was hauled by the Board's own tankers and the remainder by a number of private hauliers. Having the tanker drivers in two separate unions was an advantage during the 1979 strike when the Board's drivers did not come out.

This strike began on the 3rd January after quite a heavy snowfall which added to the great inconvenience it caused. The greatest difficulty was in Dumfriesshire where most of the milk haulage was operated by contractors who were affected by the strike.

In the counties of Kirkcudbright and Wigtown a large part of the milk collection was by Board-owned vehicles which continued to operate and these managed by extended working, to collect most of the milk at risk in their immediate vicinities. Self-help became the name of the game. With a great deal of ingenuity and innovation some quite unexpected containers appeared on lorries and trailers which formed long queues at creameries. In this way nearly all the milk at risk was transported to the local creameries for processing, having had to combat treacherous road conditions.

At the time Sir William Young commented: 'The ingenuity and effort displayed by hundreds of milk producers in the Dumfries and Kirkcudbright areas in delivering their own milk is quite extraordinary and shows their determination to save as much as possible of their valuable product. When considering the financial results of this strike the Board will certainly be making special provision for recognition of those producers who have actually delivered their own milk.'

The change to bulk collection of milk brought the tanker driver into focus. He was actually saving the work of at least two farm lorries. New responsibilities devolved on him. He had to acquire a certain technical knowledge and be much more observant than previously. At each farm he had to measure the milk in the tank with a dip-stick, take a sample for the laboratory, switch on the pump and swill out the farm tank before leaving. In addition he had to drive the bulky vehicle along narrow roads in all weathers and above all avoid delays, accidents and breakdowns.

One particular driver was not so skilful. He worked for Hayton Coulthard in Twynholm in Kirkcudbrightshire and drove one of the older tankers. At the end of his working day he had to clean his tanker which entailed him having to go inside it to hose it down. He forgot to open the outlet cock at the rear of the tanker. He was blissfully unaware of that until he felt the water filling into the top of his rubber boots.

Fig. 44 Tanker driver's strike 1979.
Jim Ross, Romesbeoch, "Supervises Operations"

Fig. 45 Tanker driver's strike 1979.
Patiently waiting to offload at Dalbeattie Creamery

Similar to the milking machine testing scheme the Board initiated a farm tank inspection scheme which quickly spotted any deterioration in the performance of the tanks. Both schemes are now administered by the Board's Farm Services Department.

To establish an efficient haulage service had its problems. Prior to the inception of the Scottish Milk Marketing Board each producer made his own arrangements about haulage. They sometimes bore little relation to the service given and there were anomalies. To those in outlying areas the costs were penal compared with those near to the consuming centres and the latter were very reluctant to give up their trading advantage.

When the Board became involved it acted as agent for the producers in the marketing of their milk. Apart from the milk purchased by the Board for their creameries, the ownership of the milk handled by the Board never passed to the Board. The Board collected and transported the milk as agents and paid the net proceeds according to the Scheme, therefore the cost of transport was largely borne by the producers.

To make the haulage more equitable an ingenious arrangement was made whereby the haulage would be based on the distance from the nearest 'haulage centre'. To avoid the impossible task of trying to set up a standard haulage for each farm, the Board created a number of distance bands in accordance with its calculated road distance from a designated haulage centre. Initially, the rates were based on the distance from Glasgow, Edinburgh and Dundee.

This greatly upset the producers in the east of Scotland. They had already felt disadvantaged with the 'pooling' arrangements for milk and they applied so much pressure on the Board that a further 12 haulage centres were introduced throughout the eastern part of the Board area; Alloa, Brechin, Crieff, Coupar, Dunfermline, Duns, Gala, Haddington, Kinross, Kirkcaldy, Perth and Stirling. This meant that by reducing the average haulage deduction, the eastern producers received a higher price.

During the 1939–45 war the Board was instrumental in ironing out many of the haulage inequalities. This was imperative when labour and fuel was at a premium. Rationalisation during this period showed clearly the economies that could be made and set a pattern for more efficient collection and delivery service thereafter. In relation to many other costs, haulage costs were well contained over many years.

There came a time when there was no longer a viable case for the perpetuation of the so called proximity value for dairy farms. The old antagonistic feelings between East and West disappeared. The greatly increased milk flow over the years, the rationalisation of dairies and creameries, the advent of the tanker collection system and the daily and seasonal fluctuations in demand from buyers, have all served to create a much more complex ex-farm haulage system, which is now far removed from anything envisaged in 1933.

For these reasons and the subsequent amendments made to the Scheme because of the E.E.C. Regulations necessitated milk becoming the property of the Board at the farm gate. The cost of the transport therefore, became a charge against the Board and not against the individual producer as formerly. Thus, the pool price became an ex-farm price throughout the Board area.

According to the Scottish Milk Marketing Scheme, 'The Board shall have the powers to specify the person or persons by whom and in the manner or manners in which the milk of any registered producer shall be transported'. The contracts and haulage rates continue to be established in the Joint Haulage Committee, comprising of representatives of the S.M.M.B. and the Road Haulage Association.

After many years of development, the complex problems of matching demand with the requisite supply was eventually undertaken by the Milk Movements Section of the Marketing Division of the S.M.M.B. This was an indispensable part of the Board's function, trying to match varying supplies of milk from farms to the even more varying demands of the dairies. This can mean a variation in requirements of a typical dairy by as much as 40% from mid-week to weekend, reflecting demands placed on it by its own customers, particularly shops who generally do not trade on Sundays.

Certainly, the Board's pricing system is geared to induce dairies to try to level out their pattern of demand to make life easier to those concerned, but there are limits to what can be achieved because of market circumstances.

Milk movement has been described as a trinity of producers, processors and distributors. In 1962 Hugh Gaitskill described it well. 'It always seems to me something of a miracle that 4 million gallons of fresh milk are delivered punctually morning by morning, day by day, for virtually every household in the country.'

No other country in the world has had such a home delivery as Britain. This is a far cry from when a family kept a cow, a goat and a hen or two in the garden, to the rise and fall of the town dairy and finally to the development of a complicated yet efficient method of delivering milk to the people of this country.

As has been noted, the responsibility for the collection of milk from farms and its delivery to the various buyers rests with the Scottish Milk Marketing Board. The individual, unless he is a retailer, has no say in where his milk is delivered and the buyer has no say in where his milk is produced. This enables the Boards to organise the most economical movement of milk from the farm to the distributor. Haulage of milk is the Board's largest single operational cost.

It is improbable that such an efficient method could have emerged without a Board and the further opportunities for rationalisation made possible during World War II.

Milk passes from the producer to the consumer in a variety of ways. (ref. chart) The original system was direct from the producer to the consumer, now referred to as producer retailing. A number of producers sell their milk to the consumer via a retailer. By far the most important sequence now is when milk passes from the producer through the arrangements made by the Boards to a wholesaler who processes, bottles and or cartons it.

The wholesaler disposes of it in a number of ways: to a retailer; sold through retail branches of the wholesale company; delivered to the consumer direct from vehicles; sold to the semi-retail trade for schools, hospitals, catering, restaurants etc. In 1960 there were about 600 buyers of milk from the Boards in Scotland. As a result of bulk handling and rationalisation the number has been reduced to about 120 (1990) and rationalisation stills goes on. The wholesalers are, however, an essential link in the movement of milk. Without them there would be few supplies available for consumption, even although some producers think that they charge too much for their services!

Since the 1960s. the pattern of distribution in Scotland has undergone considerable change in response to changing economic and social conditions. Notable among these, has been the movement away from the doorstep delivery service to shop buying, the trend away from glass bottles to other types of packaging and more recently the introduction and subsequent growth of sales low fat milk.

According to contractual arrangements, the Scottish Board has to supply its buyers of liquid milk on a 48 hours notice, but as a rule the Board tries to meet the changing demand patterns within 24 hours of notice being given, thus providing the greatest possible flexibility to dairy managers.

This leads on to the persistent problem of disposal of surplus milk, which is of course destined for manufacturing. In more recent years, this is carried out according to price priorities. Certain markets notably, evaporated milk, chocolate crumb and speciality cheeses, are serviced

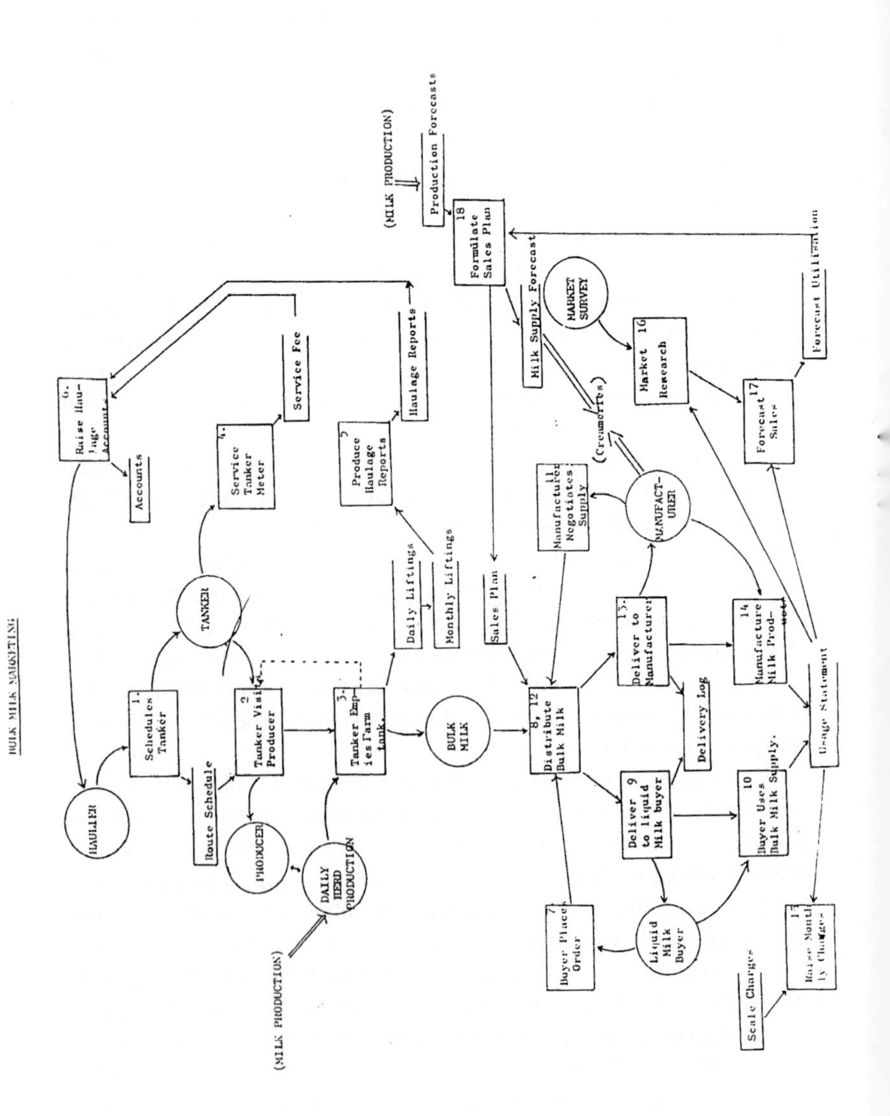
BULK MILK MARKETING
HAULIER
1. Schedules Tanker
Route Schedule
TANKER
2 Tanker Visits Producer
PRODUCER
DAILY HERD PRODUCTION
(MILK PRODUCTION)
3. Tanker Empties Farm tank
4. Service Tanker Meter
Service Fee
5 Produce Haulage Reports
Haulage Reports
6. Raise Haulage Accounts
Accounts
Daily Liftings
Monthly Liftings
BULK MILK
8, 12 Distribute Bulk Milk
Sales Plan
7 Buyer Places Order
Liquid Milk Buyer
9 Deliver to liquid Milk buyer
10 Buyer Uses Bulk Milk Supply.
Delivery Log
13. Deliver to Manufacturer
11 Manufacturer Negotiates Supply
MANUFACTURER
(Creameries)
14 Manufacture Milk Products
Usage Statement
15 Raise Monthly Charges
Scale Charges
17 Forecast Sales
Forecast Utilisation
16 Market Research
MARKET SURVEY
Milk Supply Forecast
18 Formulate Sales Plan
Production Forecasts
(MILK PRODUCTION)

according to predicted and pre-arranged patterns of supply and the balance is directed to the bulk commodity markets, cheddar cheese and butter. These thereby suffer the greatest variation in milk availability, which reflects in their higher costs of production.

THE BOTTLE

It has been noted that to carry out the vital work of moving milk, over a period of time, use was made of a variety of modes of transport, horse and pony vehicles, railways, tractors, petrol, diesel and electric lorries and bulk tankers. The sole aim has been and is to supply the housewife in the speediest and most economical manner. To eliminate a major 'bottleneck' in this movement of milk, was the production of the milk bottle.

Credit for the first bottling of milk commercially is given to George Barham, founder of Express Dairies Ltd. in 1884. The bottles were sealed with a wire cap. He was followed by Anthony Hailwood, a north country dairyman, who in 1894 started selling 'swing stoppered' bottles, similar to the old fashioned ginger beer bottles. These were filled with milk which had been partially pasteurised by heating it to a high temperature.

The progressive company United Dairies Ltd. pioneered the large scale use of bottles for delivery in the U.K. After the First World War officials of the company studied the use of bottles in Canada and U.S.A. They realised their great potential for the replacement of cans and various receptacles by which the housewife obtained her milk. The ability to completely sterilise bottles ensured that milk reached a very high standard of safety and made milk delivering so much more streamlined.

In many a household the clatter of bottles in the morning acted as an alarm clock, although many thought that they seemed to chatter and babble incessantly. When the use of bottles developed rapidly from about 1920, it drew attention to the appearance of milk and to the breed of cows which were producing the richer looking milk as judged by the cream line seen in the bottles. The test being the lower the cream line the richer the milk. Many a housewife changed her milkman because of creamlines.

Today, many forget that all the delivered bottles were washed and filled by hand. Some dairies would have 40–50 tons of milk bottled and shifted by hand before bottle washing and filling machines and conveyers came into vogue. The trick was how to sterilise the bottles without damaging them. This eventually happened.

There were lots of headaches with regard to bottles and their delivery during the war. There was a shortage of imported silica which caused problems with bottle manufacturing and increased the value of cullet (broken glass). Half pint bottles were discontinued. Cash incentives had to be paid to encourage roundsmen and women to bring back empty bottles. When this was done the bottles made on average 96 journeys. Today it is about 15. In places there was a perverse behaviour about returning empty bottles. Incidents are recorded where roundsmen discovered floors of sparerooms in tenements covered with bottles. In the 'Dig for Victory Campaign' bottles were found buried in gardens.

Also during the war, it must have been a frustrating if not a hilarious task educating women, who were directed from the Labour Exchange in towns, because of their unsuitability for other work, to harness and yoke horses into their lorries and then back them into a loading platform. If the roads were slippery with frost, screws (sharps) had to be inserted into the horses shoes to prevent them slipping. There was no grit in those days.

Time has overcome many difficulties in the delivery of milk. Some say its magic how it is delivered unseen each morning! The milkman is frequently treated as the unsung hero in the final movement of milk to the housewife. Next to the postman he is the best known public servant. A number of years ago an experiment was carried with a pedometer by a dairy. It was estimated that in a milkman's working life he would travel 250,000 miles, the approximate distance from the Earth to the Moon. The milkman has for many years and still continues to be, to some extent, an essential link in the milk movement chain.

This calls to mind words from Heredotus carved on a frieze of the Corinthian columnade in front of the New York General Post Office. 'Neither snow, nor rain, nor heat, nor gloom, stays these carriers from the swift completion of their appropriate rounds.'

In this discussion the position of producer retailers should not be forgotten and it seems a little odd that they should be mentioned towards the end of it. They have always held a special position within the industry, being the original purveyor of milk over many years.

In Scotland, there are now (1990) only 79 producer-retailers compared with 2440 in 1933. They still offer a service especially in rural areas. Formerly they were essential. Their seven day a week delivery was very welcome where other deliveries were unavailable or unreliable particularly in popular holiday places.

Since the inception of the Boards there have been many discussions, arguments and as we have seen, court cases, about the levy imposed on the producer retailers by the Boards. Some prefer to euphemistically call the levy the producer retailers' 'contribution'. This was agreed in the interests of equitability. It was felt that the producer retailers could gain an unfair advantage over the average producers because they received money for their milk sold at the retail price which was more than their receipts as a producer together with what they were entitled to as a distributor.

In former years when they were more numerous, it was thought that if producer retailers kept all the money they received from consumers and made no 'contribution' they would be so much better off than other producers, that there would be a real danger of the liquid milk market being undermined by the price cutting among the many producers who would decide to start retailing their own milk. This would be contrary to the principles behind the Agricultural Marketing Acts and the Scottish Milk Marketing Scheme and to the detriment of the whole industry.

Time and events discounted many of these fears. The imposition of the regulations for the sale of T.T. and Certified milk with their necessary stringent hygienic conditions for their production and the more recent compulsory pasteurisation of all milk, plus labour and transport costs, found many producer retailers in a disadvantaged and uneconomical position against the intense competition from large milk businesses so that many gave up. Perhaps those who remain would be interested in an old jingle!

Rich milk from the cow,
Both sweet and fine,
The doctors declare
Its better than wine.

LOCAL AUTHORITY OF STEWARTRY OF KIRKCUDBRIGHT.

CERTIFICATE OF REGISTRATION.

328.

MILK AND DAIRIES (SCOTLAND) ACT, 1914,

AND THE

MILK AND DAIRIES (AMENDMENT) ACT, 1922.

I hereby certify that ADAM GRAY

residing at Ingleston, Borgue, Kirkcudbright.

has, in terms of section 7 of the Milk and Dairies (Scotland) Act, 1914, been granted a Certificate of Registration by the Local Authority of the Stewartry of Kirkcudbright.

in respect of* premises, consisting of double and single byre and milkhouse, situated at Ingleston in the Parish of Borgue.

within the district of the said Local Authority.

Signed on behalf of the Local Authority, this twenty second

day of September, 1938.

Clerk to the Local Authority.

, 193 .

* Insert here "the premises at situated" or "(state number) carts, vans, or other vehicles from which milk is sold."

G.—MD 2.

Fig. 47 Certificate of Registration, sect. 7 Milk & Dairies Act 1914

CHAPTER 11

SELLING MILK CLEAN

For along time 'men have robbed their cows of their children so that they may rob them of their milk.' (G. E. Fussell) It has already been said that because of its perishable nature, in early days it had to be made into butter and cheese to get it to places of consumption. It took milk a long time before it was accepted as a drink in its own right. In 1825 the Board of Agriculture said that milk was only fit for swine. (Aiton). For a long time it was considered 'all right' for adding to tea, coffee and puddings but not as a liquid refreshment. Initially for the masses it was not available and if it was, it was too expensive. For many it was considered too much of a luxury. As late as 1939 enquiries showed that 25% of the unemployed families took no milk at all. The average consumption per family instead of increasing diminished with the size of the family. Skimmmed milk from butter making and whey from cheesemaking were the more common, cheaper beverages. Until about 1933, the consumption of milk in the U.K. was a quarter of that in the USA. Canada, or in Scandinavia. 'Some pasteurise, some sterilise, some criticise, but the main slogan should be we must sell more milk.' *

To sell more milk required overcoming ignorance and prejudices. Doctors and nutritionists were always supportive in the functions of selling more milk, but the general public had no confidence in its value or potential. Science had not shown what many thought, that milk was near enough a complete food for all young mammalian and that included the human race most of all. True, the whole of mankind knew its value for the very young, the original sustenance for survival.

It took the long term experiments in the 1920s of Dr H.C. Corky Main and John Boyd Orr, (later Lord Boyd Orr), who investigated the nutritional value of milk and milk products, to make the authorities and public realise their value. These experiments involved measuring the height, weight and intelligence of groups of schoolchildren over several years, from different environments. These children, in development had a diet which included one extra pint of milk compared with those who had not. This demonstrated conclusively milk was an advantage to growing children.

Unfortunately, milk was not free from dirt or disease. There were many diseases borne and easily spread by milk – brucellosis, (undulating fever) tuberculosis, diphtheria, scarlet fever, typhoid, infantile diarrhoea

* "The Milk Industry"

etc. which claimed 20% of child deaths in some areas.

'Those who live by the production, distribution or the manufacturing of milk must unite and be awake to the future which is theirs to make and rise again Phoenix-like from the ashes of the past. Milk must be fresh safe and value for money'.

In the 19th century there were odd ideas about freshness. Many Victorian wives tested their milk at the door for freshness 'by sticking their finger into the pail to see if it was still warm from the cow!' As to safety, it was a gamble. Brian Morgan in his *History of Express Dairies* graphically writes about pails, 'whether slung from the yoke of a grubby roundsman, puffing at foul clay pipe, or flung on a dray or piled on floats which are still called in the trade, "prams", which were rarely far from the rear end of a horse, it was always exposed to germ laden air.' There were Inspectors of Nuisances who among other duties were supposed to ensure that 'any accumulation of dung, soil, filth, or obnoxious matter shall be removed by the person to whom the same belongs.' A difficult task with little authoritive backing. There were too few men of the calibre of William Harley. It took many years before his pioneering principles of producing clean milk became standard practice.

The Adulteration Act of 1860 was an effort to abolish malpractices but it did not consider hygiene. This was not taken into account until the passing of the Public Health Act of 1875 which made compulsory the inspection of milk for sale. Real progress was made in the control of milk hygiene under the 1899 Sale of Foods and Drugs Act which was followed by the 1901 Sale of Milk Regulations. They laid down the minimum compositional standards of 3% butterfat and 8.5% S.N.F. 'below which milk is presumed to be adulterated.' The Milk and Dairies (Scotland) Act 1914 was the first real attempt to bring all the milk regulations to a uniform basis. Because of the war and the considerable delays, it took until 1925 to bring the operation of the Act into full force. Orders for Public and Animal Health for the first time came under this Act, as later did many dairy bylaws and orders governing the production and distribution of milk. These were ultimately revoked under the Milk (Special Designations) Scotland Order 1951, which designated the standards for milk to be sold under licence as Certified, Grade "A" T.T., Standard, Pasteurised, Heat-Treated and Sterilised.

As before, in order to qualify for these licences certain minimum standards of premises and dairy management had to be maintained. It has been said that milk has been subjected to more regulations and sampling than any other main food. Nevertheless the plethora of these achieved the objective of safeguarding the health of the public against the hazards of milk borne diseases and prevented all forms of adulteration of milk and milk products.

As the demand for milk increased it was felt that 'it would be impossible to supply large towns with milk without preservatives.' It was said that milk containing small quantities of boracic acid could be consumed without harmful results to healthy children. It was estimated that 50% of the dairymen in London used preservatives.

Experience in Denmark proved that large quantities of milk could be distributed where the use of preservatives was prohibited by law. The problem was overcome 'by the organisation of the milk traffic.' (Chalmers, 1904.)

PASTEURISATION

It was the development of the pasteurising process of milk which did most for the making of milk 'safe'. It took a long time to achieve the universal adoption of this procedure. As far back as 1893 New York had its first city pasteurisation plant. One of the earliest established in Scotland was in Edinburgh in 1923. It was, however, Louis Pasteur (1822–1895) who gave the name to the process as a result of a series of experiments leading the way to its development. The 1922 Milk Act introduced the 'Special Designated Milks' recognising pasteurised milk officially. Up until that time the process had no precise legal and scientific definition. This was really necessary as many unscrupulous sellers sold milk as pasteurised having only heated the milk to a temperature that would prevent souring and not to a sufficiently high temperature to effectively kill the dangerous organisms which caused the diseases. They used the name 'pasteurised' because it enhanced milk sales.

For a long time there were two main methods of pasteurisation. The High Temperature Short Time where the milk is heated for 15 seconds at 161°F and the Holder System where the milk is heated for 30 minutes at 145°F. Both must be cooled immediately to a minimum of 50°F.

The former method has subsequently proved the more efficient and is used in all modern dairy plants. Interestingly the Scottish Milk Marketing Board cooperated with Lord Boyd Orr when he was Director of the Rowett Research Institute, Aberdeen, in purchasing a small pasteurisation plant to be used at the Quarrier Homes, Bridge of Weir, in connection with the nutritional experiments which have already been mentioned.

From the First World War onwards there were long arguments about the acceptability of pasteurised milk. It was not until 1983 that only pasteurised milk could be sold to the housewives in Scotland, although fresh milk can still be sold in England.

The advocates of pasteurisation, the medical profession, health authorities and the section of the public who were genuinely interested in the wellbeing of the nation had to deal with some very vociferous opposition. For a long time they tended to impress the general public by pointing out all the defects of the procedure while paying little heed to make a clean safe food. The critics emphasised at great length how the treated milk did not taste the same as fresh milk. In the early phase of pasteurisation this was true, as milk tended to have an unwelcome scorched flavour due to the caramalising of the milk sugars. This was an impression which tended to linger for some time, but the refinement of the technique eventually eliminated this problem, leading to the wide spread acceptance of treated milk.

A Labour M.P. in 1939 said that, 'If God meant milk to be pasteurised, he would have made cows which worked at boiling point.' There were stupid M.P.s then – nothing has changed! The opponents, understandably put great stress on the damaging effect that the process might have on the nutritional value of the milk particularly with regard to calcium, vitamins and enzymes. Many felt that pasteurisation would encourage lax methods of production. This was easily discounted because of the number of regulations which would prevent this happening.

CLEAN MILK CAMPAIGN

The most serious cattle diseases have been largely eliminated from dairy cattle while pasteurisation has eliminated the milk borne diseases. Still remaining, are those arising from physiological and nutritional causes. Mastitis could be considered the modern scourge of dairy farming. Currently costing the U.K. industry around £100m. This is not a simple disease. It is really a generic name for a variety of infections of cows' udders. It is the one which has outrun all others being an iniquitous disease which costs the dairy industry many millions of pounds annually. Now it is studied at internatioanl level under an umbrella organisation, the National Mastitis Council based in Louiseville, Kentucky.

All Milk Marketing Boards have set up mastitis control programmes. The Scottish Milk Marketing Board was the first to provide a free cell count monitoring service, which is now generally acknowledged to minimise the losses in milk sales.

There is an ongoing, constant endeavour to ensure that milk which reaches the consumer is of the highest hygienic and compositional quality. It has taken prodigious efforts on the part of scientists, advisers, staffs from Milk Boards, processors, wholesalers, retailers and farmers to achieve the present high standards.

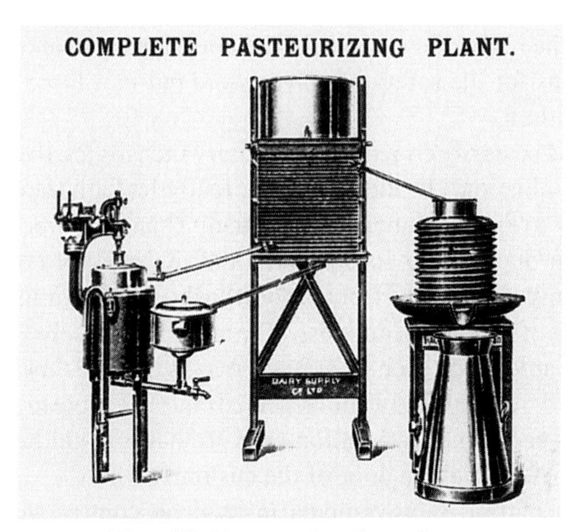

Fig. 48 Pasteurisation plant

Producing clean milk is all about preventing unwanted bacteria from souring milk. Bacteria was first discovered by Levwen Hoek c. 1675. He did this by means of a crude microscope of his own construction. He observed tiny organisms in putrifying liquids and in saliva. They were classed as 'animals' until the 19th century. This was progressed by Pasteur and others who after investigating yeasts in brewing, turned their attention to the bacteria which controlled cheese and silage making. Once various bacteria were isolated and studied, the 'germ' theory evolved and this in turn encouraged better hygiene on farms and made farmers more tolerant of measures which were periodically imposed upon them. Dairy bacteriology did not really commence until after the First World War. As a result of experiments, the new knowledge gained pushed local authorities into supervising efficiently the necessary controls, for some, too efficiently. Dairy bacteriology did not really commence until after the First World War.

Today great progress has been made in the production of milk which is clean, but it has been slow. As far back as 1878, Lord Lister, who was a pioneer in clean milk production, took many samples of milk straight from cows and poured them into sterilised glasses. After six weeks most of the samples were still fresh, showing no trace of bacteria or moulds and one of them stayed fresh for four months, proving that complete asepsis is possible all the way from the cow to the consumer! Someone said that God must never have meant a cow to produce clean milk considering how he arranged the respective organs for the emissions. Yet another said that the regulations for the safety of calves were put into force quicker than those for children.

Milk is so easily contaminated. Dairy utensils are the chief source of this contamination. In the past, milk really had a hazardous journey from the cow to the consumer, with so many changes of receptacle, each presenting an opportunity for airborne and more direct contamination. Initially the milk was passed from the cow to the 'luggy' (milk pail) via the milkers hands of varying cleanliness. The milkers themselves were known to propagate epidemics such as T.B. carriers with sore throats. The milk usually passed from a pail to a poorly sealed churn en route to a roundsman, who often tipped it into two gallon cans so that it could be more easily retailed in open jugs at the door of the customer.

On the farm, improvements in hygiene control were gradually made, enforced by the various regulations. These were in the charge of the staff of the County Councils. It took sometime for the traditional dairymen to realise the importance of clean udders, milk pails, washing buckets and udder cloths. They had to be convinced that it was not all a charade and dispel the idea that there was anything unmanly in adopting clean milk practices. The motto was 'The cleaner the cows, the cleaner the utensils and the cleaner the workers, the cleaner the milk.'

True farmers may have been tardy in their attitude to making milk safe as well as a nutritious food but for a time consumers considered the whole affair a bit of a fad not understanding that improvements to buildings, modern milking equipment and higher standards of dairy management all cost producers money for which they are entitled to an economic return. These changes were being called for in a period of difficult economic conditions, when the financial advantages were unclear to the uninitiated.

Robert Stenhouse Williams, a physician and bacteriologist, who in 1923 became the first Director of the new National Institute for Dairy Research at Reading was a motivating force in 'The Clean Milk Campaign'. He and his staff gave many lectures and demonstrations to all involved to educate and try to overcome their many prejudices. He had some himself, believing that pasteurisation lessened the food value of milk and that it must be regarded as a necessary evil. However, a quote from a speech he made in 1919 has a familiar ring about it; 'If our milk supply be considered as a national problem it is clear that our first function is to ensure that milk be available to our children in the most nutritious possible form and at a reasonable price, since it is quite probable that efficient nutrition is the most important single factor in the development of a nation.'

The previously mentioned Milk and Dairies Order of 1926 greatly emphasised the necessity for correct procedures, two of the most important being the cooling of milk and the sterilising of the utensils. The milk was required to be cooled within 5 degrees of the water supply temperature and all utensils had to be well scalded with boiling water. The introduction into farm dairies of large steam chests for the sterilising of the milking machines and all the related equipment led to vast improvements. These improvements were monitored by the testing facilities of the local authorities, Agricultural College and latterly by the Milk Marketing Boards. By 1926 chemical sterlisation was being considered creating widespread discussion. However, it was not until the 1950s its use was permitted throughout the industry.

The Scottish Milk Marketing Board took over the routine testing of milk by setting up a central laboratory in 1965, adjacent to Hogganfield Creamery on the north side of Glasgow. The latter was sold for retail developement in 1978, leaving the Laboratory in isolation, but it was later replaced in 1986 by a new building adjacent to the Board's head office at Paisley.

Various tests are applied to producers' milk to check on the composition and hygienic quality, plus freedom from the presence of antibiotics and extraneous water. In 1965 a Hygienic Quality Payments Scheme based on the modified resazurin test was introduced. Premiums and penalties were applied to the pool price according to test results for individual producers. Because of the influence that fat and protein have on the product yield of milk, especially for butter and cheese, a Compositional Quality Premium Scheme based on total solids, was introduced in 1965. All this ensured a steady progress in the final aim to guarantee milk safe and healthy from the cow to the consumer. Provided the necessary precautions are taken today's pasteurised milk has a shelf life of about 10–14 days.

To stimulate the right attitude to clean milk production, the first competitions for it were organised by the Bacteriology Department and County Staff of the West of Scotland Agricultural College from 1926. They were held in Renfrewshire (50 farms), West Stirlingshire (7 farms), West Perthshire (18 farms), Craigie and Symington district of Ayrshire (28 farms) and Dumbartonshire (36 farms). These competitions undoubtedly served a useful purpose in focussing the attention of farmers and the general public on the problems associated with producing clean milk.

This lead to a scheme being started in 1927 to enable farmers to have their milk tested at regular intervals. Farmers who joined the scheme were able to demonstrate to the Public Health Authority and general public that they were endeavouring to put pure wholesome milk on the market and therefore it was worth more.

Further to this, when Certified and Grade A (T.T.) milk became more available a Scottish Certified and Grade A (T.T.) Milk Producers Society was formed in 1927. There were 80 members, all certified milk producers. They were scattered throughout Scotland,though the majority were in the south-west. This society was supported by some creameries. It did not trade but carried a programme of advertising and personal canvassing in hospitals and institutions. (Plunkett, 1932.)

After the Second World War, Clean Milk Competitions were again held in various counties. The first was organised in Stirlingshire where Sir George Wilson, chairman of the Scottish Milk Marketing presented the silver cups and certificates.

From 1950 onwards the old attitudes changed remarkably, due to many more young farmers going to universities and agricultural colleges, due to increasingly good advice from the agricultural services, the Milk Boards and also due to constant contact with progressive commercial firms.

SELL THE MILK

If you whisper down a well,
About the milk you have to sell,
You will not make as many dollars
As the man who climbs the tree and hollars.

(Lord Leverhulme.)

The Milk Marketing Boards' basic objective is to market all the milk consigned to them and pay the highest possible net price to its producers. That the consumer had confidence in it, the milk had to be, 'clean and safe.' How much of this was accomplished has been noted. It then became necessary to tell the consumers how good the milk was and they are still requiring to be told, so that more milk is drunk.

Whatever the ticket you hold may declare,
Milk is always first class and the country's best fare,
Then let us be proud of milk cream and cheese,
They are the best in the world so enjoy them please. (Anon.)

The initiative for this began in England. 'To start a nationwide propaganda drive to raise the level of consumption.' A meeting was held in London on the 24th February 1920. It was recorded inauspiciously, 'in a plump, black, school exercise book.' A resolution was passed that, 'In the opinion of this Committee representing all sections of the dairy industry, it is desirable that a National Publicity Campaign should be instituted to make known in the interests of the nation, the value of pure milk. The meeting, also resolved that the committee should be known as the National Milk Publicity Council'.

For a few years the new council experienced difficulties in acquiring sufficient funds to launch their generic milk publicity campaigns. There was also difficulty in convincing those who doubted the necessity of advertising. Dr Johnstone in 1759 said that, 'The advertisements are now so numerous they are very negligently perused.' Two centuries later they are perused more than ever due to their attractive presentation. It is not so long ago that Lord Leverhulme was reported to have said that he was sure that half of his expenditure on advertising was wasted but, he did not know which half.

Captain Wright, who was an unpaid Hon. Adviser to the N.M.P.C., made many speeches throughout the country and wrote articles to pacify the said doubters. He said that publicity was nothing new to farmers, the first farmyard advertisement was the hen's cackle after she had laid an egg. He further said that, 'We must believe in advertising, it is a fertiliser which will better the soil of consumption.' From these beginnings the N.M.P.C. has gone from strength to strength in the vast field of advertising and promotion. One of its original slogans being, 'You'll feel a lot better if you drink more milk.'

In Scotland, particularly in the Scottish Milk Marketing Board area, publicity was originally handled by the Publicity Committee of the S.M.M.B. which was advised by the Scottish National Development Council. To launch the first plans for publicity, the Board approved an expenditure to a maximum of £8,500 from the Board's funds for the year 1935. From then till 1939, milk consumption increased by 12%. This was done without consumer subsidies.

Following on the success of the N.M.P.C. and having gained a lot of support from it the S.M.M.B. motivated the inauguration of the Scottish Milk Publicity Council in 1958. The original members were those who were appointed to the Permanent Joint Committee. Representing the S.M.M.B. were William Young and J.G. Inglis; representing the Scottish Milk Trade Federation, George P. Ross, from Ross Dairies Ltd. and John Stevenson, Stevenson's Dairy Farms, Cumnock; representing the Scottish Cooperative Milk Trade Association, A.C. McMillan, Assistant Manager, Milk Department of the Scottish Cooperative Milk Trade Association, 84, Morrison Street, Glasgow and representing the Scottish Association of Milk Product Manufacturers was K.W. Pocock from Edinburgh and Dumfries Dairy Co. Ltd. West Bryson Road, Edinburgh. F.J. Burns Reid was appointed secretary. Mr Burns sadly, died on the golf course during a match between the Scottish Milk Marketing Board and the Scottish Dairy Trade Federation.

In the first discussion on finance, each representative agreed to finance the proposed advertising campaign in principle. However, Mr Pocock intimated that while the Manufacturers agreed in principle he added that 'they were at the second remove in this matter' and recommended that the advertising 'be not confined exclusively to liquid but be extended to milk products.' The chairman intimated that 'it was in contemplation that the Government contribution would be some £10,000.' At this meeting, Mather and Crowther, who had operated successfully in the South, were appointed as advertising agents initially for twelve months. They were asked to submit plans costing no more than £30,000 'on how the interests of the Council would be best served by employing them for the Scottish campaign. Subsequently, a "Standard Term of Business" was drawn up by Mather and Crowther Ltd. under which it was agreed that they would operate.

On Advertising, for publications, outdoor, transport, radio, cinema, theatre, advertising, the agents would charge the gross amount which was charged to them plus 15% and credited to the Council any commissions received by them.

To begin with the Scottish Milk Publicity Council understandably adopted many of the principles and campaigns of the experienced National Milk Publicity Council. Interestingly, it did not follow the latter

Fig. 49 Zoe Newton whose face became known nationally as a result of milk publicity. 1955

in using Norman Wisdom, the nationally known popular comedian on the publicity material carrying the slogan, 'Milk drinking was not only healthy, but was fun.' However, the Scottish Milk Publicity Council was very enthusiastic about their adoption of the popular Zoë Newton in their advertising campaign similar to that of the National Milk Publicity Council. The posters, featured Zoë as an attractive, vivacious girl with the slogan, 'Be healthy. Be happy. Drink your health in milk everyday.' Of course, there was a nationalistic angle when the Scottish advertising depicted photographs of this young lady in highland dress.

In 1955, three in depth surveys were conducted for the N.M.P.C. to measure women's acceptance of the milk slogan, 'You will feel a lot better if you drink more milk,' and in particular their acceptance of Zoë Newton. The Council was delighted at the overwhelming favourable reaction enabling it to proceed with confidence with their advertising and publicity programme which featured the well liked Zoë. She became one of the best known photographic models in the world. She was so versatile. 'She clowned, improvised, was completely professional, did everything the press photographers asked, rode on the backs of cows, crawled inside boilers in North-country factories, kissed the right people, was at home

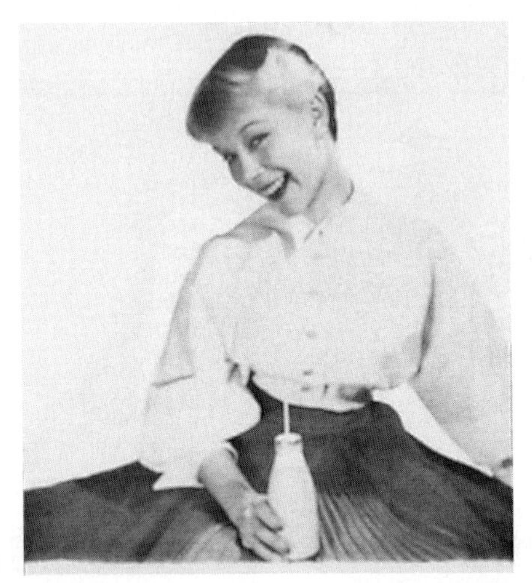

Fig. 50. Zoe Newton promoting Scottish Milk. 1955

with everyone and was intimidated by nobody.' It is doubtful if there has been such a successful milk advertising campaign since that 'Drinka Pinta Milka' era with Zoë Newton.

In the 1950s the cinema was still very popular and had a wide receptive audience. In 1954 the first 20 second filmlets were shown in about 250 Scottish cinemas for seven alternative weeks. They were provided by the National Milk Publicity Council, later lengthened to 2 minutes. The filmlet cost £310 of which the S.M.P.C. paid 2/3rds i.e. £68 plus 13s 9d per copy.

In 1955 the National Milk Publicity Council devised a Seven-Day Milk Diet in order to combat the craze of 'crash diets' such as a milk and banana only diet. This was to seek a proper attitude to balanced diets. To this end the S.M.P.C. in 1956 carried out an experiment to prove that an overweight person could lose 5lbs. per week on a balanced high protein diet. Six volunteers, readers of the Glasgow Daily Record who sponsored the experiment, had to report to a doctor daily in a quiet hotel on their weight loss. The results proved that an average weight loss of 10lbs. in a fortnight could be achieved. This encouraged thereafter, a lot of publicity on how to slim effectively. A debate which has been going on ever since.

Alongside the ongoing advertisements, promotions and publicity, there were some special features adopted which in their time were very successful. At the Scottish Dairy Show held annually in the Kelvin Hall, Glasgow, the Scottish Milk Council in conjunction with the organisers and the Young Farmers Clubs organised events which were very popular especially with the young folk. The popular activities held in the main arena included displays by several Scottish Country Dancing teams, accompanied by famous Scottish dance bands such as Jimmy Shand and Ian MacLeod. There were also gymnastic displays. The final contests for Milk Beauty Queens, later called Pinta Princesses were a major attraction. Earlier, heats for these were held all over Scotland. There were other young farmers' competitions and 'farm frolics of various sorts.'

In 1958 there was an ambitious project set up to bring milk and dairy foods in a real way before the public. 'The policy would be so to conduct the business as to raise milk bars out of the disrepute into which they had fallen in London and elsewhere.' A dairy shop known as the Scottish Milk Centre, was established in Gordon Street, Glasgow, an excellent venue. The premises were leased by the Scottish Milk Publicity Council and the project financially backed by the Scottish Milk Marketing Board. The Milk Centre included a quality self service restaurant, coffee lounge and a dairy shop, displaying and selling various dairy foods, showing that there were many excellent alternative dishes to the customary ones. The concept was first class but was difficult to sustain commercially. Because of the need for more capital for refurbishment, the Centre was closed in 1973.

Another popular and much publicised annual event, sadly now defunct, was the Scottish Milk Bicycle Race. This developed from a local one day event to a major international 5 day event, becoming the fourth biggest amateur cycling event in the world. To coordinate these activities and to keep the media informed, in 1956, Malcolm Miller was appointed as a Public Relations Executive at a salary of £500 per annum. This he did with great acceptance.

Thus from 1954 the Scottish Milk Publicity Council has continued in its prime objective to 'safeguard and strengthen the market for milk and milk products in Scotland.' The dairy councils with the support of the Boards have developed far in all the fields of activity pertaining to advertising, publicity and public relations, mainly through television, radio and press, advertising and promoting milk and cream which reflect the higher return available from that market.

The Scottish Milk Publicity Council now trades as the Scottish Dairy Council. The Dairy Councils in England, Scotland, Aberdeen and North of Scotland are unique organisations in that they are organised and run by representatives from producers, trade and manufacturers. It is the only time that these representatives get together with the well being of the industry and the consumer at heart, without any problems of defending their own individual positions within the industry. It is a forum where there is mutual trust and cooperation on all sides, to achieve the common objective of selling more milk. The Councils are regarded by the industry as 'umbrellas in defence and weapons in attack.'

Alongside the functions of the Scottish Dairy Council, the Scottish Milk Marketing Board is very active in the field of milk and dairy product advertising and sales promotion. Over the years, this has developed into one of the most conspicuous aspects of the Board's work. The main objective was to keep the public constantly aware of the food value of milk and its products, especially in the catering trade and in schools. The promotional work now covers a wide spectrum of activity. This ranges from promotion in shops, the support of school milk bars in all Scotland, the production of cookery books, the whole running of the milk dispensing business for caterers and shops, all to support milk at the point of sale.

The people of the country have become a race of 'grazing consumers', eating on demand rather than by the clock. Every effort has to be made to get as much milk as possible from the back end of cows over the throats of the consumers, with 'taste appeal.'

MILK IN SCHOOLS

> 'Cows are our foster mother, they have been for centuries.'
>
> (*Hoard's Dairyman.)*

It is important that young people appreciate milk in all its forms and understand its benefits compared with the many other beverages that are available. It is of comparatively recent times that milk has become available in schools in its present day sophisticated manner in very attractive milk bars and milk dispensers. Cool for School!

Milk in schools has had a chequered career and at times a high political profile. The first school milk scheme began in 1927 as a result of experimental work carried out in the 1920s. In 1922 the National Publicity Council started an experiment with the cooperation of the Birmingham Educational Authorities. Fifty undernourished children were supplied with a pint of milk for two months and showed a gain in height and weight in comparison with children not given the additional milk. A woman teacher who had supervised the experiment wrote, 'Everyone noticed the children's eyes, they shone with health and high spirits, the children filled out and their skins cleared as if by magic. A little boy when asked what he would do without his milk, replied', 'Cry, Miss.'

In 1926 and 1927 Lord Boyd Orr supervised an experiment on behalf of the Scottish Board of Health. It was much more extensive and detailed than the work he did between 1903 and 1912. It was conducted among 1400 boys aged 5–14 years from seven centres of population, Peterhead, Aberdeen, Dundee, Edinburgh, Glasgow, Paisley and Greenock. They were divided into four diet groups: ordinary home diet; ordinary home diet plus extra milk; ordinary home diet plus separated milk; ordinary home diet plus one biscuit. The results showed that milk could bring about a 20% increase in height and weight and 'an improved general condition.' At first this work was hindered by the difficulty of getting suitable cups. Coincidentally this was overcome when bottles and straws became available about that time. Similar experiments were carried out by Dr H.C.Corry Mann. He divided boys between 6–11 years old at a boarding school into seven groups, each group receiving a different diet;ordinary diet (control)and ordinary plus milk; sugar, butter, margarine, casein, or watercress, for 12 months. Boys who were given one extra pint of milk showed an increase in height, weight and improvement in health compared with those boys on the control diet. Since then, other experiments in this and other countries continued to confirm the value of milk in the diet of schoolchildren.

In 1927 the National Milk Publicity Council introduced a milk scheme whereby 1/3 pint of milk could be obtained at 1d per bottle. Under the Milk Act of 1934 the operation of the scheme was taken over by the Milk Marketing Boards. Government subsidies made it possible to supply 1/3 pint for ½d to all children in primary schools, though the administration left much to be desired.

This is alluded to in this author's book, *'Borgue Academy'*, a story about a village school. There is a comment made about the scheme by the pawky humoured headmaster, John Henderson. 'On 1st April 1935, the Milk Marketing Board's Scheme for supplying milk to school came into operation today. The day's response was poor, only 29 participating out of 176 on the roll. At a County Council meeting, allegations were made that the milk was in fact being poured down the drains. A solemn declaration has been made that nothing of the kind has happened in Borgue, but a serious problem arose when two bottles arrived only part full and one minus a cover. The children cannot be expected to drink this milk, it cannot be poured down the drains, the suppliers refuse to take it back and there is no cat on the premises.'

This sort of thing, plus milk being left in the sun in the summertime and beside the school radiators during the winter, gave milk a bad image which lingered a long time in the memory of many people. This made it much more difficult to encourage the consumption of more milk. During the war the scheme was considerably extended by the Ministry of Agriculture.

In 1946, as a result of the 1944 Education Act all children at state maintained or recognised independent schools received 1/3 pint per day free. This ceased for children in secondary schools during 1968 and in 1971 for those from 7–11 year old, except for those designated as "in need". The 1980 Education Act removed the last statutory obligation for local authorities to provide free school milk to children under 7 years. At that time great concern was expressed by many about the possible harmful effects the withdrawal of the school milk would have on the nutritional status of the schoolchildren. There were many passionate speeches made in Parliament. Mrs Thatcher who was then the Minister of Education was labelled 'Thatcher, the milk snatcher.'

Fig. 51 Children drinking school milk. 1937

As a result of successive Government cutbacks, the position of milk in schools went from one of having it available free, to that where the Education Authorities were no longer required to provide any free milk whatsoever. This aroused a lot of emotion. It had been generally accepted for a long time that it was highly desirable that children should be encouraged to drink milk. The demands that this should happen became more voluble when it was realised that there was a substantial E.E.C. subsidy available which was not being taken up. In early 1980 this reduced the cost of 1/3 pint to just over 1.1p. compared with 7p which was the cost in the home.

A great deal of intensive work was done by Dairy Councils and Milk Marketing Boards to lobby opinion formers in Regions to persuade and encourage headmasters, awkward teachers and school meal supervisors to have milk available in schools. R.M. Kennedy and Tim Russell successive Directors of Sales and Market Development of the Scottish Milk Marketing Board were the prime motivaters. Milk in school has now moved from being the unwanted drink at 'elevances' to a prime position in milk bars and vending machines installed in schools throughout Scotland with a throughput of some 11 million litres.

Fig. 52 Wartime advert for Milk

Fig. 53 Southbar Cattle Breeding Centre, Inchinnan, Renfrewshire.

Fig. 54 Semen tanks awaiting despatch

CHAPTER 12

CATTLE BREEDING

'The Cow is a noble representation of Motherhood in the Animal Creation.'.

(*Hoard's Dairyman*)

No cows no milk. The better bred cows generally lead to more efficient milk production. However, there is no royal road to success in cattle breeding. Many have tried to find this road but few have succeeded. Genetics is complex and can be confusing. There are also many who are driven on by ambition and prestige guided by the depth of their pocket plus hope. Some of those who have been successful in cattle breeding would admit to good luck rather than good guidance.

Until the advent of the enclosing of land and the cultivation of turnips, improvement in cattle breeding was impossible. An improved level of nutrition allows positive selection for milking performance to commence because they were dependent on each other, without one the other was of no avail. For many years before this happened, cattle were used more as draught animals and beasts of burden than for producing milk or meat. Until well into the 18th century large areas of land were still unenclosed. Much of the arable land in a parish was cultivated in large open, unfenced, fields sometimes without rest or rotations. All the livestock of the farmers were grazed on the common land in the summer and over the arable land in the winter. Indiscriminate breeding was the norm. This was further aggravated by many cattle not being castrated at a young age. It really was a haphazard affair where it was the 'union of nobody's son with anybody's daughter.'

Early efforts to improve cattle was done by farmers cooperating in buying a 'parish bull'. Evidence of a township's bull shed can be seen at Auchin drane, Ayrshire. Under range like conditions the earliest form of selection was by colour and the ability to adapt to local conditions and became 'hefted' (remained) there. For example the West Highland breed becoming suited to a wet climate and a mountainous area, whereas the Aberdeen Angus were right for the drier, fertile North East. The various strains of local cattle evolved into breeds named after their county of origin. As Thomas Hale wrote in 1758, 'Bulls differ only in their size according to the counties in which they are bred. The various parts of this kingdom afford so different pasturage for cattle, that when they are brought into other places, they are after the name as that from whence they came.'

From early 18th century onwards, each breed's improvement tended to be dominated by one or two men. While some of them may be mentioned here, their work and that of others has been well recorded elsewhere. Robert Bakewell improved the Longhorn cattle and Leicester sheep; Robert and Charles Colling, English Shorthorn; Thomas Bates and George Coates, the Dairy Shorthorn; Amos Cruickshank, the Scotch Beef Shorthorn; Benjamin Tomkins, the Hereford; Hugh Watson and William Mc Combie, the Aberdeen Angus; Francis Quartley, George Turner and the Davys family, the Devon and the McNeils of Barra, Macdonalds and Mc Kinnons of Skye, who were the Island landowners, improved the Highland breed.

With the rapid spread of dairying and Ayrshire cattle in the South West of Scotland, the Galloway breed was usurped in many areas. History does not record being very dominated by a few breeders such as the foregoing. It is said that there was a prevalent fear that by intensive breeding and selection the breed would lose its inherent vigour and hardy constitution. Nevertheless, the breed had and still has its enthusiasts for breed improvement. The Sproats bred 'Cumberland Willie' whose progeny dominated many herds. Thereafter, the Biggar, McTurk and Graham families have long played an active part in bringing to the fore the Galloways as witnessed by successes in inter-breed competitions.

The improvers in dairy breeds are mentioned elsewhere.

In these modern times agricultural shows are sometimes denigrated for being outdated and offer little to the improvement of today's cattle population, being considered as little more than social occasions for the country folk. Or as one vociferous critic was wont to say, 'Make the shows over to something akin to greyhound or football, from very fine spectacles for the betting farmer into an important factor in his progress as a business.' This is always a good subject for debate at Young Farmers' Speechmaking Competitions, which will be bypassed here!

In bygone times early fairs, markets and agricultural shows were great incentives to the improvement of livestock. Fairs are of ancient origin. Franchises or charters to hold them at a given time or place were granted by the king or feudal lord. Fairs were held in China in ancient times and were operating in Champagne and Brie in 427 A.D. In 660 a cattle market was chartered in Utrecht, Holland where butter and cheese fairs were held.

During Angle-Saxon times, market transactions were concluded before the 'reeve' or acceptable witnesses for legal security. Buyers and sellers congregated at fairs and markets which tended to stabilise the prices. Fairs which were often and larger and gayer than markets increased greatly after the Norman Conquest.

Agricultural shows evidenced the first real efforts at cooperative improvement of cattle of which there are records. There, comparisons and judgements were made on different breeds and types of animals bringing the results of the master breeders before an audience of farmers who would try to emulate them. In spite of some criticisms the agricultural shows are still acclaimed as a method for yet further livestock improvement.

EXOTICS

Gerry Rankin who was a noted breeder of Beef Shorthorn and Aberdeen Angus cattle often said that the definition of a master breeder was one who had ruined more than one breed in his lifetime. Was this why there was an invasion of so called exotic cattle from Europe in the 1960s and 1970s? Food for thought but a bit unkind.

After the Second World War there was a gradual change in consumer demand away from the traditional large Sunday roast because families were becoming smaller, and more women were going out to work. Compared with other foods meat was considered too expensive and there was growing pressures coming from the anti-fat lobby. All this went against the consumption of meat and therefore reduced the profit margins of beef enterprises.

The main beef breeds, Aberdeen Angus, Shorthorn and Hereford over the years had become smaller and fatter driven by the very high prices paid by the American, Canadians and Argentinians for bulls. When they were crossed on dairy cows from which came two thirds of the country's beef came, the calves especially females acquired too much fat before they grew into an economical weight.

There became an obvious need for a larger, leaner. quick growing animals which would give a better return over a shorter period. This led breeders to look overseas. Tony Harman, John Mackie and Alex Anderson and colleagues after viewing Charolais in France agitated forcefully for them to be imported into the U.K. It was said that when Alex Anderson returned home from his first visit to France he burned all his clothes in case he brought Foot and Mouth disease into this country. It was this fear and the strong objections from the breed societies which delayed importations for a number of years.

A powerful deputation from South West Scotland travelled to London to lobby the Minister of Agriculture against the importation of Charolais cattle. Interestingly, many members of this deputation subsequently became enthusiastic Simmental breeders. Enthusiasm for Simmentals was clearly illustrated by Messrs. Jimmy Todd and Dave Hogg, when they paraded a bull at the Aberdeen Angus dinner at a Perth bull sale. The bull obligingly defecated at the door of the hotel before entering!

In 1961 26 Charolais bulls were allowed in on an experimental basis. The results were very impressive especially their characteristic of liveweight gain. It took another four years of wrangling before foundation stock of 200 heifers and 19 bulls were allowed into the country under very stringent veterinary conditions. At this time two bulls Sujet and Salomon were introduced to the S.M.M.B. A.I. stud.

This was followed by years of intensive campaigning for the Government to 'liberalise' their policy on the importation of breeding stock. Those who had been so obstructive never visualised that Charolais breed would dominate the beef industry.

The Government relented in 1970. A Committee was appointed under the chairmanship of Professor O.G. Williams, Agricultural Director of Fisons and a past Regional Director of the National Agricultural Advisory Service to monitor the imports of breeding livestock and to allocate licences to several Continental breeds. Immediately 26 breeds from eleven countries made applications. Between 1970–76 eleven new Breeds of cattle arrived in this country from the Continent and the Murray Grey from Australia.

They were Simmental, Limousin, Maine-Anjou, Blonde D'Aquitaine, Gelbvieh, Braunvieh, (Brown Swiss), Meuse-Rhine-Issel, Chianina, Romagnola, Marchgiana, Belgian Blue and Murray Grey. There are more than 800 breeds of cattle world wide, it is estimated that 120 of them are currently at risk of extinction. How many of the new imports will survive in this country?

Health regulations did not allow cattle to be sent direct from the European countries to America and Australasia, this resulted in a tremendous overseas demand for British bred calves at exorbitant prices running to £6000–7000. This led the critics to say that the U.K. had changed from being the stud farm of the world to being the quarantine station of the world. In spite of that, the importations of the 'exotics' has had a profound effect in improving the efficiency of cattle breeding in this country.

ARTIFICIAL INSEMINATION

In recent years the popularity of artificial insemination has revolutionised breed improvement. Although its use is usually considered a modern technique, in reality animal historians report that artificial insemination was practised as early as the 14th century. An Arabian chief is said to have mated a prize mare with a stallion of a rival chieftain by stealthily collecting the semen from the stallion and then artificially inseminating his mare in 1322. Inseminating of bitches was successfully carried out in Italy in 1799. By 1938 as many as 1.2 million cattle and 15 million sheep had been inseminated. The Danes started their first A.I. in 1936 and by 1955 80% of all the cows in Denmark were bred to A.I. (Mingay,1982.)

In thc U.K. much of the pioneering work was done at Cambridge under the aegis of John Hammond, Arthur Walton, Joseph Edwards, (M.M.B.) et al. In 1941 their work was given ministerial approval leading the setting up of cattle breeding centres throughout the country.

In Scotland the use of artificial insemination was first used by a number of enterprising farmers in Dumfriesshire who opened a Cattle Breeding Centre at Hoddam Castle in 1947. Mr A.R.Semple Charlesfield, Annan, who became a S.M.M.B member, was Chairman and a founder member of the Dumfriesshire Cattle Breeders Association Ltd. The Scottish Milk Marketing Board became involved at the beginning by taking up two hundred £1 shares in this organisation.

The success of this organisation was observed by some well known breeders in Renfrewshire and because the availability of semen was limited to that of one Ayrshire and one Friesian bull, moves were made to establish an artificial insemination centre in that area.

Robert Urquart reports an interesting anecdote about the proposed siting of a centre. 'An officer of the Scottish Milk Marketing Board was looking around the centre of Scotland for a building in which to house a proposed cattle breeding centre. He drove up to an impressive building in the Lanark area and rang the bell. To the senior uniformed lady who answered, he explained the purpose of his travels and asked what this building was used for. The haughty reply informed the officer that it was a maternity home thus quickly ending that part of the research! It transpired that this was the Fairhaven Nursing Home in which Jack Lawson the current Chief Executive of Scottish Livestock Breeders Ltd. was born.

The result of this research was the opening of the Southbar Cattle

Breeding Centre at Inchinnan, Renfrewshire, on 1st. December 1949. In preparation for this in the December 1948 News Letter, which was the title of the Board's earliest Milk Bulletin the following announcement appeared:

'Have you a bull for A.I.? The Board will shortly required a number of pedigree Ayrshire and Friesian Bulls for their Southbar Cattle Breeding Centre. If you have a bull you consider suitable for this purpose, you should write to the Secretary of the Board or to your Regional Officer for a Pedigree Form on which to supply the particulars.'

The number of cows inseminated by county in the first year of A.I. were: Argyll 347; Ayr 1920; Bute 256; Dumbartomn, 495; Lanark 666; Renfrew 1196; Stirling 248; Total 5128. In the second year the numbers rose to over 15,000

In 1952 the Board took over the Dumfriesshire Cattle Breeding at Hoddam which was subsequently closed in 1954.

As the demand for the service increased throughout Scotland and from the world over, it became necessary to open another centre, preferably situated further north than Glasgow. Newlands at Scone near Perth was the selected site, but a Public Enquiry was required before commencement in 1954. This proved a very good site which has been developed into the most modern in Europe. There is now available from it semen from 5 dairy breeds, 45 beef breeds and 10 dual-purpose breeds being administered by 65 highly trained technicians offering a 363 daily service. In 1993 there were 161,196 inseminations carried out.

Fig. 55 Bull semen, colour coded to show breeds, is kept at low temperatures in liquid nitrogen

Fresh semen has a limited 'shelf life', a maximum of about four days following collection, though rarely used beyond the second, whereas ram semen should be used within two days.

Because of this perishability cattle breeding sub-centres covering the country were necessary to act as collecting and distributing points. One has to appreciate that there was a daily scramble to rush the fresh semen to point of use utilising all types of transport available, cars, trains and planes. Jim Swanney, who was a former Director of the Board's Cattle Breeding Services, used to say that in the earlier days the standards of some of the cars used were such that some of the inseminators had to wear rubber boots because the floor boards were not water proof. There were no M.O.T. tests in those days.

As semen was usually collected only once or twice weekly from the bulls, this meant that farmers received from a variety of bulls which was a frequent cause of complaint. This was not the only complaint that was levelled at the early proponents of the use of A.I. had to withstand. Some thought that it was immoral, expensive and others feared that as the semen was in those days mixed with a protective fluid which included egg yoke, the resultant calves would be covered in hen feathers!

The progress in the use of A.I. in this country has been slow compared with other countries, which inevitably meant that the U.K. dairy cattle breeding fell behind. Initially too many farmers had trepidation about the unknown. There was some hostility on the grounds that it was 'agin nature'. There were too many wrong ideas prevalent about what A.I. could or could not do. A great learning curve was necessary. Some thought that it would correct all breeding difficulties; some thought that it would be possible to have cows breeding at any time, whether or not they were in season.

Pedigree breeders complained that they would be deprived of a considerable part of their income as fewer bulls would be required. They vehemently objected that the Boards and not the Breed Societies determined the criteria upon which bull purchases were made. This was understandable because all good cattlemen know that, 'A good bull is half of a herd and a bad bull is all of it.' There were further disappointments due to careless handling of semen, poor technique in inseminating the cow and poor sanitary practices, all resulting in a slow uptake of the practice.

To be licenced to sell semen each organisation had to have an advisory committee. Its members comprised of representatives from breed societies, commercial milk producers and the Department of Agriculture. This comprehensive committee did much to ameliorate the apprehensions held by many potential users of the A.I. service.

It was unfortunate that the vociferous detractors masked the advantages of the A.I. service. At the Annual General Meeting of the Scottish Milk Marketing Board the complaints were frequently numerous and sometimes unjustified. Similarly at meetings of the Board itself it has been known that a project costing thousands of pounds could be passed quickly and thereafter, there would be long discussions on A.I. when everyone suddenly became an expert! There must have been times when Archie Campbell, Director of the Cattle Breeding Service, his Deputy, Jim Swanney and Jim Isbister, Technical Director would be very frustrated. Those three enthusiasts devoted most of their working lives to the development of the A.I. service in Scotland and the shores beyond.

Thanks to the pioneering work of Dr. Chris Polge at Cambridge, Jim Isbister and colleagues elsewhere in the world, the perfecting of the technique of processing and freezing semen revolutionised the entire practice of artificial insemination. New ideas emanated from space travel to assist this important work on how to freeze the most specialised cell in the body, the sperm cell, store it for long periods and to bring it back to active life when it still retained its ability to fertilise an egg. The experience gained in the handling of rocket fuels was used in the design and manufacture of vessels to store liquids at extremely low temperatures. This coupled with changing the packaging material for semen from glass ampoules to plastic 'straws' enabled the slogan, 'Any bull, Anywhere, at Any Time,' to become a reality.

This great breakthrough meant that breeders had unlimited access to the best bulls when they could 'breed the best to the best.' A top bull could fertilise thousands of cows thousands of miles away years after he was dead.

The uptake of the A.I. gradually increased as the benefits of the more sophisticated methods of breeding practice were adopted. Breeders realised that the only sure way of predicting the genetic value of a sire was by progeny testing. As the Bible says, 'By their get ye shall know them.' Professor Robertson of the Animal Genetics in Edinburgh, developed the contemporary method of assessing a bull's breeding merit. This method was based on comparing the performance of daughters of the bull on test with daughters of other bulls milked in the same herd at the same time. This formula made the assumption that the contemporaries with which the test daughters were compared would be daughters of 'average' bulls. Because so many of the contemporary heifers were themselves daughters of proven bulls this formula has been modified. Now breeders have access

Fig. 56 AI Advisory Committee 1981

1) Bob Strathie, John McColm, Andrew Wilson, Jack Rennie, Jim Shanks, Jim Isbister, David Yellowlees, Ian Marr, Frank Young, Jim Biggar, M. Taylor, Alan Mathieson, Bideon Rutherford

2) Ian Gilmour, Archie Boreland, Adam Gray, Brian Speight, John Caldwell, K. Mair, John Logan, David McKerrow, J. McGregor, John Allan, Robert Woodburn, John Jamieson

3) Archie Campbell, Bob Lammie, William Young, John Marshall, Logan Forrest, Robert McKendrick, Jim Swanney

to top class proven bulls from all over the world.

The first A.I. progeny test was carried out in conjunction with the British Oil Cake Mills Co. at South Cathkin in Renfrewshire, with four Ayrshire bulls namely, Rottenrow Wonderman, Skerrington Vernon, Gree Gay Lawrence and Carbrook Flash. Initially, it was quite a problem for the staff of the organisation to get breeders to use young bulls for proving. They offered little cooperation due to their independent instincts and they thought that the young bulls would be too inferior to proven bulls or their own unproven stock bulls.

The introduction of cash incentive improved the situation. These have been changed over the years in the light of some expensive experiences. In the first scheme the owner was paid £200 when the bull went onto the Centre. A further £800 was paid to the owner when the bull was proven and accepted by the Board and at the same time a bonus was paid according to the performance of the bull's daughters. There were also incentives to the owners of milk recorded herds to use the young bulls. There was a reduced insemination fee of £1.25 with repeats free and a £2 bonus per calf or bull, resulting from a young bull mating which was limited to 50% of the herd.

An example of these incentives is illustrated by the handsome cheque of £3,848, which was paid by the Board to John Jamieson, Roundbush, Annan, when Ellerton Double Merit was proven. This cheque represented the £1,000 purchase price and the balance was the bonus paid on performance of the bull's daughters. A survey of 39 of them showed that Double Merit could raise the yields of his daughters by 180.4 gallons which was 25% better than his contemporaries. He became one of the most lucrative bulls which the S.M.M.B. purchased.

Jack Lawson who became then the Director of Cattle Breeding Services of the Scottish Milk Marketing Board in 1984 once said after seeing the results of the early progeny tests, 'It quickly became clear that neither price nor prefix had anything to do with performance.' This rather shattered some of the so called master breeders of the dairy world.

Now that A.I. is a highly acceptable method of mating cows with the herd usage of A.I. over 80%, there are quite a number of farmers who think that by inseminating their cows under a 'Do-it-Yourself' scheme, the conception of the cows is higher than if they are inseminated by the itinerant inseminator employed by the Cattle Breeding Stations. So far statistics show that there is little difference in the percentage of cows which conceive after the first whether mated naturally by a bull or via the technician service or by the 'Do-it-Yourself' artificial insemination.

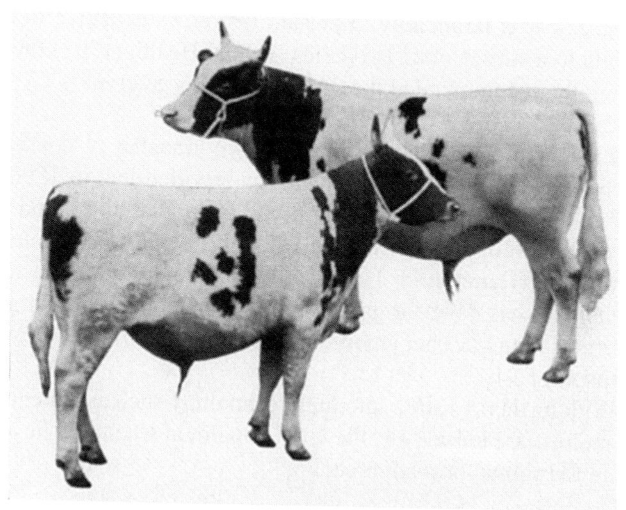

Fig. 57 The first AI progeny test was carried out with 4 Ayrshire bulls, pictured here are
Rottenrow Wonderman; Skerrington Vernon; - 1955

Fig. 58 Some "Weel Kent" faces from the past; visiting South Cathkin Progeny Centre
Alex. Kirkpatrick; James Howie; Archy Campbell; Robin Dunlop; Sir William Young & the Cathkin Manager.

Nevertheless, it is financially important that cows conceive timeously. According to a survey done by Genus Animal Health (1992) the cost of exceeding the recommended the 365-day calving interval is £3 per cow per day.

Like artificial insemination, embryo transfer is considered a relatively recent technique, yet it has been reported that in 1890 Heape transferred a fertilised ova from one rabbit to another and found that the genetic characters of the implanted young were not affected by those of the foster mother. (Hammomd, 1955.) Its development has done for good cows what A.I. has done for good bulls. A cow chosen for her superior characteristics can have her embryos stored or transported at will without high transport costs.

With further research into high technology such as genetic engineering, molecular biology, etc. the mind boggles at what may lie ahead in the future for animal or plant breeding.

BOBBY BOUTFLOUR 1890–1961

Half the pedigree goes in by the mouth. It took a long time for this simple truth to be established. Robert Boutflour showed the way. Bobby Boutflour, as he was affectionately known, in his forthright, pugnacious way; with a fine sense of humour, did more than anyone to spread new and better ideas about cow feeding and management throughout the dairy industry of the U.K. When he became Chief Agricultural Officer for Wiltshire County Council in 1922, he was put in charge of agricultural education in face of strong opposition from many local farmers, who thought that it was quite unnecessary. They did not want to hear the poppycock about the new ways of feeding cows which they had done all their working lives.

His principles on feeding cows were based on the foundation work done around the beginning of the century on assessing the feeding values of various foodstuffs by Kellner and other scientific nutritionists. In the 1870s palm kernal cake was introduced and with bean meal and brewers' grains began to be used as concentrates. Meals made of legume seed caused constipation and had to be corrected by adding bran which had long been considered good for milk production. Their work was made available in a practical way by Professor T.B.Wood in his book *'Rations for Livestock'* in 1921. In the many succeeding editions this book gave typical analyses and digestibilities for all foods that farmers might feed to their livestock.

The principal factors Boutflour laid down were the feeding of concentrates strictly according to individual cow's yield and at the same time reducing the bulky roughage as the concentrate levels increased. The traditional ration for feeding milk cows was 56lbs. roots; 14lbs. chopped straw and a 7lbs. mixture of linseed cake and Egyptian cotton cake, with a handful more to the high yielders. The theory of the time, which continued to be popular in many areas until the advent of well made silage was that the chaff or long oat straw was to counteract the linseed cake and roots.

The improvements in milk yields came easily when it was established that the dry matter requirement of a 10–11cwt dairy cow was approximately 30–33lbs. Naturally the heavier the cow, the more dry matter she required. But the bulkiness varies with the quality of the roughage and the amount consumed is inversely proportional to the indigestible matter fed. In other words, if the cow is fed too much roughage especially of a poorer quality, she suffers from indigestion and milk yields fall.

By the sheer strength of his personality and his ability to persuade, together with the magnetism of his lectures, which he gave to many hundreds of farmers meetings over the length and breadth of the country, many farmers threw away their chaff cutters and stopped feeding roots which Boutflour described as 'expensive water.' He continued his countrywide lectures when he was appointed Director of Dairy Husbandry at Harper Adams College 1926–1931.

The ration he propounded at the time was:

1 part Decorticated groundnut cake.
2 parts Maize meal.
1 part Rice bran
2 parts Palm kernel meal.

This was fed at the rate of 3½lbs. per gallon.

Further to this he introduced pre-parturition feeding which he called 'steaming up'. This was supposed to reduce the high incidence of milk fever.

The many lectures he gave were always well attended. Farmers were drawn to them by his stream of paradoxes, witticisms and calculated overstatements. The hard bitten farmers who rarely attended meetings usually enjoyed his offensive remarks because of the humorous manner of his delivery. A number are well worth noting.

'Never keep anything you can't manage, except your wife.'
'If camels gave more milk than cows, we would keep them in spite of their humps.'
'An old cow was grunting. In point of fact she was trying to say, "Oh what a skinful I've got, what an ass I was to eat so much and what a fool that man was for giving it to me.'
'If it is sensible to associate efficient mammary glands and consequent high yields with big stomachs in cows, it is equally sensible to associate big stomachs with big muscles. By such reasoning the men with big corporations should be capable of the most work.'
'If your cows go up in yield on going to grass then you do not know how to feed them indoors. The more they go up the worse your management is.'

While Boutflour was critical of the current management of dairy cows he had a number of caustic comments to make about pedigree breeding and cattle showing, which at times did not endear him to the enthusiasts. His views modified when he studied progeny testing and the proven sire system in America. At times it was his wont to say –

'Pedigree is based upon the supposition that like begets like. It may or it may not. Have a look at your brother!'
'A recipe for breeding cows is ½oz. of breeding, ½lb. feeding and ½ a stone of good luck.'
'I can see the breeder's point of view, for if he can find enough mugs to buy unproved sires, why should he prove them?'
'The show ring may be described little else than a glorified form of fortune telling, where one or two fortune tellers walk round a bunch of cows, pronounce upon their hidden mysteries. What humbug!'
'An expert is an ordinary fellow a long way from home.'
'To read old books is one of the best way to lose conceit.'

He thought that show judges looked as wise as owls and reminded them that when an owl looks wise he is asleep and when he is awake he is asleep. Nevertheless, in spite of his critics the Boutflour system of having a well balanced ration for milking cows became well established throughout the country by 1930 and 2000 gallon cows were not unusual. The twenty cow dairy herd he established at the Harper Adams College averaged 1400 gallons which was very high average in those days when the average size of herd in England was 15 cows.

His philosophy was widely adopted by the farm feed company British Oil and Cake Mills Ltd. whom he freely advised. They put the J.R. Milk Ration Nuts on the market which was thought to be about the first balanced ration for milk production. There have been many so called 'perfect' dairy feeds since!

From 1931–1958, Bobby Boutflour was principal of the Royal Agricultural College, Cirencester, the oldest institution of its kind being founded in 1845. The College had gone through an 'unhappy financial history' but with his dynamism and support of his admirers and business connections Boutflour established it to be an institution of influence in the agricultural industry. On his passing in 1961, Guy Chipperfield, C.B.E. said he was 'the most capable, colourful, eloquent and forceful character that ever adorned the fields of agriculture.' (Boutflour 1965).

CHAPTER 13

AYRSHIRE CATTLE

R..L. Stevenson once wrote:

The friendly cow all red and white
I love with all my heart,
She gives me cream with all her might
To eat with apple tart.

This is a sentimental but true description of the Ayrshire cow.

The Ayrshire breed has spread the world over, giving high quality milk ideal for drinking and manufacturing. Its prominent position in Scotland has now been overtaken by the Black and White breeds in recent years. Nevertheless the Ayrshire breed has been so critical to the development of the dairy industry in Scotland that it is well worthy of some discussion.

The Ayrshire is one of the most distinctive breeds. When studying its history it is difficult to be clear whether the breed should be considered as an new variety imported into a new district and modified by its surroundings or an improvement of an existing breed by selection locally and crossed with importations from outside of Scotland.

Prior to its development from the late 1700's, the countryside had scattered on it many non-descript cattle mainly black with some brown and 'speckled' colours. Cattle breeding in those days was a haphazard affair when any bull's son sired any other's daughter! In a very general way it could be said that the native Celtic breeds were black, the Anglo-Saxon tended to be of a red colour and any imported Dutch or French cattle were broken-coloured. In reality there is a whole fascinating area of speculation about the Ayrshire breed's early history.

Prof. Cossar Ewart wrote to John Speir about 1908, that the Bos Longrifrons or Brachyceros was apparently the only breed in Britain when the Romans came, i.e. the Celtic type with inward pointing horns. Before this period civilsation had advanced to such a stage that boats had been built of a size sufficient to cross from France or Belgium to Britain and from Wales or Scotland to Ireland. No other breed could have been brought from either of these countries, as at that date they only had the same breed as was in Britain. At the Roman invasion it therefore seems as if there was only one breed of cattle in Britain and at that time it had not been previously crossed with any other. Early writers say that this breed came into Britain with the arrival of the Celts from the continent.

Confusion, however, can arise about the colour black. In earlier writings the black was a generic name used for all bovine which could include white, dun and broken colours, the latter sometimes called brindled. These black cattle were mainly longhorned and over the centuries, when cattle were driven and sold into England they were the main source of agricultural income in Scotland. Efforts were made to breed cattle with smaller horns or no horns at all. It was fortunate that polling is a dominating breeding factor which enabled the progressive farmers in the south of Scotland to evolve the Galloway breed. These cattle having no horns made them popular for droving in large herds.

The term cattle also, can lead to some confusion when reading old papers. The word was synonymous with chattels and later, capital, to the extent that cattle could include horses, sheep and even bees in the days when they were an all important source of food and energy.

There is a well known adage of unknown antiquity often quoted about Ayrshire and Galloway:

Kyle for a man,
Carrick for a coo,'
Cunningham for butter and cheese,
And Galloway for woo'.

The county of Ayrshire is formed into three districts:

Kyle, between the rivers of Kyle and Doon, is said to take its name from the name Coilus, King of the Britons, (Old King Cole), whose daughter was lauded by one of the earlier poets as a virgin of such exceeding beauty, "that of all the ladies of the country of Brettayne, nane was sae fare." (Shaw J.E.) Another opinion is that Kyle is derived from Coille, a Celtic word for wood, hence cows of the wood. (Aiton Wc. 1812).

Cunningham, to the north, formerly Cunegan (1153); Cuninham (1180); derives its name from Gallic, cuinneag, 'a milk pail' and ham or hame, Anglo-Saxon for 'the place of'. Thus Cunningham district must have been renowned for milk production from early times, back to the days when cows belonging to the family were grazed and milked away from the 'ferm toune' and the milk would be carried back home in cuinneags. On unenclosed land with one or two cows per household this would be easier done than driving the whole mixed herd.

Carrick, to the south, is said to come from the Gaelic, 'carraig' meaning 'a sea cliff or rock.' The indigenous 'black' cattle were predominant in this area for quite a time after milk was being produced for sale in Cunningham. Interestingly, Ortelius, in his Description of the World, published about 1573, says, that in Carrick, a district of Ayrshire, 'are cattle of great size, whose flesh is tender and sweet; and another kind which never becomes fat, but yield rich milk.' Could these be of similar characteristics to the Galloways? William Aiton in 1811 said, 'The Galloway cow, so well known and so highly valued in the English market, was till of late, the only breed known in Carrick and in former ages through the whole county of Ayr and although the dairy breed has been lately introduced and is fast increasing in Carrick, still the Galloway is the most common in that district of Ayrshire.'

Fullarton (1793) reports that 'among the Galloway breed, many cows are found which yield great quantities of milk.' Aiton estimated that the Galloway cow gave about 225 gallons in a 5–6 month lactation. Youatt, (1834), wrote that 'Galloways are not good milkers'. It was estimated that their yields then were not more than 175 gallons in a lactation.

It was about this time that Galloway cows stopped being milked and suckled alternately and became single suckled and crossed by a Shorthorn bull producing the renowned Blue-grey cow.

Galloway, now comprising of the counties of Kirkcudbright and Wigtownshire, was once a formidable kingdom, it formerly included the districts of Carrick in Ayrshire and Nithsdale in Dumfriesshire.

The name Galloway was derived from Gall meaning stranger or foreigner and Gaidhel, the Gaels, giving the name Gallgaidhel – foreign gaels, being a mixed race of Gaels and Norse. The present province was originally covered by a large forest and the only access to it was via the Cree and Dee rivers.

The 'black' cattle mentioned were triple-purpose used for draught and beef and milk production. As time went on there was a degree of selection done. The daughters of cows which reared the best calves were hand milked for the production of butter and cheese. The production of those milkier strains of cows was greatly enhanced with the enclosing of land and the growing of 'new crops' already mentioned. This illustrated the old adage which is still true today – 'The cow gives her milk by the Mou'.'

It is generally agreed among earlier writers that the county of Ayrshire was the cradle of specialist milk production on any scale.

Col. Fullarton of Fullarton wrote in his General View of the Agriculture of the County of Ayr in 1794 which was submitted to the Board of Agriculture:

'In Cunningham, or the northern division of the County, a breed of cattle has for more than a century been established, remarkable for the quantity and quality of their milk in proportion to their size. They have long been denominated the Dunlop breed, from the ancient family of that name in the parish of Dunlop, Dunlop being the name of a parish in Cunningham, where the breed was first brought to perfection and where there still continues a greater attention to milk cows and dairies than in any other part of Scotland.' He also says that these cattle were generally 'black or brown, with white or flecked faces with white streaks along their backs.' These have also been referred to as Calder or Cadder cattle after a district north of Glasgow in the county of Lanark.

There has always been speculation as to the origin of the various colours associated with the Ayrshire breed. It is understandable that there are doubts about these origins. There can be many inaccuracies about time scale and descriptions because many incidents of history were passed around by word of mouth due to the lack of communications and authoritative records.

Colonel Fullarton was a progressive landowner and an M.P. for a time. In 1793, Prime Minister William Pitt established the Board of Agriculture with Sir John Sinclair as president and Arthur Young as Secretary. Surveyors were appointed to report on the agriculture in each county. These reports combined with those of William Marshall, who was active before the Board was formed, provide indispensible information on farming of the period. The Board was one of the casualties of the era of change following the Napoleonic wars and it was dissolved in 1822. It was re-established in 1822 in response to the findings of the Richmond Commission (1879–1882) on Agricultural Distress. It was renamed the Ministry of Agriculture in 1919.

When Col. Fullarton was transferred to other duties, the Board of Agriculture selected William Aiton, who was born in Ayrshire, to write a new report in 1811. It seems reasonable to suggest that because Col. Fullarton and William Aiton were both 'local boys' and genuinely interested in the wellfare of agriculture living in the era of rapid expansion of dairy cows their writings should be taken as being credible.

Apart from his report to the Board of Agriculture, William Aiton also wrote in 1825 a comprehensive treatise on the *Dairy Husbandry of Ayrshire* with an account of the Lanarkshire Breed of Horses and a number of other articles on cattle. He was a practical farmer in the county so was well placed to observe the farming changes. He wrote in 1811, 'I am old enough to remember, nearly, the commencement of enclosing of land and the introduction of ryegrass as a crop in the parish of Kilmarnock. The popular prejudice and the extraordinar clamour, among the tenantry against the innovations was very strong....... The tenants were disposed to consider every movement they were required to make on their possessions, as tending only to augment their labour and increase the rent rolls of the proprietor.'

Fullarton's colourful description of the local cattle must come from a number of sources according to the breeds that were introduced over a period of years.

It is logical to think that the earliest introduction of new bloodlines into these black cattle would be the other indigenous Scottish breed, the Highland or Kyloe, at one time the most numerous breed of cattle in Scotland. As the name suggests this breed is native to the Western Highlands and Islands of Scotland. Their recognised colours embrace various shades of red, yellow, dun and cream, as well as brindled and black. The black colour formerly prevailed but is now very rare. Their characteristic upward spreading horns to a degree was passed onto the Ayrshire breed, likewise their hardiness.

It was known that some Highland herds were kept in Dumbarton whose milk was made into butter and cheese. One eminent breeder said that, 'In breeding for the dairy, the Kyloes have the preference to every other breed. This superiority they have no doubt attained by judicious selection and breeding exclusively from such animals that secreted the most milk, as well as persevering experimental observations. Good judges can now pretty accurately point out a profitable dairy cow from the development of certain points in her conformation.'
(Farral, 1876.)

It was also known that there was an infusion of Highland blood later. John Speir (1908) is categoric in saying that the foundation of the famous Swinlees herd at Dalry belonging to Theophilus Paton was based on crossing of a West Highland heifer and an Ayrshire bull. 'Theo's brother Will, was a Highland cattle dealer. Swinlees Ayrshires were noted more especially for their size of body, volume of udder, neatness and perpendicularity of a large corky teat, brown colour, with very dark sides of head and neck.'

Other well known herds of the time that were alleged to have been founded from this nucleus herd were, Parker of Nether Broomlands, Irvine; Reid of Auchengown, Lochwinnoch; Love of Threepwood, Beith; and Robertson Hall, Neilston.

When the Romans came to Scotland about 80 A.D. they brought with them white long-horned cattle. They were larger and stronger boned cattle than the native Celtic breed, ideally suitable for draught purposes. Considering the vast amount of work and building that was done by the Romans during their stay in Britain, large numbers of draught animals were required necessitating frequent crossing with the local breeds. It is believed that these cattle are the ancestors of the present British White Cattle. There will be no doubt that they will be the ancestors of the Chianina whose society claim that it is the oldest and largest cattle breed in the world. Along with the Romagnola cattle they were imported into Britain in the 1970s.

Although those Roman cattle were mainly white, the implication that they were responsible for the white colour in the Ayrshire breed seems a little farfetched. It has been suggested that the black, white and black and white Welsh cattle originated from crosses between the original native black shorthorn cattle and the white longhorned Roman cattle.

John Speir says that the reason for the proportion of Ayrshire cattle being mostly white was because in the years between 1865 and 1880 'several bulls with a large amount of white in their colour became noted prize-takers. These were largely bred from and in a few years their progeny were widely distributed over the south-western counties...... so that the presence of white among Ayrshires at the present time is easily enough accounted for without any occasion to go further back than in our own time.'

The invasions of the Anglo-Saxons from 500–900A.D. had a great deal to do with the development of agriculture in Britain in general and the cattle stocks in particular. They were considered real farmers, they cleared forests etc. ploughed and sowed. These 'invading farmers' brought with them cattle which were mostly red in colour which became widely established in the south and east of England. They in turn are alleged to be the ancient ancestors of the present day red breeds such as the Sussex, Hereford, Lincoln Red, Devon and Red Poll.

When the Norsemen arrived in Britain they are supposed to have brought with them cattle which were 'small, short-legged narrow-backed, big-bellied creatures, with scythe shaped hind legs, usually light dun in colour and hornless.' It is believed that they are responsible for the polled character of Galloways, Aberdeen Angus and Red Poll, three breeds which originated in areas occupied by the Norse invaders. From such an unprepossessing description it was fortunate this breed contained the polling factor! It has been said that the polling factor was also introduced by the Romans. Nevertheless John Speir noted that, 'The Norwegians had a firm hold on some Western Islands and to some of these they seem to have introduced one of their breeds. What is known as the present Telemark breed of cattle is a horned dairy breed, somewhat smaller than the Ayrshire, white on the belly and legs and along the spine. The white markings along the back have a short herring bone appearance.' This is the origin of the cattle that have previously described as Cadder or Calder cattle.

Perhaps, however, this description is too disparaging to this imported breed. Its successor, Suffolk Dun cows at one time had a very high reputation for milk production. If reports from early writers could be believed their yields would not be out of place today! Arthur Young in 1794 writes 'This Suffolk Dun was always polled, so small that when fat it seldom exceeded 50 stone in weight, the possessor of a large carcase on thin legs, with a 'ridged ' backbone above and narrow loin and a large loose udder below exhibiting the most pronounced milk veins. There is hardly a dairy of any consideration in the district that does not contain cows which give, in the height of the season...eight gallons of milk in the day and six are common among many for a large part of the season.' Writers about this breed have said that had the Suffolk Dun survived, unimproved by beef entusiasts, it would have been among the premier British milk breeds today. (Trow-Smith 1958.)

Up to this point in the discussion about the history of the Ayrshire breed, the direct influence of the imported breeds from the 'invasions' has got to be conjectural and best ignored. Mention has been made of the whole coloured Celtic black, Roman white, Saxon red and Scandinavian dun, each invader bringing his own kind of cows. Unfortunately there are few written records in Scotland about its cattle prior to 1600, so it rather speculative to discuss the longterm effects that cattle from overseas had on the cattle population of Scotland and on the Ayrshire breed in particular. In fact there was a period of some seven hundred years before any great progress was made in cattle breeding. This was associated with a non-military 'Dutch Invasion' between 1500 and 1700.

DUTCH ORIGINS

Although early documentation on cattle is rather sparse in Scotland, there were quite a number of writers on the subject in England, particularly between 1500 and 1600, some of whom throw some light on cattle coming into this country during that period. There was also a close association between England and Holland in the wars during that period to the extent that there were English volunteers in the Dutch army and Dutch volunteers in the English army. A large majority of these men would be countrymen, the more discerning of whom such as officers would appreciate seeing new breeds of cattle.

There were two well known writers at this time, Leonard Marscal and Gervase Markham, who wrote about various aspects of farming. Leonard Marscal travelled on the continent, studied farming and thereafter published several books. In 1596 he wrote one on the 'Government of Cattel' in which he said, 'Also for oxen to labour, the black oxe and the redde oxe are the best and the browne oxe and the greezled oxe next, the white one is the worst of all colours.' About cows he says 'the browne colour mixt with white spots is good.'

Gervase Markham, an ancestor of a well known farming family, who as a young man he served as a soldier in Holland, later published several books on farming from 1608 to 1631 which contained many references to cattle: 'As touching the right Breed of Kine through our nation, it generally affordeth very good ones, yet some counties do far exceed other counties, as Cheshire, Lancashire, Yorkshire and Derbyshire for black kyne; Gloucestershire, Somersetshire and part of Wiltshire for red kine; and Lincolnshire for pide kine.' Pied or pyde cattle are those which are brown and white, similar to the average colour of the present Ayrshire cow.

Furthermore, there was a close association in England with the Dutch people when the Fen lands were being drained in the 16th and 17th centuries. Because of their expertise, many Dutchmen worked in that area for long periods and brought over their cattle. During the 17th century it was illegal to import cattle into England but not so into Scotland, such as to Leith or Ayr which was at that time the principal port for the west of Scotland before the Clyde was properly opened up. There are further references about Dutch cattle by other writers of the 18th century.

In 1756 T. Hale wrote in his book – *A Compleat Body of Husbandry*, 'Yorkshire oxen are in general black all over and they are very large and form a valuable kind in every respect. There are none that exceed them for labour and few feed like them....The oxen of Lincolnshire are in general red and white, they are very bulky and are equal to any in value.' It is understandable that the writers of that era should mention bullocks as most cattle then were all considered to be dual purpose and in many areas triple purpose, but they were still looking for the strains that would give the most milk.

Arthur Young on his tour of the north of England about 1770 mentions that 'In Yorkshire the common breed was the short horned kind of cattle called Holderness, but really the Dutch sort.' Holderness being a district near the river Humber.

In his book on *'Observations on Livestock'*, George Culley in 1786 is more categoric about Dutch importations 'I remember a gentleman of the county of Durham, Mr Michael Dobinson, who went in the earlier part of his life to Holland in order to buy bulls, those he bought were of much service in improving the breed and this Mr Dobinson and his neighbours, even in my day were noted for having the best breed of shorthorned cattle and sold their bulls and heifers for great prices.' He also says that there were few of this type of cattle in this country 'except along the east coast, facing those part of the Continent where the same kind of cattle are still bred and reaching from the southern extremity of Lincolnshire to the borders of Scotland.'

Later, in 1864 W. Youatt published a book the *Complete Grazier,* in which he remarked that, 'The shorthorned cattle under which the denominations are included the Holderness and Teeswater breeds, have been supposed to have derived their origin from a cross with some large bulls that were imported by Sir William St Quintin nearly a century ago

Fig. 59 The Holderness Cow

from Holland to Yorkshire and in the east and north ridings of which county the two latter breeds have been long established and deservedly esteemed,...and it is from some of that stock , so maintained, that the present improved shorthorn cattle sometimes known as the Durham breed, is supposed by some to be descended.'

It would seem from the foregoing that over a period of some two hundred years 'the flecked or pyed red and white breed had filtered into England and had a unique part in the development of the Shorthorn breed. How it progressed into the two distinct types now named the Beef Shorthorn and the Dairy Shorthorn is another story. The interest for the present is what part did these importations play in the development of the Ayrshire breed.

From a consensus of earlier writers namely Marchal (1596), Marham (1608), Mortimer (1707), Hale (1756), Young (1770), Culley (1786), Col Fullarton (1794), William Aiton, (1812), George Robertson (1829), and John Speir (1908), there seems little doubt that Dutch cattle were imported into Eastern England bred there and crossed with native cattle which had origins from the Anglo-Saxon invasions and 'found' their way into Scotland by various routes.

It has been implied that while there were import restrictions on cattle coming into England in the seventeenth century a number of cattle were sent direct to Scottish ports where there were no such restrictions. Another little recorded route would be by droving. There is plenty of literature referring to large herds of cattle going south but little about cattle being brought north which is understandable for the cattle going south were for fattening. However, it seems unlikely that the mercenary minded drovers would not miss an opportunity of walking back north with a 'return drove'. There is every chance this would include crosses of the Dutch type of cattle. Is it more than coincidental that droving south reached its peak about 1835 at a time when brown and white cattle spread all over the central and south west Scotland? After all the nucleus stock in Ayrshire at that time would not be very numerous.

Col Fullarton and William Aiton are often quoted as being two of the authorities of the pre-twentieth century writers on the evolution of the Ayrshire breed. Aiton is inclined to maintain a more parochial opinion, 'in a great measure the native indigenous breed of the county of Ayr improved their size, shapes and qualities chiefly by judicious selection, cross coupling feeding and treatment for a long series of time with much judgement and attention by the industrious inhabitants of the county and principally by those of the district of Cunnungham.' Col Fullarton on the other hand, considered that the breed was not an improved variety of a previously existing one, but an entirely new one. 'It appears that this mottled breed is of a different origin from the former flock.'

Some individuals are quoted to have brought in cattle from the east of England which formed a nucleus which was alleged to have spread over the country. Col. Fullarton wrote that 'It is asserted by a gentleman of great skill and long experience, Mr Bruce Campbell that the breed was introduced into Ayrshire by the present Earl of Marchmount and afterwards reared at the seat of the Earl of Glasgow, whence they are said to have spread all over the country.'

Aiton's writings in early 19th century on the evolution of the Ayrshire breed are confusing. In 1812 he recalls that 'Among other crosses with foreign cows or bulls, I understand that the Earl of Marchmount about 1750 purchased from the Bishop of Durham and carried to his seat in Berwickshire several cows and a bull either of the Teeswater or other English breed of the high brown and white colour now so general in Ayrshire and that Bruce Campbell then factor of his Lordship's estates in Ayrshire carried some of that breed to Sornbeg in Kyle, from whence they spread over different parts of the country.' He goes on to say that 'I have been told that John Dunlop of Dunlop brought some large cows from a distance, probably of the Dutch, Teeswater, or Lincoln breeds and much of that breed of Cunningham proceeds chiefly from that origin. John Orr of Barrowfield, now part of Glasgow, brought from Glasgow or some part of the east country to Grougar, about 1769, several very fine cows of the colour now in vogue, one of whom I remember cost £6, which was more than twice the price of the best cow in that quarter.'

The following year in the *Farmers Magazine*, Aiton writes, 'Prior to 1760 and 1770 there seems to have been about Glasgow and in the possession of several noblemen and wealthy gentlemen kept at their country seats, milk cows of a brown colour and of a much greater size than the native breed of Scotland; and some of these have been carried from time to time into different parts of the county of Ayr and being generally placed on richer pasture and better fed than the ordinary farm stock were at the time. They yielded a greater quantity of milk and the farmers became to procure calves or crosses with them, in the hopes of getting similar returns from their progeny. I have been anxious to discover from what quarter this stranger breed came, but I have not been fully satisfied as to their origin. I remember to have heard them forty years ago termed Dutch cows by some and English cows by others, but whether from the one country or the other, or from whence I have not been able to ascertain.'

'But from whatever quarter they may have come, it is from them that the brown colour, now so universal in the Ayrshire dairy breed, has become fashionable. Perhaps something of the other qualities of that breed may have also descended to the Ayrshire dairy cows by crossing with them, but I am not of the opinion that the present stock of Ayrshire are either completed descended, or that their superior excellence has been entirely derived from these strangers. I have been persuaded that they have been brought to their improved state chiefly by their better feeding and treatment.'

The dates that Aiton mentions about the introduction of imports from the south are not substantiated by G. Robertson in 1832 only twenty years later than when Aiton was writing. Robertson says that 'This Mr Bruce Campbell was, I presume, of Milrig in the parish of Galston and was born around 1730 as I know from family history and the Earl of Marchmount alluded to, must have been Alexander Hume Campbell who married Campbell, heiress of Cessnock and became Earl of Marchmount in 1724 and died in 1740. The introduction, therefore, of this dairy stock must have happened betwixt these two dates... My own conjecture is that they were either Holderness breed or derived from it judging from the varied colour or what is still better evidence, the small head and slender neck and in 1800 I found a similar breed in the lands of Colgarth, the property of Dr Richard Watson, Bishop of Llandaff, by the Windermere in Westmorland, which had been there from Holderness.'

The question could be asked did the red and white cattle of Holland pre-date the now common black and white cattle? John Speir (1908) concludes that to be so, judging from the evidence from 17th century paintings examples of which were to be found in the art galleries of Holland and Britain. Practically all such paintings depicted the Dutch cattle of the period as being red and white. Dr Bakker, 1948, is quoted to have said that 'It is evident that there is sufficiently valid foundation for the claim that Dutch cattle belonged to the uniformly red Germanic breed forming part of the longifrons group....The old breed known in literature as the old Friesian breed disappeared for the most part in the years 1713–1769 and was replaced and crossed with the Jutland cattle imported from Denmark, which were black and white. (Stanford 1956).

Irrespective of their milking ability then, there is every possibility that the landed gentry of yesteryear who were importing these cattle would include cattle of a different colour for novelty rather than commercial reasons. Quite a different attitude was of course taken on the importations of the 19th century onwards.

THE ALDERNEY QUESTION

When the 'Dutch' cattle were crossed with the local breed in Ayrshire, the offspring were considered to be 'illshaped, mongrel appearance, their bones being large and prominent.' These cattle eventually became more refined and credit for this has been given to the importations of Alderney cattle. Youatt in his book the *Complete Grazier* claims that Alderney cattle were used on the evolving Ayrshire cattle. It would appear that this contention is supported by the fact that Field Marshall Conway and Lieut-General Andrew Gordon succeeding governors of Jersey, sent cattle to both England and Scotland between 1772 and 1806.

At that time the term Alderney encompassed Jersey and Guernsey cattle, as well as those which came from Normandy and Brittany. It has been suggested that the original were saved from the ships in the Spanish Armada.

Quale who wrote an agricultural survey of Jersey, declares that Ayrshires were an Alderney cross. References in Custom House books 1719 et seq., indicate that substantial numbers of the Channel Island cattle came into England. By the middle of the nineteenth century there was an annual importation of 1,500–3,000.

There was an Alderney cattle company, owned by Mr Fowler and his four sons which brought in those cattle to supply the town dairies of London. They eventually found their way into the South West of Scotland. Fullarton writes in his Review that 'Alderneys and Guerseys have been introduced in order to give a richness and colour to the milk and butter.' There was a Guernsey herd established near Castle Douglas in that era. There is no doubt about the influence of the Channel Island cattle on the evolvement of the Ayrshire breed. The conformation of early twentieth century cattle bear witness to this.

According to John Speir(1908), the first herd of Ayrshires to be moved from their native county was when James Fulton took his herd from his farm in the parish of Beith to Jamestown in the parish of Maybole in 1790. From then on reports on agriculture refer to cattle from Ayrshire being introduced into the counties of Dumbarton, Lanark, Dumfries, Roxbourgh and Wigtown. The reports on Banff, Moray, Peebles, Berwick, Perth and West Lothian refer to Holderness being introduced.

William Aiton in the *Farmers Magazine* in 1812 reported that, 'Not fewer than a 1000 cows of the proper Cunningham breed have been carried from Ayrshire annually for several years to other counties of Scotland and England and some of them may now be found in every shire from Caithness to Kent, while the demand for them is every year increasing.'

One of the earliest references to the prices of Ayrshires is found in the Agricultural Report on the county of Renfrew, referring to the parish of Mearns, 'It is all enclosed. The parks or enclosures consist of from eight to ten acres, renting from £1.10s. to £2. They are stocked with the finest milch cows anywhere to be seen, mostly of a brown and white colour, purchased chiefly in Ayrshire when in calf at from £8–£10 each.' With farm wages at that time about £20 per year that makes an in-calf heifer having a present day value of £4000! On the other hand, from the deed of settlement of Giles Blair, Lady Row, who lived in Carrick, executed on 31st August 1530, it appears that a cow at that time was worth 2s.2d. an ox 2s.6d; a two year old 1s.1d. and a stirk 8d. (Gillespie 1877)

The Rev. William Donaldson, minister of Ballantrae, is credited with being one of the earliest writers to name the Cunningham breed of milch cows, 'Ayrshires' when he wrote in the Transactions of the Highland Society of 1812. Earlier it has been noted the original dairy breed of the county was named the Dunlop breed as a tribute to the pioneering work in dairy cattle breeding by the Dunlop family in the parish of Dunlop. Thus as the Ayrshire cattle spread throughout the country their name changed from Holderness, Dunlop, Cunningham, to Ayrshire.

It is intriguing to wonder how there were quite a number of black and white Ayrshire cattle. It has been noted earlier that they were a result of crossing with some of the later importations of Dutch cattle. One possibility which is rarely mentioned by earlier writers is that they may have been descended from Black Cattle of Fife.

THE FIFE CATTLE

When the Highland Society decided in 1835 to award premiums to encourage improvements in cattle breeding it specified the Shorthorn, West Highland, Polled Angus, Polled Aberdeenshire and Galloway beef breeds and the Ayrshireas a dairy breed. This action lead to the demise of the Horned Aberdeenshires and the dairy breed of Fifeshire.

Understandably records about the Fifeshire dairy breed are scarce. Only brief references can on this occasion made. Rev. Charles Rogers read an essay to the Lunaw and Vinney Water Farmer Society, Forfar, in July 1804, on the rearing of horses and cattle saying that, 'Prior to the reign of James I, Alexander, Earl of Mar, imported horses from Hungary; while

James I who was himself a promoter of farm stock, introduced on his lands at Falkland in Fife a superior species of milk cows .... and suggested that the tops of carrots should be used in the feeding of milch cows.' Previously, Henry VII presented Margaret Tudor and James IV with cattle from England on the occasion of their marriage which were later called Fife cattle.

In 1794 Robert Beatson writing in the *General View of the Agriculture of the County of Fife* says about the Fife Breed of Black Cattle that 'as the breed of black cattle in this county has been brought to confiderable perfection and is getting every day more and more into repute, the following description of them, it is hoped, will not be unacceptable.'

Average length from the root of the horn to the rump, 6 feet 6 inches.
Breadth at the hough bones, 2 feet 6 inches.
Height at the fhoulder 4 feet 9 inches.
Weight when grafs-fed, from 22–24 ftone.
Price of a cow, at the age from 3–4 years and near calving, from L6 to L8 sterling.
The breed is commonly horned.
Cows in their prime give, at an average, from 10 to 12, or 13 Scotch pints of milk per day. (Two Scotch pints make one English gallon.) and they continue to give milk to within three months of their calving.
For feveral months after the milk will produce 1lb. of butter per day and 10 lbs. of cheefe per week.
A calf properly fed for the butcher, at 5 to 6 weeks old, will give 25 to 30 fhillings.
If kept for breeding and fold at 10 to 12 months old, it will fetch L3 to L3. 10s Sterling.
When 2 years old, from L4 to L4. 10s.
When 2 years old and fold fat from L5 to L5. 10s.
When 3 years old for breeding, from L5 to L5. 10s.
Or, if fed for the butcher, from L5. 10s to L6 Sterling.
When 4 years old full grown, from L6 to L8.
Sweet milk is found to be the beft food for calves.
Oxen, 3 to 4 years old, fetch from L8 to L10 Sterling.

In 1840 James Jackson wrote in his *Treatise of Agriculture and Dairy Husbandry*, (T.H.A.S.S. 1840) 'The cattle of the Highlands of Scotland are of different varieties, owing perhaps to circumstances, such

Fig. 60 The Fife Cow. c.1835

the treatment of herbage and climate. The most esteemed of those are of the West Highland and Isles called the Argyllshire Breed and frequently Kyloes. It is thought that this breed might be much improved by judicious crossing as was seen in the case of the Ayrshire Kyloe. This breed is rather handsome in appearance; the horns are long and upright, head large, the neck short and deep, legs of a good length; and the beef is in general estimation. The Fifeshire cattle are supposed to be nearly allied to the Kyloes, which they resemble in appearance very much.'

J. Lawrence in 1809 wrote that the Fifeshire cattle were 'of considerable size, black lively, up-horned, ...they feed quick... and are fit for labour (and) have the character of giving rich milk, rather than any of great abundance.'

The Aberdeenshire breed is said to have been produced by crossing with the Fifeshire and the ox thus obtained is considerably larger than the original of the county. The are commonly of a black colour but this varies from red to spotted. Compared with the West Highland cattle, they are thinner in the buttock deeper in the belly and they yield a much more abundant supply of milk. The Aberdeenshire breed here was the Aberdeenshire Horned Cattle which for a time was popular in the English markets. However, as has been mentioned the Highland Society encouraged the breeding and developement of the Angus Polled cattle which were improved in size by being crossed with the Aberdeenshire Horned Cattle resulting in the evolvement of the world famous Aberdeen-Angus breed. Nevertheless, old paintings show a strong resemblance between the Fifeshire or Falkland cattle with former Ayrshires for example one by artist William Shiel illustrated in Professor Low's book Domesticated Animals of the British Isles (1842). Professor Low believed that the Fife farmers should replace these cattle by a beef breed such as a Shorthorn.

In the search for the origins of the black and white Ayrshire cattle consideration may have to be given to the role of Arran cattle. MacNeilage, (T.H.A.S.S.1912) says that 'The native Arran cow, portraits of which adorn the pages of books published in the early years of the nineteenth century and from its appearance closely akin to the Kerry, is extinct. There can be little doubt that the presence of black and white colours in Ayrshire cattle is due to the strains of blood from this source which commingled with the Teeswater strains to build up the modern Scottish dairy breed. The Arran cow was not restricted in its habits to its island home. It was to be found in Cunningham or North Ayrshire and the sprightly of the modern Ayrshire is in large measure derived from this source.'

It seems logical to conclude that because of early indiscriminate breeding which was unavoidable with few enclosures, various colours in cattle would appear in different parts of the country. Black and white cattle of above average conformation with a big head and upward sweeping horns would be very attractive to discerning dairy farmer. In the early days of the Herd Book there were some animated discussions as to whether black and white cattle should be allowed to be entered.

In more recent times there was a strong demand for them to cross with the increasing numbers of Friesian in order to improve the appearance of the latter's udders. William Cruickshank, Rattra, Borgue had a well known herd of black and white Ayrshires and the Ramsay family in Wigtownshire still do.

Ayrshire cattle have always been important at any agricultural shows and Ayrshire breeders have always been prodigious showers of cattle, they still are. Nowhere is showing entered into with such spirit and enthusiasm. The Farmers' Club of Kilmarnock was established in 1786 and held its first cattle show in 1793. Gilbert Burns, brother of Robert Burns, in discussing the improvement of Ayrshire cattle said that 'Although much has been done of late in this country in proper selection of the species to breed from yet much remains to be done. That particular attention ought to be given to the whole appearance of the animal, as well as to colour and horns. That much attention ought to be given in the selection of the cow as well as of the bull.'

The poet Robert Burns, when he moved to the farm of Ellisland in Dumfriesshire in 1788, brought Ayrshire cows with him. John Dunlop had given Cunningham cows to Robert and Gilbert when they started farming at Mossgiel. These cattle must have done well with Burns because two of them sold for £40 each at his sale when farm wages at the time were £7 for the year. How much is that today? As an aside it has been said that Burns was not a progressive farmer yet Col. Fullarton in his Report metioned how Burns advocated the dehorning of cattle. 'In order to prevent any danger arising from cattle in studs and straw yards, the best mode is to cut out the budding nob or root out the horn while the calf is very young. This was suggested to me by Robert Burns whose general talents are no less conspicuous than the poetic powers which have done so much honour to the countryside where he was borne.' He also introduced the use of lime when it was considered the 'road to utter ruin.'

To encourage better cattle breeding, the Highland Society itself established in 1784, gave annual premiums in district competitions from 1789. The first premiums for Ayrshires were offered in Kyle in 1814 by the Highland Society. On that occasion the 1st prize for bulls was awarded to Mr Hendry, Highfield and the second prize to Mr Morton, Brownhill. For Heifers, the first prize was awarded to William Pollock, Galston and the second prize to Thomas MacLellan, Mauchline. This was the first public occasion when the press gave this breed of cattle the present name 'Ayrshire'.

When the Highland Society Show was held in Glasgow in 1826 Ayrshires were considered to be the main feature. On that occasion the Duke of Montrose was the most successful exhibitor.

As early as 1850 began the controversy between the 'yeld stock' type of cattle and the 'vessel bred' type which continued for over a hundred years which was to the longterm detriment of the Ayrshire breed. One faction put the showing emphasis on a light weight cows with 'a delicate appearance and a well set udder' whereas the other faction preferred cows which were bigger and more capacious. There were also breeders who showed only cows and others who showed only yeld stock. The anomalous situation was summed up by Mr A.Y.Allan, Runnoch, Dalry, 'We find one man year after year exhibiting yeld stock, while with cows he is nowhere to be found; and we find another man with milk stock always to the front, while his yeld stock are never to be seen. Now there is something wrong in all this! 'Eild' or 'yeld' is a Scottish expression to indicate cattle, whither male or female, that do not yield milk. Fortunately this was ameliorated by the formation of the Ayrshire Cattle Society in 1877.

However these traditions continued for many years. If there had been fewer of the small perfect show specimens with their 'thimble teats and well shaped udders' and more of 'the larger productive type' in the 1950s and 1960s the Friesian breed would not have expanded so quickly in Scotland and as personally witnessed in Canada and New Zealand in the 1950s the exports of Ayrshires to these countries would have expanded further than it did.

There was more controversy as to whether Ayrshire cattle should be dehorned. Many thought that such an act would detract from the symmetry and character of the breed. Fortunately practical thinking prevailed. After all Robert Burns advocated that this should be done!

At Ingleston when about eighty cows were dehorned in one day the byre was flowing with blood. Adam Gray (1895–1971) who had experienced three years in the 'bloody' battles of First World War looked in to see the operation in progress. He immediately retreated because he could not stand the sight of so much blood.

Fig. 61 Pant Treasure 6th. "An animal that has been cleanly and neatly dehorned, and whose head shows true Ayrshire character, shall not be penalised." ***"The Stockman's Guide to the Ayrshire."***

From whatever conclusion can be made on how the Ayrshire breed has evolved it is hardy and adaptable. As Scott Burn said in 1875, 'For dairy purposes in cheese districts, the Ayrshires are justly celebrated; indeed, they seem to possess the power of converting the elements of food more than any other breed into cheese and butter.

For a long time the Ayrshire was named 'the poor man's cow.' Not nowadays.

For many years what is the right type of Ayrshire cow has been debated. Many changes in the ideals have been made. The following ingenious versification was published under the authority of the Ayrshire Agricultural Association before the formation of the Ayrshire Cattle Society. How would it measure to present day requirements?

Would you know how to judge a good Ayrshire cow ?
Attend to the lesson you will hear from me now;
Her head should be short and her muzzle good size;
Her nose should be fine between muzzle and eyes;
Her eyes full and lively, forehead ample and wide;
Horns wide, looking up and curved inwards beside;
Her neck should be a fine tapering wedge,
And free from loose skin on the undermost edge;
Should be be fine where 'tis joined with the seat of the brain;
Strong and straight upper line without hollow or main;
Shoulder blades should be thin where they meet at the top;
Let her brisket be light, nor resemble a crop;
Her fore-part recede like the lash of a whip,
And strongly resemble a bow of a ship;
Her back short and straight, with the spine well defined,
Especially where back, neck and shoulders are joined,
Her ribs short and arched, like the ribs of a barge;
Body deep at the flanks and milk veins full and large;
Pelvis long and straight and in some measure flat;
Her tail long and fine and joined at her back;
Milk-vessel capacious and forward extending,
The hinder part broad and to the body fast pending;
The sole of her udder should just form a plane,
And all her four teats equal thickness attain;
Their length not exceeding two inches or three;
They should hang to the earth perpendicularly;
Their distance apart when viewed from behind,

Will include half of the udder you will find;
And when viewed from the side, they will have at each end;
As much of the udder as 'tween them is penned;
Her legs should be short and bones fine and clean;
The points of the latter being quite firm and keen;
Skin soft and elastic as the cushions of air,
And covered all over with short woolly hair
The colours preferred are confined to a few,
Either brown and white checkered or all brown will do;
The weight of the animal leaving the stall,
Should be about five hundred sinking offal.

A more modern concept of an Ayrshire cow might be that she is able to combine high milk yields and excellent yields of solids, particularly protein from relatively low inputs with an economic efficiency that most other dairy breeds simply cannot match.

Key to the superior performance is the breed's ability to use low cost forages to the full producing excellent margins without excessive use of costly concentrates. Added to this the low investment to buy Ayrshires, high stocking rate, superior longevity and robust health and the breed comes out well on top.

Ayrshires have spread to all corners of the globe. The modern breed is still continuing to show its adaptability, being the majority breed in countries as climatically opposed as Finland and Kenya.

The Ayrshires' conformation is the ideal design for a dairy cow with a wide muzzle, the head carried well, the neck and shoulders fine and sharp with a clean throat and brisket forming the classic thin end of a wedge shape. The body is deep with well sprung ribs and hind quarters shaped to minimise calving problems and carry the udder high with evenly balanced quarters and teats. Milk veins are apparent and with udder attachments strong to withstand continuous high yields.

The breed is still improving in terms of milk production, faster than most of its competitors. The bank of genetic material has been boosted strongly in recent years by the importation of semen from around the world.

Fig. 62 The Ayrshire Bull, from *"The Book of the Farm"*; 1851

Fig. 63 Ayrshire cow. "Dairymaid",
1st Prize Winner H. & A.S. Show 1906

Fig. 64 Ayrshire Bull, "Commander",
1st Prize Winner, H & A.S. Show 1907

Fig. 65 Part of herd of Ayrshires Lessnessock Farm, Ochiltree,
Ayrshire. 1932

AYRSHIRE CATTLE SOCIETY

Before stock could be moved around regularly they 'hefted' in one area. They generally became adapted to the conditions in which they were placed. The animals became naturally suited to the locality to which they had become acclimatised, such as the West Highlander in the north or the North Devon in the south.

Stock in one part of the country tended to be of the same kind and very often took their breed name from their county of origin, such as Ayrshire, Aberdeen Angus, Hereford and Devon etc. The breeders knew one another and how their respective stock were bred. When stock began to be moved about, the interested breeders wished to keep track of them and to be sure that they were kept pure and not crossed with local stock. These breeders bandied together and formed a breed society with a number of rules relating to the type of animal they wanted to see developed, including details of colour, in dairy cows, the shape of body and udder etc. This lead to the publishing of Herd Books, in which the pedigrees of the animals of the respective breeds were registered. One cynic said about the formation of breed societies, 'they allowed each breed to have what each breeder chose to make it!'

The idea to have a Herd Book for Ayrshire cattle originated from Mr David Tweedie of Abington, Lanark, in a letter to the Ayrshire Agricultural Association. On the death of Mr Tweedie, Mr Farral of Aspatria progressed this idea and published a 'Register' of 17 bulls and 59 cows in 1877. He called it the Ayrshire Herd Book and it was printed in Whitehaven, Cumberland. Because he was too far from the centre of the Ayrshire world Mr Farral's efforts were not successful, whereupon in the same year the Ayshire Agricultural Association appointed a committee, which called a public meeting to be held in County Buildings, Ayr, on June 26th, 1877.

The committee, having held preliminary meetings on May 15th and June 12th, was convened one hour before the inaugural meeting on June 26th 'to revise the list of Committee to be proposed at the Public Meeting....' as the Hon. Greville R. Vernon of Auchans House, Kilmarnock, said in a note asking the committee members to come early.

When Mr Vernon presided at the public meeting at 12.30 p.m., nearly 90 gentlemen were present. Sixty-five names were on the sedurunt, '....also twenty others whose names could not be got owing to their having gone in by the side door.'

A resolution was adopted, 'That it is, in the opinion of this

Meeting, desirable to form a Society for the purpose of Establishing a Herd Book containing the Pedigree, etc. of Ayrshire Cattle." At the close of the meeting 32 'gentlemen' were enrolled right away; presumably including some of the duly elected (revised) Committee and possibly some of the intruders!

Entries for the first Herd Book closed on the 31st December 1877 and this volume containing 117 bulls and 446 cows was issued in 1878. The Duke of Buccleuch was the largest with 110 cows and 21 bulls. Dead animals were eligible and a bull called 'Rob' was entered by Mr Robert Dunlop, Aulton, Kilmaurs, as owner, the breeder being Mr John Parker, Broomlands Irvine, who supplied many of the young bulls of that period.

In 1884 and again in 1906, the Society published scale points for the judging of Ayrshire cattle. Though the idea was sound it added fuel to the fire about the ideal type of Ayrshire cow. However, progress was made in resolving these arguments at Ayr New Show in 1921 when new standards for judging were introduced based on both conformation and production and thereafter have continued at many shows. This 'new thinking' bore fruit in 1923 when a team of six cows made Ayrshire bred history by winning for the first time the coveted 'Bledisloe' Challenge Trophy over all breeds. The cows were A & A Kirkpatrick's Barr Amelia; A.Y.Allan's Aitkenbar Kate 3rd; A & A Kirkpatrick's Barr Flirt; George Dunlop's Barstibly Helga; Thomas Barr's Southside Kirsty; Lt-Col. R.E. Cecil's Netherton Queen Greenfield 4th.

At the 'New Show' held Ayr in February 1921. The Ayrshires were judged by a Canadian. As one would expect, he had his critics.

There was a subsequent report in the Scottish Farmer:

The Ayrshire 'new show' is over and gone. As a show or display it was an unquestioned success. In making his awards, Professor H. Barton, from Macdonald College, Quebec, had not pleased everbody in that he was not singular but the system of judging by points and the introduction of the milk record as an element in the final placing created a novel situation.

Professor Barton clearly put greater stress on size and strength and appearance of robust health than is commonon the part of the judges at home.'

Fig. 66 Advertisement in the Scottish Farmer. 1953

Fig. 67 Glasgow Dairy Show. 1955

FIRST PUBLIC MEETING

26th June, 1877

Court House of the County Buildings,
Ayr, 26th June, 1877

At a Public Meeting of those interested in the proposal to start a Herd Book for Ayrshire Cattle, convened in the name of the Honourable Greville R. Vernon by Circular and Public Advertisement of which the following is a copy.

AYRSHIRE HERD BOOK

As I have been requested to take steps to form a Society for establishing a HERD BOOK for AYRSHIRE CATTLE, and having already received promise of much support from Proprietors and others interested, I HEREBY CALL a MEETING of all those favourable to the Formation of such a SOCIETY, to be held within the COURTHOUSE of the COUNTY BUILDINGS, AYR, upon TUESDAY first, the 26th current, at Half-past Twelve o'Clock.

G. R. VERNON.

The favour of your attendance is requested.

G.R.V.

PRESENT

The Hon. G. R. Vernon
Captain Hamilton of Rozelle
Mr. Cochran Patrick of Woodside
Mr. Adam of Tour
Mr. Hunter, Adamton
M. Whigham, Ayr
Mr. Drennan, Auchinlee
Mr. Guthrie, Crossburn
Mr. Holm, Japston
Mr. Wilson, Kilmarnock
Mr. Baxter, Ladyburn
Mr. Cunninghame, Shields
Mr. Rodger, Eastwoodhills
Mr. Paton, Stonecalsey
Mr. Caldwell, Knockshoggle
Mr. Lees, Carngillan
Mr. Howie, Burnhouses
Mr. Stevenson, Hillhouse
Mr. Hunter, Guiltreehill
Mr. Connar, Drumdow
Mr. Wright, South Sanquhar
Mr. John Dykes, Jnr., Glasgow
Mr. Caldwell, Bogside
Mr. Allan, Munnoch
Mr. Clelland, Knockinlaw
Professor James McCall, Glasgow
Mr. Cranston, Thornhill
Mr. Cunningham, Trees
Mr. Wallace, Braehead
Mr. Brown, Castleburn
Mr. Mair, Townhead of Drumley
Mr. Ligertwood, Mounthamilton
Mr. Wallace, Auchenbrain
Mr. Parker, Crooks
Mr. Latta, Whitletts
Mr. Gilmour, Orchardton
Mr. McHay, Garpin
Mr. Hyslop, Tower
Mr. W. H. Dunlop, Ayr
Mr. Murray, Carston
Mr. Lindsay, Townend
Mr Drummond, Bogwood
Mr. Campbell, Torcross
Mr. Gray, Tongue
Mr. Paton, Trees
Mr. Murray, Jnr., Carston
Mr. Macarthur, Ayr
Mr. Millar, Alloway
Mr. Craig, Guelt
Mr. Shaw, Ayr
Mr. Smith, Chanlochfoot
Mr. Gray, Midton
Mr. Reid, Clune
Mr. Russell, Craigie
Mr. Kerr, Milton
Mr. Hayman, Dumfries House
Mr. Gerrard, Dustyhall
Mr. Ralston, Lagg
Mr. Dunlop, Aulton
Mr. Meikle, Clockston
Mr. Meikle, Brownhill
Mr. Macrorie, Ayr
Mr. Cunningham, Chapeltoun
Mr. Smith, Glenmanna
Mr. Houghton, Factor, Craigowen

As also about Twenty others whose names could not be got owing to their having gone in by a side door.

Fig. 68 Proposal to start a Herd Book for Ayrshire Cattle. 1877

The ubiquitous and anonymous 'Butterman' was moved to verse.

Ah, what a show we had at Ayr!
T'was really something new.
That brought the crowd from everywhere
Tae see a Record coo.
But what we saw was half a coo.
Their Better-Halfs were deid.
Their records written in review
For visitors to read.
Their sires and dams for ages past
Were there in eerie clouds.
The very place was overcaste,
Wi' ghosts in record shrouds.

Although for many years afterwards the rivalries continued, nevertheless, the breed is backed by one of the most progressive Societies in the U.K. which offers numerous services to its members. The Society runs its own commercial company, Cattle Services (Ayr) Ltd., to supply semen from top Ayrshire bulls and arrange import and export of both cattle and semen.

The secretaries who made this society so successful were, James Mc Murtrie, (1877–1899); John Howie, (1900–1922); Hugh Bone, (1923–1948); John Graham, (1948–1962); John Madge, (1962–1969); Jack Lawson, (1970–1984), Stuart Thomson, (1984–).

The increasing popularity of the Ayrshire breed throughout the U.K. fortuitously coincided with the eradication of tuberculosis. Because the milk producers in the South of Scotland pioneered the eradication of tubeculosis especially in the post war era there was a phenominal demand for accredited Ayrshire stock from other areas especially in England. There were special sales held in the bigger markets, noteably, Ayr, Paisley, Lanark, Castle Douglas, etc. As many as 1400 heifers were sold at a pedigree Ayrshire sale at Castle Douglas in one day.

A number of well known breeders and dealers both sides of the border were involved in this trade such The Earl of Eglinton and Winton, Lt. Col. Cecil, Adam Montgomerie, W. Gibson, Dr. Constable Hayes, F.N.Mathews, F.H.Sanderson, A.W.M.Sillars, the brothers Dougal and William Mackay, Robin Dunlop, Reg Roberts, William Cochrane, Hendrie Bros, T.C. Bell and many others.

Really from the inception of the Ayrshire Cattle Society in 1877 the Ayrshire Breed developed into a world renowned breed the history of which is well worthy of another book.

CHAPTER 14

BLACK AND WHITE DAIRY CATTLE

Mention has already been made about black and white cattle with reference to those colours in the Ayrshire breed, not to be confused with black and white cattle, namely Friesians, which has had a dramatic influence on the dairy cattle herds of this country. At one time the Dairy Shorthorn was the most popular dairy breed in England and the Ayrshires reigned supreme in Scotland. In 1908 Beef and Dairy Shorthorns in Britain totalled two million of the nearly seven million in the country whereas there were only 100,000, Ayrshires. Now all this has changed. How has this come about? To give a full answer to this is really outwith the scope of this book, sufficient meantime is a synopsis.

Initially, it is worthy of note that of all the breeds of cattle, horses, sheep and pigs which made British livestock breeders respected throughout the world before the Second World War, only three, the Friesian cow, the Percheron horse and the Merino sheep originated from outwith the United Kingdom. (Watson and Hobbs 1951)

Friesian cattle have a long history. Tacitus, the Roman historian, wrote that in A.D. 28, Drusus, the father of Germanicus, imposed tax of hides upon the Friesians, 'which his Lieutenant, Ollenius, required should come up to the standard of certain terga urorum (skins of the urus) which he picked for the purpose.' This would indicate that a high standard of cattle breeding has been required in Friesland for a very long time, in an area which has been devoted to grassland and dairying for centuries. (Hobson 1918).

The impact of Dutch cattle on the development of the Ayrshire and Shorthorn breeds has also been noted. During the Middle Ages there must have been a considerable number of cattle imported because King Charles thought it necessary to pass three Acts of Parliament in 1666, 1668 and 1680 in an attempt to exclude European cattle as a precaution against the hazards of disease. Even at that time the Dutch cattle had a reputation for milk production. In 1716, Mortimer writing in '*The Whole Art of Husbandry*' says, 'the best sort of cows for the pail are the long legged shorthorned cows of the Dutch breed, which are to be had in some places in Lincolnshire but mostly in Kent; many of these cows give two gallons of milk at a meal.' At this time these would be red and white cattle.

For an in depth study into the development of the Friesian breed, authorative sources are, *'A History of the Dutch Cow'*, by Professor Dr

D.L. Bakker, of the University of Wageningen, Amsterdam in Rundvee, (1948); E. Parmalee Prentice, *'Breeding of Profitable Dairy Cattle.'* (1935); George Hobson, *'History of British Friesian Cattle'*, (1930). J.K. Stanford, *'British Friesians'*. (1956). Professor Gordon Mingay, *'British Friesians'*, (1982). There is a fund of information in the British Friesian Journals, dating back to 1920.

While references are made to Friesian cattle throughout a long period of time these cattle were subjected to the horrors of floods, disease and ravages of war. For example in 1744 a very infectious 'murrain' or foot and mouth disease wiped out two thirds of the entire livestock in Holland. As has been noted earlier, they had to be replaced by cattle from Denmark which were mostly black and white, whereas the cattle which were killed out by the disease were red. (Bakker 1948). Dr Bakker concluded that the breeds in the Netherlands as we know them today, became 'definitely established mainly in the second half of the eighteenth century'. It is interesting to note that in the earlier part of the nineteenth century 'because the quality of the Dutch cattle had considerably deteriorated and especially in comparison with English breeds they lagged far behind,' Shorthorn cattle were imported into the Netherlands.....'as it turned out this was a complete failure.' It was hoped that this infusion would improve the type of the local cattle. However this proved abortive when the resultant crosses lowered the milk yields.

Thereafter, the cattle breeding industry recovered from all its traunmas so successfully that in the years 1862-1864 over 528,000 head of cattle were exported to Prussia, Belgium and England, of which 301,000 came to England. From 1872–1891 cattle 'were landed regularly at London, Harwich, Hull, Leith, Aberdeen, Inverness and other parts of the east coast of Scotland and England" at the rate of nearly 50,000 a year. (Hobson 1930). Between 1852 and 1905, 7757 animals were imported from Holland to America, 5,103 being shipped from 1883–1885. (Mingay 1982). Between 1872 and 1876 the large number of black and white cattle imported were chiefly bought for town dairies to replenish the cows, which had been slaughtered due to the cattle plague at a time of increasing demand for milk. They had also already established a reputation for giving more milk than the local breeds.

Before 1877 imported cattle were not normally slaughtered. Between 1877 and 1889 the majority of the imported cattle were killed to augment the beef supplies. From 1889 to 1892 they were allowed to enter, subject to inspection. In 1894 further restrictions were imposed and in 1896 imports of live cattle were prohibited altogether by an amendment to the Contagious Diseases of Animals Act. (Hobson, T.H.A.S. 1918.)

Because there was a big export trade, the progressive Dutch dairy farmers realised the advantage of having a Herd Book, at first they were more like address books. In 1875 the Netherlands Cattle Herd Book was founded followed by the Friesian Cattle Herdbook in 1879. Initially all the dairy breeds whatever the colour were registered in the Netherlands Cattle Herdbook. These colours could be black, black and white, red and white, dun, dun and white and blue. When breeds became more identifiable, about 1902 there were three sections for the main breeds. Holland-Friesian (black and white); Groningen, (black with white or black with white heads); and Maas-Rijn-Ijsell, (red and white). From then onwards dairy cattle breeding in that small country really got underway when Mendel's laws of heredity, which had been first published as far back as 1865, became more understood.

It was the ability to persistently produce comparatively increasing yields over all other breeds and to fatten into a good killing out carcase that made the Dutch Friesian cow so universally popular. In his book *'How to Choose a Good Milk Cow'*, (Dutch Breed) in 1853 J.H. Magne writes 'A good cow, which consumes in proper food what is equal to from 30 to 33 pounds of hay, is able to give $3^1/_2$ to 4 gallons and up to $5^1/_2$ gallons after calving.' There was quite an exportation of butter from Friesland to England in that era, said to be from cows yielding 200lbs. per cow, a creditable figure for the time.

It was only about 30–40 breeders with vision, faith and perseverance, who kept their herds pure for breeding. Among the earliest herds established before the formation of the breed society were those belonging to, T. Rumbal & Sons, Upper Clapton & Harlow, who kept 115 cows on about 115 acres, which was dispersed in 1900; The Tatton Herd of Earl of Egerton in Cheshire, dispersed in 1909; The Colton Herd of Hugh Brown in Dunfermline, dispersed in 1923; The Hawkrigg Herd of John Twentyman in Cumberland, dispersed in 1903; The Hedges (originally Marden) herd of Messrs A.J.Brown in Hertfordshire, dispersed in 1927; The Terling Herd of Lord Rayleigh in Essex. There was also David Spence of Dunninald and his brother Andrew of Commieston in Angus whose family moved up to Scotland from Cambridgeshire.(Stanford 1956.)

Being so few in numbers there was little scope for breed development. The situation was aggravated by a number of factors. Because of the increasing demand for urban liquid milk high prices were being paid for cows to go into town dairies and then were immediately slaughtered at the end of their milking life. This meant that the commercial breeder was not interested in pedigree breeding resulting in indiscriminating crossing by using any type of bull. 'Anything with four legs and a tail was good enough.' Furthermore, because of health restrictions no good bulls could be imported from abroad. There was also opposition from the established breeds such as the numerous Shorthorn, Ayrshire, Channel Island and other regional breeds as seen from the Agricultural Statistics of the United Kingdom which were first compiled in 1866.

An illuminating report of the current situation appeared in The Livestock Journal 1900. 'Some of the Dutch breed were squarely built, broad across the hips with well sprung ribs and with medium- size spread horns, handsome in form and good milkers. Others are about as ugly in form as a cow can be made; angular with drooping quarters, want of width between the buttocks, slender fore quarters and crumpled horns. Some of these ugly beasts proved excellent milkers and some were so ugly and so poor in appearance that they almost shamed their owners.'

Because of the foregoing circumstances, the publication of a herd book and the formation of a breed society was slower than for other breeds, in this country and overseas. The earliest herd book published was The Coates Shorthorn Herd Book in 1822, followed by the Hereford in 1846. The Shorthorn Society was established in 1875, the Hereford in 1876, the Ayrshire and Galloway in 1877 and the Aberdeen Angus in 1879.

It is interesting to note the number of societies which were formed in an era of an agricultural depression. This was motivated by the opening up of the cattle ranges in the 'new countries' who demanded pure bred bulls of quality to improve their own cattle. While the development of the Friesian breed may have been retarded by various difficulties, at the time of the formation of the Society, it was moving into an advantageous position.

For many years there had been a great deal of aggravation within the Shorthorn breed. Two factions each with their supporters had evolved. There were those and the more numerous in England who wanted to promote the milkier dual purpose animal and those mainly in Scotland wished to have a beefier type. This discord delayed the formation of the Dairy Shorthorn Society until 1905 only four years earlier than that of the Friesian breed. If this had been done a number of years earlier it is possible that the demand would not have been so great. By the same token if so many Ayrshire breeders had not been so mesmerised by showing dainty cows and developed their true milking potential, Friesian cattle would not have had such a successful invasion into the 'Ayrshire stronghold.' It is to the everlasting credit of the early Friesian breeders that they saw the opportunities available to them and took them up with such enthusiasm.

On 23rd June 1909 in the Royal Showground at Gloucester, Mrs Agnes Brown, of Hedges, Messrs. Hugh Brown of Colton, William J. Clark of Bakewell and Henry P. Ratcliff, Pebsham, met with a view to forming a society to 'foster the interests of the black and white breed.'. This was a collective endeavour to preserve purity within the breed. The first title of the organisation was 'The British Holstein Cattle Society'. The first Council members of the Society were Messrs. E.D.Brieant, Hugh Brown, John Brown, William MacBean, Henry P. Ratcliff, Adam Smith, Gerald M. Strutt and C.H.Westropp who acted as chairman. In 1910, H.R.H. Prince Christian of Schleswig-Holstein became the first president of the Society.

To establish the breed on a good foundation some 1000 males and 6,000 females were inspected by 1912. As there were few records entry registration had to be based on inspection instead of upon ancestry. This was a marathon task considering the lack of modern transport. Hugh Brown, who travelled the whole of Scotland 'with no other company than his pipe, his Burns, his thoughts and sense of duty.' When he was shown a very moderate bull, his owner said it had a 'marvellous pedigree'. He succinctly replied, 'I have never seen a beast that needed it more.'

By the end of the first year 56 members had joined the Society and 300 after 4 years. Hugh Brown became President of the Society in 1920.

It is worthy of note that the formation of the U.K. Society was tardy in being established compared with America in 1872, Holland in 1879 and Canada in 1891. This was mainly because these countries concentrated on breeding programmes based on scientific guidelines necessitating accurately kept data. In 1914 the name of the Society was changed to "The British Holstein-Friesian Cattle Society. Because of the prejudice against Germany after the First World War. Holstein was dropped from the name of the Society. Holstein was originally a province in Denmark which was overrun by Germany in 1864 and as Schleswig-Holstein remains a province of German. In 1988 the name was changed back to 'The British Holstein-Friesian Society,' in the interests of being good Europeans.

Since the first importations of Friesian cattle into this country and its subsequent progress to being the most numerous breed, Scottish breeders have played a very active part throughout its history. Among the pioneers were, Hugh Brown, William MacBean, Adam Smith, Alex Munro, John Houston and Dr William Sinclair and the Spence brothers. In Volumes I & II of the herdbook there was 71 herds entered, over a quarter of the total. It was understandable that a number of them were established in the centre of Scotland being nearby the town dairies and that Paisley became the main marketing centre efficiently organised by the well known firm of auctioneers, Robert Wilson and Sons, now A & J Wilson. The foundation animals for some of these herds were bought from the Caledonian Railway Company who kept a herd at Govan. This company had imported cattle from Canada before the formation of the Society.

As the breed became more popular a number of herds which became well known nationally and internationally were established in various parts of Scotland, some of them are now owned by the grandsons of the founders. R.E. McKendrick, Craigends, was President of the Society in 1962. His father founded the Dennistoun herd in Renfrewshire in 1910 and was registered in the first herd book of the Society. Jim Shanks surprised the 'locals' of Borgue parish in Kirkcudbright by starting a Friesian at Rattra in 1921 by purchasing six heifers at Paisley. He was born at Deapstone, Ayrshire and saw service for twenty one years in the Ayrshire Yeomanry before moving to Nutholm, Lockerbie in 1935. His son, James G. Shanks with a colourful, forthright personality, took with him the Rattra prefix to found a herd at Standhill farm, Hawick. James G. was the Society's President in 1977. His brother Robert also founded a notable herd in the Borders at Queenscairn.

In 1919 the world renowned doyen of Clydesdale horses James Kilpatrick started a Friesian herd at Muirside in the heartland of the Ayrshire breed. This was based on heifers purchased at the dispersal sale of the Colton Mains herd near Dunfermline. Under the management of his son William it achieved notable successes, including breeding a record holding 3,007 gallon cow, a number of 2,000 gallon cows and Register of Merit sires. Grandson William has kept up the family enthusiasm for the breed, having been President of the Society in 1993 and 1994.

Other Scottish herds of renown for a number of years include the Douneside herd in Aberdeenshire whose owner the American born Lady Rachel McRobert was in 1937 one of three women who has been President of the Society. The others were Mrs G.M. Strutt and Mrs C. Jarmay. There were also George Prentice's herd at Raithill, the Powis herd, owned by the Logans, the Bourtrie herd of John Collie who was President of the Society in 1979, the Airies herd belonging to Hugh Robertson which was founded by his father in Wigtownshire and the Boclair herd owned by one of the greatest enthusiasts of all, Jack Brewster, President of the Society in 1991. This herd originated at Hattrick. The Parkhouse herd is one of the oldest in Scotland was founded by Tom Allan in 1912 in one of the bleaker districts near Biggar, Lanarkshire. He became President of the Society in 1955.

Because of the lack of good animals for selective breeding, the Friesian breed benefited enormously from a number of importations. They were necessary to supply high quality stock to bring about improvements in a breed which was expanding rapidly. For a long time after Friesians were introduced into this country they were subjected to much criticism. Like a lot of criticism some of it was justified and some was through fear and jealousy. Their type then, as described by George Hobson in a 1939 British Friesian Journal was, 'angular, leggy, shelly, narrow, sickle-hocked rather ewe-necked, frequently with an ungainly and excessive udder and a very drooping goose-rumped hindquarters.' So bad were their udders that some breeders preferred leggier cows so that their udders would not swing in the mud. Their milk was generally low in butterfat that the cows were called 'just pure milking machines' or 'water carts from an irrigation breed.' Nevertheless, because of their stamina, great body capacity and ability to give comparatively large volumes of milk the British Holstein Friesian today makes up about 85% of the British dairy herd and can also claim to be the most important single breed for beef.

On studying the history of the breed it is remarkable to see the number of cows which produced very high yields without the benefit of modern day scientific aids in breeding and feeding. In 1914 Eske Hetty was the first officially recorded British Friesian to give over 2,000 gallons, 2413 gallons at 3.33 % in 365 days. She averaged 1623 gallons in four lactations. The severe criticism about low fat milk was overcome later when the Society instigated an upgrading system with respect to butter fat content. This was motivated by the introduction of quality payments and the fact that a well defined creamline in the bottle on the doorstep helped the sales of milk.

The breed, however, made slower progress in Scotland than elsewhere in the U.K. In 1960 the distribution of the dairy herds in Scotland was 79% Ayrshire, 18% Friesian and 3% others. Whereas in England it was 19.2% Ayrshire, 51.1% Friesian, 14.5% Dairy Shorthorn and 9.5% Channel Breeds.

By 1975 the distribution in the herds of Scotland was, 47% Ayrshire, 27.9% Friesian and 24% Friesian/Ayrshire crosses, compared to England with 3.6% Ayrshire, 81% Friesian, .9% Dairy Shorthorn, 5% Channel Breeds and 9.5% others. (U.K. Dairy Facts & Figures.)

The long standing allegiance to Ayrshire cattle with its economical production of milk slowed the progress of the Friesian breed in Scotland. These cattle were fed on the products of the traditional four-coarse-rotation, oats and or barley supplemented with a protein cake plus plenty of roots, hay and straw. The full potential of the Friesian was not realised until better grassland techniques were adopted with greater use of artificial fertilisers and more sophisticated methods of silage making. These resulted in producing quality roughages more conducive to higher milk production. Added to this there was a greater value attached to the Friesian bullock and the cast cow compared with the Ayrshire by-products.

The Holstein Friesian breed now accounts for over 90% of the nation's milk production and the Society is the largest in Europe with around 13000 members.

IMPORTATIONS

The importations of Friesian cattle into the U.K. over a number of years played an integral part in the improvement of the breed in this country. It was the 1914 importation of Dutch Friesians into England which marked a new era in the breed's history. It had been felt for some time by breeders that the breed had too many mongrel type cows within it. To remedy this, on the evening before war was declared, 40 bulls and 20 heifers were brought in from Holland and put into quarantine for three months at Byfleet farm then occupied by Trevor Williams, the newly appointed president of the Society. During this period one bull died. The cattle were selected from milk recorded stock with a minimum of 900 gallons. The average yield of all cows in Friesland was about 900 gallons and those on best land averaged 1100 gallons in about 320 days (Stanford 1956.)

The Council members, not the Society underwrote all the financial risk of this importation. The cattle cost £2,488, in Holland. At the sale held at Byfleet farm they realised £14,936, an average of £257 for bulls and £244 for heifers. Needless to say breeders of today will not be surprised to learn that the cattle which made the highest prices at this sale were not necessarily subsequently the best breeders. After all expenses paid, the Society benefited by £10,300, which put it on a sounder financial footing. By all accounts this venture was an outstanding success. 'To such an extent has the modern Friesian breed been built upon the foundations laid by this historic transaction that it is scarcely too much to say that the real story that the rise of the bred from obscurity to pre-eminence commences with the 60 animals secured from Friesland in 1914.' (Hobson, 1930.)

In the post war boom some of these animals changed hands for ten times their cost price. Trevor Williams, reflected sometime later, 'Other breed societies at that time were pleasantly asleep but since....they had improved thanks possibly, to the example of the newcomer.'

To put in perspective those enhanced prices for the imported cattle and to illustrate the increasing demand for registered stock at sales in the few years before the importation, some average prices are quoted. In 1911, 56 lots averaged £17, 9s., the highest price being £48; 132 animals averaged £17 3s., £29 being the highest price; 47 lots averaged £20 6s. In 1912, 44 head averaged £31 7s., the top price being 50 guineas; 111 animals averaged £26 17s., the top price being £70. In 1913, a sale of 62 lots sold for the satisfactory average of £28 8s. and 87 averaged £42 with a record top price of £120, 15s. (Hobson, c.1920).

During this euphoric period, tentative approaches were made to the Canadian Society with a view to buying cattle from Canada. These came to nothing as it was reckoned that there was not enough animals available with the required production standards. Changed days! The Council proposed to borrow £100,000 to finance this importation. Admittedly, from the present day standpoint the request that the dams of the 100 young cattle asked for had to yield not less than 2,000 gallons, looked ambitious. As a result of this, attention was turned to South Africa, Holland being ruled out because of the current disease problems.

After a series of negotiations, the South African Society selected the animals according to the standards laid down by the British Society. There were 83 lots comprising of 103 animals, from 19 herds imported in 1922. Via demand and speculation these were sold by their owners for the phenomenal average of £1,242 15s. 10d. For the betterment of the breed this importation was not nearly so successful as the 1914 importation, in spite of the fact that the dams of the imported South African cattle averaged 1,432 gallons at 3.48% butterfat.

This lack of success was alleged to be due to the different climatic conditions in this country! More than likely it was due to the financial losses incurred by the buyers later, due to the onset of the agricultural depression 'giving the South African cattle a certain measure of undeserved unpopularity.' These cattle in reality would have a greater difficulty in making an impression on the British cattle than those of 1914, because in the decade following that importation the breeding and management standards of dairy cattle in this country had improved.

Fig. 69 CRAIGIEMAINS VICTORIA 29th
Born 19th May 1945 Supreme Champion at RHAS Show 1948
Reserve Female champion at Royal Show 1948

Fig. 70 "Powis Tension" on 17th August, 1967.
Aged 6 years 4 months.

There were, however, two plus factors. A bull was bought by Gerald Strutt for 3,900 guineas and was named Terling Marthus. He was outstandingly successful in the Terling herd and in turn so also was his resultant progeny. In 1959 Harry Hobson, the well known auctioneer was wont to say, 'It is doubtful if any dairy bull ever exerted a greater influence for good than did Marthus and it is surely no exaggeration to describe him as the greatest dairy sire of all time.' From a commercial angle, the South African cattle possessed more beefing qualities than the home cattle which increased an interest in the ability of the breed becoming more dual purpose than hitherto.

Whether it was this latter thought or not, there was a further demand for a second importation of South African cattle which the Society tried to stop as too few of the cattle were up to their standards. Nevertheless, the cattle arrived and were sold at Reading in 1927. The average paid for them was under a modest £81 which disappointed the South African exporters but was more in line with the current pedigree prices, which like all other prices had at that time fallen. There was further disappointment for the buyers because it was ruled that they were ineligible for registration in the Herd Book and only after a number of heated discussions were they allowed to be entered in the Supplementary Register.

This Register was established in 1921 as an auxiliary section of the Herd Book. This enabled the offspring of a cow passed by inspection to acquire pedigree status after four top crosses by a pedigree bull. This was conditional of the final cross having given 700 gallons as a heifer or 1,000 gallons as a cow. In 1922 an Advanced Register was instituted and subsequently replaced by the present Register of Merit, designed to raise the standards of production and quality. Many of the well known herds in Scotland were established by being graded up originally from Ayrshire cows.

It is inevitable when a breed becomes suddenly successful expansion is rapid. Too many want 'in on the act' especially when prices for commercial cattle were high. This resulted in a lot of poor cattle coming on to the market which in turn not only depressed the prices but threw the breed into disrepute, similar to what has been seen in recent times with some Continental cattle. The Friesian breed experienced this for a period during the 1920s. This incited a report in the breed journal in 1924, 'Most of the cattle at a sale at Reading needed bullets not bids. Such a sale does an infinity of harm.'

During this era of falling milk prices, producers began to look seriously at the beef attributes of the Friesian cattle and their crosses. This was being noticed in the showring and it prompted a well known Dutch judge to comment, 'It is a very great pity that the breeders make their animals far too fat in trying to make them look beef cattle.' There was a theory accepted at the time that milk and beef type were not incompatable. This was encouraged in Holland where beefier calves were in demand for the veal industry. Again this was encouraged by the successes at Fatstock shows up and down the country. For example, at the 1921 Smithfield Fat Stock in London, Messrs J.& B.M. Dale showed a Friesian bullock weighing 19 cwts. at 2 years 10 months, the heaviest animal at the show. At the same show in 1925 the Friesians had the highest daily liveweight gain over all other breeds. (Hobson, 1930.)

It would not be exaggerating to say that it was the merits of the dual purpose aspect of the Friesian which enabled it to usurp the dominant position of the Ayrshire in Scotland. In truth this lead to a strong difference of opinion among breeders about the dual-purpose propensity of the breed which carried on until the upsurge of the Canadian Holsteins in the 1980s.

The membership of the Society fluctuated because of the agricultural depression and to a degree an antithesis which had developed against the breed. From 1920 to 1924 the number of members rose from 1,431 to 2,098 the highest in any breed society except the Dairy Shorthorn, with 4,490 members. This fell back to 1,371 in 1935.

However, in the 1930s thoughts were stirring about the importation of Canadian cattle, to which end some were imported directly to members and non-members of the Society. This did not meet with the Society's approval and there were threats to set up a rival organisation. There were also thoughts about bringing in another consignment from South Africa. Because of the desire to improve the butterfat content about which there had always been severe criticism and hopefully to improve type it was decided to go back to Holland for more cattle.

By this time the economy of agriculture was improving. A deputation comprising of President G.B. Radcliffe and Messrs. Strutt, Hall, Weightman and Gilbert with secretary G. Hobson went to Holland and bought 47 bulls and 49 females. The bulls cost around £300 and the females £45 to £70 in Holland. These cattle were allocated to those who had ordered them, 'without any assurance other than that the Committee would do their best for them.' On his return George Hobson reported that the general average of the Friesian herds in Holland was higher than in Britain. 'Cow starvers in Britain would be surprised at the condition and quality of animals that remain indoors throughout the winter as with wealth of written information concerning pedigree and performance available.' As was said earlier they no longer kept their Herdbooks as 'address-books for cattle of good appearance.'

This importation had a decided benefit on the quality of the milk from Friesian cows. It has been said that this importation and the cattle subsequently brought in by others influenced the reduction in size which made breeders turn their attention to the cattle in Canada and later the U.S.A. This was endorsed by the results of the third Dutch Importation in 1950. The buying commission on this occasion was Messrs. F.K. Abbey, G.J. Curtis, F. Loftus and J.E. Moffitt (Dalton). Great care was taken in selecting the seventy animals on this importation costing in Holland £42,000 out of which seventeen bulls purchased for £9,200 were allocated to a number of A.I stations. The remainder of the consignment were auctioned at Peterborough where over 3,000 people witnessed a fabulous sale where 40 bulls averaged £3,572 and 12 heifers £3,587.

Initially, animals from this sale did well in the showring as did some of their progeny. Unfortunately, all that is gold does not glitter. Some bulls were unsuitable in the A.I stations their progeny did not

Fig. 71 Mr Jack Brewster studies his renowned Boclair herd.

measure up to the desired standards including being too small or breeding malformed calves. There was, however, some satisfaction derived because other bulls such as Hunday Adema 88. did breed well by increasing butterfat percentages and improving the hind legs, both very much required. On discussing how the cattle were becoming smaller in size, one critic remarked that 'the smaller animal could never be expected to provide the same factory for milk production.'

For some time cattle in Canada and subsequently in the U.S.A. had been looked at by enterprising breeders, especially those who were interested in maximum milk production without the issue being confused by thoughts on beef production. As has already been noted, during the sales boom time of 1919 an abortive attempt was made to import cattle from Canada. This fell through because the information given by the Canadian Government could not be substantiated. There were also other privately organised imports in the 1930s.

In late 1947 the Dutch government kindly gave 500 animals to the British Flood Distress Fund as an expression of sympathy for the British farmers who had suffered great losses during the very severe winter of 1946–47. Without wanting to appear ungrateful the Society were concerned in case too many of the animals would not be up to their standards and not pass the necessary inspections. In the end all was resolved and the better cattle were allowed into the Supplementary Register, which proved satisfactory.

As a result of the disenchantment of the Society which followed the last Dutch importation and the problems with subseqent unofficial importations, any further demand for overseas cattle was left to the breeders individually or collectively under the supervision of the Ministry of Agriculture and the Society. A meeting of the Council concluded in 1956, 'to allow the breed to settle down with its own blood without if possible any further disturbances or distractions by new introductions.'

According to George Hobson writing in the 1919 Journal: 'Without question a fortune awaits the breeder who is first to own an extensive herd of females, each producing a calf annually and averaging 1,000 gallons of milk testing 4% of butterfat, each animal to be correct in type and symmetry and able to pass the tuberculin test.' It would seem a tall order when comparable heifers which could easily be sold for £400 were a short time later, were being sold for £40. Time did prove George right.

Having discussed the effect the Dutch importations had on the dairy cattle in the U.K. it may come as a surprise what happened in Canada and U.S.A. over the same period. When Dutch settlers went to America in 1621 they took Friesian type cattle with them and further importations were made by the West India Company for their dairy business. For many years afterwards there were sporadic shipments sent. After three unsuccessful attempts to establish the Holstein breed, it was successful in 1861 with the importation comprising of a bull and four cows bought by Mr Winthrop W. Chenery, Belmont, Massachusetts. From then until 1905, 7,7000 cattle were imported. To become established they had to withstand intense competition from the Jerseys in the same way as they had to in England from the Dairy Shorthorns in earlier times.

The first Herdbook was published in 1872 before any in the Netherlands. 'The the fundamental purpose is to increase public interest in the breed, to provide an equal incentive to all breeders to improve their herds, to aid in such improvement and withal to build up a reputation for the breed in which all would have a common pride.' From the outset production performance and recording was the aim without too much attention being paid conformation. When the Babcock test was invented in 1890, it was quickly adopted for the official recording of of butterfat production. Very high yields, comparable to the present day were recorded between 1871 and 1888. For example in 1884 Echo 121 produced 23,775 lbs. of milk; in 1886 Clothilde 1308, 26,021lbs and in 1888 Pieterje 2nd produced a world record production of 30, 318 lbs. which was not overtaken until 1914. (Hobson 1930).

Dr Edwards reported in 1923, 'for a very long time the Americans have been breeding 'on paper using sires and dams exclusively for their production records and taking little thought for their conformation and type.' By the introduction of type classification and special awards this was remedied which lead John Moffit (Hunday) to comment in 1968 after an extensive tour that the overall type was quite impressive and that the udders of the cows were of a better confirmation.

The American cattle have now impressed breeders around the world as witnessed by their establishment in all the main dairying countries.

It is sometimes not realised that the Canadian Holsteins originated from the U.S.A. There were of course black and white cattle taken into Canada with Dutch settlers about 1664, but it was the cattle brought in from the U.S. in 1882 and 1883 which laid the foundations for their establishment in Canada. Until 1891 the pedigree cattle were registered in the American Herd Book when the Canadian Herd Book was started.

In 1941 when Britain was in dire straits during the war the Canadian Holstein-Friesian Association made a generous gift to various seamen's charities £2,650 which was the proceeds of a sale of a hundred selective heifers. In the subsequent two years further gifts were sent. These were augmented by donations from the British Friesian Society. Between 1941 and 1944 the two Societies donated £28,815 to various charities.

Because of this generosity the British government were very supportive in encouraging the first post war importation from Canada in 1946. The British Holstein Herd Book commenced with this importation. The cattle there were well known for their well shaped udders and high yields of both milk and butterfat which were much sought after in the U.K. This was largely due to the Canadians ready acceptance of innovating techniques, including milk recording, artificial insemination, progeny testing and intensive selection unbedevilled by the unrealistic criteria of the showground. In other words the adoption of sound genetic principles with no thought about beef production.

At a time when foreign exchange was at a premium the government allowed £60,000 for spending on the importation which comprised on 54 bulls, 67 first and second calf heifers and 99 younger heifers. This importation proved on the whole successful although as one would expect there were the critics especially amongst some Ayrshire breeders, who thought that the cattle were too extreme in type and slow maturing. It lead an ardent Ayrshire breeder George Templeton from Carnell to say that, 'They maybe give a lot of milk but they must be gae hard to look at every day.' It is noteworthy that many of today's leading Holstein breeders are former successful Ayrshire breeders.

At the same time many Friesian breeders were very critical of the extreme Holstein types. For a long time there was an ongoing debate on the direction the Friesian breed should go with reference to whether it should be a dual purpose breed or not. During the inter war period when agricultural prices were low an extra good income from the dairy herd was most welcome. The Spence family in Scotland and others were well known for producing quality beef from Friesians. Mr Trevor Williams, who was an outstanding President of the Society, 1914–1919, made a prophecy in 1917 at the Society's Annual General Meeting, 'What we want to see is the British Friesian winning outright at Smithfield and winning outright at the Dairy Show. All these things are possible and, I may say, likely...I believe you will have the finest dual-purpose animal in the world.' It has certainly been very successful at Dairy Shows.

After the advent of peace in 1946 beef was scarce. The supplies from the beef producing countries such as the Argentine dried up and the farming policy was to produce as much food as possible from home resources. Beef from the dairy herd was encouraged via calf subsidies. It was claimed that 'the Friesians could have produced three times as much meat as all the pure beef animals put together.' This would not have been impossible because as has been noted the cattle which were imported from Holland were of the beefier type which helped to 'flesh up' the home bred cattle. This approach was specially prominent in England, firstly, because of the demands from an increasing population and secondly, the Friesian cows usurped the Dairy Shorthorn a recognised dual-purpose breed.

One definition of dual-purpose was 'one just good enough to be at the bottom of two show classes, one for milk and one for beef!' Eventually the theory that milk and beef production traits were compatible collapsed. The Holstein breeders showed the way having as a principle 'that the natural ability of their breed to produce milk has to be combined with careful attention to functional type.' The Friesian breed policy changed to being 'single purpose with a dual result.' This continued till the present time. Now strenuous efforts are being made to amalgamate the two black and white breeds with one aim in view to produce more milk. Black and white cattle are still being imported.

Had William Youatt the modern cow in mind when he published the following lines in his book on *'Cattle'* in 1834 ?

She' long in her face,
She's fine in her horn,
She will quickly get fat without cake or corn,
She's clean in her jaws & full in her chine
She's heavy in her flank & wide in her loin.

She's broad in her ribs and long in her rump
A straight and flat back,
without ever a hump;
She's wide in her hips
and calm in her eyes,
She's fine in her shoulders-
And thin in her thighs.

Black and White Dairy Cattle

She’s light in neck
and small in her tail,
She’s wide at the breast
and good at the pail,
She’s fine in her bone
and silky of skin,
She’s a graziers without,
and a butcher’s within.

LOCAL AUTHORITY OF THE STEWARTRY OF KIRKCUDBRIGHT

MILK (SPECIAL DESIGNATIONS) (SCOTLAND) ORDER, 1951.

PRODUCER'S LICENCE AUTHORISING THE USE OF THE SPECIAL DESIGNATION "TUBERCULIN TESTED"

The Local Authority of the Stewartry of Kirkcudbright hereby authorise Messrs A. & A. Gray

of Ingleston, Borgue.

to use the special designation "Tuberculin Tested" in relation to milk produced from a herd kept by ~~XXX~~ them at Ingleston

in the Parish of Borgue and sold by wholesale at or from these premises.

This licence is not transferable, and is subject to the conditions prescribed in the Milk (Special Designations) (Scotland) Order, 1951, and unless suspended or revoked will remain in force until 31st December, 1961.

Dated this First day of January, 1957.

[signature]

Clerk to the Local Authority.

Fig. 72 Poducer's licence authorising the use of the designation "Tuberculin Tested"

CHAPTER 15

DISEASES IN DAIRY CATTLE

The presence of disease was and still is a very important aspect in the discussion of milk production. The dairy farmers' war against disease is a vast subject on its own. It is sufficient to mention the diseases which caused the most havoc in the past.

Diseases began to be written about by the 16th and 17th centuries. It was in the 18th century that their identification became more specific. Live cattle for slaughter were imported from Europe to satisfy the demands of town dairies and to augment the beef supplies to feed the expanding population. With them came some dreadful diseases. Rinderpest from Eastern Europe first appeared in Essex in 1745, Foot and Mouth appeared in 1839 and Pleuropneumonia in 1841 from Holland.

It is said that you cannot have livestock without deadstock, which is true, but no one wants disease disasters in the animal world. Rinderpest, commonly known as Cattle Plague, originated in Egypt and spread into Eastern Europe. It is alleged to be the same disease that Moses refers to in the Bible. It decimated many herds and bankrupted many farmers throughout the country causing the death of about 233,000 animals. In Scotland 22,000 cattle were affected two thirds of which died or were killed. In Great Britain in one week in March 1864, over 10,000 cattle were killed. It really destroyed many town herds in a wholesale manner especially in London. The cattle being kept all the time in the close confines of badly ventilated buildings propogated the spread of the disease resulting in those sheds never being filled again.

It is a virus disease which attacks all ruminants, the most susceptible being bovine, especially domestic cattle. The stricken animals are blinded and choked from the discharge from the mucous membranes. The mucous pores are rope like from the nostrils. The discharge is highly infectious, contagious and persists in the pasture. The mucous discharge is immediately followed by diarrhoea and dysentery, completely emaciating the animals. Death follows quickly. The course of the disease is rapid and irreversible.

The epidemic must have been horrific to witness. One farmer was determined to record his disaster for posterity when he had written on a gravestone. 'Near this place were buried 43 cows, 7 calving heifers, 5 yearling heifers, 1 bull, 20 calves, that died in the months of February and March 1866 of Rinderpest then reigning in Cheshire, belonging to John Suction of Moston Manor.'

The Cattle Diseases Prevention Act was passed in 1866 in an effort to eliminate these scourges. This was followed by the Contagious Diseases (Animal) Act 1869. A Cattle Plague Department was established in 1865 to control all movement of cattle from abroad and at home. This Department started as a branch of the Home Office and was transferred to the Privy Council which delegated powers to the Justices of the Peace to appoint inspectors to enter farms to slaughter and bury infected animals, to prohibit movement of diseased stock and to close fairs and markets. Four years later the Cattle Plague Department was renamed the Veterinary Department. For the first time compensation was paid, £20 for a slaughtered animal 'or half its value when well.' This compensation was to come out of the county rates and the local authorities were allowed to borrow for it.

When King George III opened Parliament he called for a special report on plague and a special prayer was prepared for the churches in order to bring divine aid into the battle against the pestilence.

Prior to the passing of the Acts which authorised the compensation, some enterprising farmers in Wigtownshire set up the LOCAL MUTUAL CATTLE INSURANCE SOCIETY, later renamed the RHINS & GALLOWAY CATTLE INSURANCE CO. LTD. It was financed by members paying one shilling per head annually for every animal insured, until a capital sum of £5,000, was built up. The landlords subscribed two shillings per £100 rental to this company. This encouraged the stamping out of pleuro pneumonia and cattle plague. To prevent the spread of these diseases each infected animal was bought and slaughtered by the company.

However, the execution of the law was not done without some criticism. The Acts in total were fairly comprehensive in their powers, but the enforcing of these powers was not very strict.

'Even the dishful tale told in inimical words about the cattle plague of 1865 and 1866 had made little impression, by the tone of the press particularly. It is due much to the want of organisation and slow progress which has marked the efforts to annihilate the scourges that now threaten to destroy our herds and our flocks. The communications down to local level was poor. The local clerks and magistrates either had no copies of the regulations or did not understand them.'

A prevailing magistrate and M.P. who was chairman of the cattle committee for one county said, "cow doctor for the neighbouring village will be appointed, but it is not contemplated at present to do anything. When the farmers notified the disease as required by law, no one did much about it. The vets offered assistance but this was often declined so the police were appointed instead who, in some cases, were not allowed to consult the vets ' in the interests of expense.'

The farmers did not like the appearance of the police on their premises which 'was regarded as espionage and a direct violation of liberty and privacy.' The vets, on the other hand did not want to be inspectors for fear of alienating their clients. 'There is also too, great reason to fear that bribery played no insignificant part in keeping secret the existence of the disease.' Sometimes foot and mouth and pleuropneumonia raged because the isolation regulations were not carried out. Sales, markets and fairs were allowed to continue in some infected areas.

In spite of the criticisms the Government eventually did take firm action. Rinderpest was completely eradicated by 1871 and pleuro-pneumonia by 1900. Foot and Mouth disease was not so easily stamped out. It is a more debilitating disease than fatal. Of the earlier designated diseases it is the only one that still reappears such as in 1869–70, 1912, 1927, 1952, etc. Fortunately it has limited impact now, due to the current stringent measures of isolation and slaughter policy under the supervision of the Minister of Agriculture.

TUBERCULOSIS

Tuberculosis is a disease that caused a lot of misery to the people of this country. There were various reports on how lethal it was among children. When the disease was unchecked there were estimates that 2–3000 children were killed every year. Many others who were infected went on to lead a 'life in death' existence, through a broken crippled adolescence. It made invalids of thousands both young and old. As late as the 1950s, the people of the U.K. suffered more from T.B. than any other comparable country. Such was the reputation of the British milk that during the Second World War, the American forces stationed in this country were not allowed to drink it. Instead the milk was imported.

Because of its effect on the lungs and chest it was commonly known as 'consumption' or the 'wasting disease.' In the 18th century the term consumption covered other diseases as well as T.B. So many died from it because there was no known cure. There was little alleviation from it until the advent of streptomycin. Many were confined to a sanatorium where they were exposed to as much fresh air as possible. Fresh air was regarded as a very important part of the healing process. At times one could see on the verandas rows of beds with red noses and water proof covers to protect them against inclement weather.

As T.B. was such a menace to the population, various investigations were made into the prevalence of the disease in the national dairy herd. As far back as 1895 John Spier, pioneer farmer and writer, wrote in his report to the Royal Commission on Agriculture in the counties of Ayrshire, Dumfriesshire, Kirkcudbright and Wigtownshire; 'My enquiries lead me to believe that throughout the stocks of Ayrshire and Wigtownshire this disease has become more prevalent than anyone ever supposed. Throughout a proportion of Ayrshire and Wigtownshire the losses are enormous and in many cases amount to what would be a fair annual profit to the farmer. This was most prevalent in the Rhins of Wigtownshire where there was little breeding done. The cows were purchased when 3–4 years old from Ayrshire and Argyllshire.' Further, he reports that many herds were wiped out over a period of 5–7 years.

At that time the butchers in Ayrshire formed an Ayrshire Butchers' Society comprising of 200–300 members, 'for the purpose of compensating those of their members who may have animals condemned which have been purchased at a public sale and at prices between £9 and £20. When this became too expensive, the Society threatened not to purchase fatstock, unless the farmers provided a warranty that they were free from disease, especially when medical science was demonstrating that T.B. could be conveyed from cows to human beings through the medium of infected milk or infected meat.'

Another report about the presence of T.B. in cattle is in Robert Wallace's *Farm Livestock in G.B.* (1907). 'Excluding farm animals kept out of doors and calves, about 30% of all cattle slaughtered in this country are reported to have tuberculosis.' A survey done in Edinburgh in 1925 found that 48% of the cows slaughtered in the city showed T.B. lesions in some form or other. In 1934 the Minister of Agriculture estimated that 40% of all dairy cows in the country were infected. By 1947 it was again estimated that no more than one in seven cows came from a herd that had been tested free from tuberculosis.

In earlier times the disease was essentially of man and animals living unnaturally in overcrowded and unsanitary conditions. The disease was easily spread in excretions and discharges from infected animals. The germs coughed up from the lungs got into the surrounding atmosphere and spread rapidly when in badly ventilated, hot dirty byres. Feeding calves on infected milk greatly aided the spread of the disease.

The causal bacteria, Tubercle bacillus, was discovered in 1882 by a German bacteriologist Koch. He caused confusion when he maintained the bovine tuberculosis was not transmittable to human beings. This opinion coming from such an imminent scientist resulted in the setting up of a Royal Commission and it hindered the thinking about eradication of the disease.

Tuberculosis is such a virulent disease and so contagious. It is easily spread from cows to their milk and on to humans. Cattle and humans can infect each other. Tuberculosis can attack any organ in cattle, also lungs, digestive system, udder and bones. Once it is established in one part of the animal it may move in the blood to any other susceptible part. It eventually leads to debility and death. Fortunately, after a great deal of research, it was conclusively established that the disease does not pass directly to the new borne offspring.

When it was realised that the disease was so rampant, a controversy arose about the merits of its elimination. There were those in 1932 who considered that 'it was impractical to stamp out the disease at its source,' because one million out of the three million dairy cattle were thought to be reactors. The disposal of these would upset the entire milk supply of the country. As there was no satisfactory method to combat the disease many were afraid to do anything.

When tuberculin free milk became available it sold at a higher price. This too, had its critics. Andrew Mc Dowall, Girstingwood, Kirkcudbright wrote in the *Gallovidian Annual* in 1935; 'There is, great talk of removing tubercular reactors from dairy herds, but if the milk of this improved standard is to be retailed at round about sixpence a pint, I doubt whether the general health situation will be much improved. As a matter of fact more Grade A (T.T.) milk is now being produced than can be consumed at the price and farmers are considering whether they would be better to give up their high grade production while still maintaining their herds free of disease. They would then be able to sell surplus stock to buyers who, owing to their favourable location, are able to sell all their Grade A (T.T.) milk they can produce and who, owing to accidents, have occasionally to fill a blank in their herds. In the Galloway area, however, the price of Grade A (T.T.) milk (in view of the surplus produced) is so low that, on balance, the local producers consider they would be better to cut their high grade production costs and sell their product as ordinary commercial milk at ordinary market.' (c. 11.2d. per gallon)

Compared with the U.S.A. and Canada the progress of eradication in this country was slow. They had the advantage that there was not the same degree of infection initially which allowed a more drastic method of eradication to be adopted. From an early stage in their campaign all reactors had to be branded and slaughtered with the Government paying compensation at two thirds of the commercial value. On the other hand there were no special premiums for T.T. milk. If producers wanted to produce milk it had to be graded or they went out of business.

It took the reports of three Royal Commissions, 1890, 1894, 1904 and a period of fifteen years, before any action was taken. National legislation was eventually introduced in 1909, whereby compensation was paid to owners of cows which were condemned because of T.B. This was paid out of the rates for which the owners of the land were largely responsible. They, however, used their political muscle in conjunction with the Chamber of Agriculture, the forerunner of the National Farmer Union, to have this legislation withdrawn. It was reintroduced in 1914 when a sum of £60,000 from the taxes was set aside for the purpose because it was thought that 'public health was a national concern'.

Some local authorities under the Burgh Police Scotland Act 1903, took the initiative to acquire powers to introduce local regulations preventing the sale of milk from cows known to be carriers of the disease. Some counties, Ayrshire, in particular, took up this initiative to voluntarily clean up their herds. When one farmer decided to get rid of the reactors in his herd his neighbour followed. There evolved local 'islands' free from T.B. from which cattle were sold at enhanced prices to like minded farmers elsewhere.

The first official recognition to have tuberculosis eradicated from the herds in the U.K., came under the Milk (Special Designation) Order of 1923. This made provision for herd owners to become licenced for the production of Certified or Grade "A" Tuberculin Tested Milk (T.T.). i.e. if the cows did not react to the tuberculin test and provided that certain regulations regarding methods of production of milk were complied with.

This was followed by another order in 1925 which stated that all animals clinically affected with T.B. were to be compulsorily slaughtered so as to limit the spread of infection and so reduce the incidence of infected milk. However, this Order failed in its aims. There was not a strict enough control made on the movement of the 'reactors'. These were cows which failed the test but did not show any clinical signs of infection. The unscrupulous had no compunction in selling those animals in markets. They adopted the doubtful philosophy that they could not do much harm as 'they were going amongst their own kind.' This of course did not make it any easier or less costly to clear out the disease.

Another hindrance to eradication was the position of tenant farmers, who at that time were about two thirds of the farming community. Many of their premises were not suitable for the production of graded milk, nor were their landlords in a position to face the necessary expenditure. On the other hand many tenants had not the vision to make an effort which would ultimately be worth their while. These problems were eventually overcome.

In 1935 the Attested Herds Scheme was launched. This was a major step towards the eradication of this scourge. The movement of cattle was strictly controlled. Special bonuses and capital grants were given to encourage more progress. Herds which qualified for these were termed 'Supervised'.

This scheme was suspended from the outbreak of the war in 1939 until 1944. In 1937 the Scottish Milk Marketing Boards were directed to pay a premium of 2d. per gallon for T.T, milk sold. This was increased in 1943 to 4d. per gallon for Attested and T.T. milk and 1¼d for Standard milk.

The Scottish Milk Marketing Board being fully aware that clean milk and the health of the dairy herd was a key factor in selling 'safe' milk, had a Clean Milk Sub-Committee appointed.

From 1935 onwards when the authorities were endeavouring to stamp out T.B. the Board, in an effort to facilitate this, invited producers who had not had their herds tested to have one tuberculin test carried out at no charge. The cost was one shilling per animal if carried out by local authority vets.

Within the Scottish Milk Board area, in 1939 there were 565 producers holding certified T.T, licences out of a total of about 8000. They were mostly family farms in Ayrshire and Bute. By October 1939 this rose to 1460. At the end of 1946 it had reached 4010, i.e. 50% In England with about 150,000 herds the comparable figure was in the region of 10,000 i.e. about 7%. The milk sold from graded herds commanded a higher price which focussed attention on attaining higher status herds and at the same time directed attention on the keeping quality of milk.

To make a more positive attempt to stamp out T.B. as soon as it was physically and administratively possible, a Compulsory Eradication Scheme was started in 1950. In 1952 Eradication Areas were declared. The first in Scotland included the counties of Ayrshire, Dumfriesshire, Kirkcudbrightshire, Wigtownshire, Renfrewshire, Dumbartonshire, Lanarkshire and Bute.

It was understandable that the administration of the Scheme should focus their attention on the West and South West of Scotland where there was a high stocking rate of dairy cattle. It was an area from which a large number of surplus dairy cattle were sold. This gave an incentive to establish nucleus herds in other parts of the country. Compared with elsewhere, this area took the initiative and showed more enthusiasm to rid the country of the disease.

Herds were tested with free tuberculin and bonuses were enhanced to encourage the voluntary entry into the Attested Herds Scheme. This was greatly stimulated when the premiums paid reached 4d per gallon for milk sold through the Board for four years and 2d per gallon for a further two years. Later herds were compulsorily tested and all reactors slaughtered for which compensation was paid.

The Milk (Special Designation) Scotland Order 1951 revoked the previous orders and designated the milks to be sold under licence as Certified, Grade "A" T.T., Standard, Pasteurized, Heat-Treated, Sterilised. As before, in order to qualify for those licences, certain minimum standards of premises and dairy management had to be maintained.

On March 1st 1953, Ayrshire, Dumfriesshire, Kirkcudbrightshire, Wigtownshire, Renfrewshire and Bute were declared an Attested Area free from tuberculosis. On 1st October 1959 the whole of Scotland reached this status. By 1961 the national herd was declared free from tuberculosis thus following rinderpest, pleuro-pneumonia into the limbo of the past. Thankfully, we no longer see the 'trade of childhood, glands in the neck.'

BRUCELLOSIS

Brucellosis, like Tuberculosis is a very contagious disease. It can cause cows to abort, leading to infertility, reduced milk yields and loss of calves. Humans in close contact with such animals can be infected, sometimes seriously causing great distress. The symptoms are similar to severe flu. The disease has been known for a long time. If it becomes rampant in a herd, the losses can be catastrophic. In earlier years such were the losses that many farmers even the most efficient, were driven to bankruptcy.

Unfortunately, there are many reasons for abortion which causes the interruption of pregnancy, variously known as 'slinking', 'slipping', 'warping', 'casting' and 'picking'. It is called 'kebbing' in sheep. The causal bacillus, Brucella abortus was isolated in 1897 by Bang who gave the original name to Bang's disease. The contagious nature of the disease for a long time escaped observation. Even when modern science took over, there was difficulty and confusion about the identification of the 'carrier' animals, i.e. infected animals which do not themselves abort.

Because of difficulties in identification etc. a lot of mystique surrounded the disease as to 'cause and cure.' Dairymen were confused as to the cause of the disease. Some dairymen thought that if the cows were allowed outside for an hour or two at midday, this would induce the disease, whereas others thought that if they were allowed outside it prevented the disease! It was said that this difference of opinion arose from the fact that Galloway cows, who spent most of the winter outside seldom lost their calves prematurely.

There were other spurious theories about the causes of abortion. Some said that it was due to the 'imaginative disposition' of the cow when 'she was highly irritable' during pregnancy, or cows being terrified by an unusually violent thunderstorm. There was the 'Sympathy' factor which was prevalent in this country and also on the continent. This theory assumed that when one cow aborted, the other cows in the same herd or in the same building were prompted to follow suit by the mere knowledge that one of their companions had been in labour! Another theory quoted was 'Cows drinking water off ironstone or out of ponds, where tributaries are impregnated with the impurities from the steading are more apt to cast their calf than those drinking off limestone, granite, greywacke or from a pure pond.' It was well recognised that malnutrition and feeding unsound foods such as mouldy hay or feeding large quantities of frozen roots could cause isolated cases of abortion but did not explain outbreaks on a large scale.

Apart from the theories on the causes of the disease, there was one theory on the prevention which claimed success till comparatively recent times. Until some time after the Second World War it was not uncommon to see especially in England, a billy goat running along with the dairy cows. The Principal of Wye College at the time declared that the practice was a superstition but it worked. His argument was that after farmers had tried every remedy, apparently without effect, they reluctantly fell back on a piece of folk-lore.

The progress of the disease in a herd was usually of a volatile nature. When infection was introduced especially into a clean herd, the result could be disastrous. There would be a few abortions initially, which were often attributed to accidents. Usually no action was taken immediately allowing the disease to spread until there was an 'abortion storm' with disastrous results. Because animals do not usually abort for the second time, the disease often flared up spread through the herd and died down again. The infection lingered in the herd and the disease was known to reappear several years later before corrective measures were taken.

Unfortunately it took some time before an effective contagion to the disease was proven. During this period there was a wonderful opportunity for quack medicine manufacturers. Farmers in the midst of an abortion storm having dramatic losses would try any cure. There were no laws in the country then, to prevent the marketing of quack medicines. By the time the farmer found out about a 'new cure' and administered it, the abortions were usually becoming less and the active disease dying down, but it was the "quack" medicine or the presence of the billy goat that was given the credit. These medicines were found wanting if they were administered at the earlier stages of the outbreak, by which time a large profit had been made enabling another 'quack' medicine to be financed.

Over the years voluntary control measures were taken, a) by blood testing and the elimination of reactors, b) control by vaccination. Progress was hindered because of poor isolation facilities on many farms and the availability of 'clean stock' as replacements for the reactors. Some farmers were frustrated in their efforts to eliminate the disease because while the blood test was very effective in detecting the presence of the disease it did not pick out "as positive" an animal which had just become infected.

It was a great step forward when the vaccination of calves proved an effective method of prevention. As far back as 1906, Bang showed that vaccination of non-pregnant heifers with live cultures reduced the number of abortions when the animals were exposed to infection during pregnancy. Before there was legislation earlier vaccines were of a variable quality with expected doubtful results. This method of prevention became more widely used when a low virulent live strain, 'Strain 19' was produced. This originated in America. Calves were vaccinated between 4–6 months. It had the effect of causing the calves to react to a blood test but by the time these animals matured and came to be served they usually had thrown off the infection and were negative to the test. This vaccination was prohibited when the herds became attested and the use of the vaccine was made illegal in the whole of Great Britain from 1st November 1979.

A Brucellosis (Accredited Herds) Scheme was introduced in 1968. Because of a lot of apprehension there was little enthusiasm for herds to become accredited. This attitude changed when the Milk Boards provided a milk ring test for all registered producers to enable them to ascertain the brucellosis status of their herds. This screening encouraged many to have their herds blood tested, to register in the Brucellosis Incentive Scheme of 1970 and eventually reach Accredited status. Alongside this scheme there was a compulsory area eradication programme.

The Brucellosis Incentive Scheme was designed to accelerate the pace of voluntary eradication provided the applicants had a suitable system of livestock husbandry, a sound herd management policy and a well drained and fenced farm. The Scheme made premiums available through the Boards for milk sold and for every beef animal qualifying for the Hill Cow and Beef Cow Subsidy which were paid by the Minister of Agriculture. The premiums for herds which became accredited after 1st April 1971 were paid for a period of 5 years from the date of accreditation. The rates from 1971 were .176 pence per litre and £5 per beef animal. There was the expected animated discussions between the National Farmers' Union and the Government regarding those rates and many wrangles about there being no compensation for reactors. For the latter, the producers were expected to insure against consequential loss. However, at the expiry of the incentive period compensation of 75% of market value subject to an upper limit, was paid for reactors slaughtered.

The eradication of the disease was accelerated. By 1972, 51% of the herds in Scotland were accredited and a further 24% were in the Scheme 'pipeline'. On the other hand, throughout the country there were herds which were so severely infected that the incentive scheme bonuses were not attractive enough to encourage their owners to join. To rid the country of these serious sources of infection a compulsory area eradication programme commenced in November 1972. In these eradication areas all herds not in voluntary schemes were subject to blood tests, movement restrictions and other ancillary measures. In March 1976 the Ministry introduced free 45/20 vaccines to assist farmers with actively infected herds in those areas. Compensation was payable to herd owners (excluding herd owners taking part in the Brucellosis Incentive Scheme) whose animals were found to be reactors or dangerous contacts and compulsorily slaughtered. By November 1976 the whole of Scotland was covered by the compulsory eradication measures.

On 1st January 1980 the whole of Scotland was declared an Attested area for brucellosis and 'for all practical purposes it is free from the disease.'

Fig. 73 A Meeting of the staff of The Scottish Milk Records, Association

CHAPTER 16

MILK RECORDING

For a long period of time, a great deal of effort has gone into the improvement of the management and trofitability of dairy herds. Progress rolled gradually as better feeding regimes became available, be they concentrated feeding-stuffs or improved grasses, the latter being assisted by manurial policies ranging from farmyard manure being applied solely to very high applications of artificial fertilisers.

One of the best aids to management was the realisation of how important milk recording was. Although the advantages of recording milk yields had been known for a long time and cows have been officially recorded for almost 100 years,the number of cows recorded in Scotland is still less than half, about 44%. It is true that many producers being the individuals that they are, with their high degree of stockmanship and knowledge of cows, feel that they do not need to milk record. The question often asked 'What percentage of milk cows are culled for low yields only?' Arguments still persist.

In earlier days many pedigree breeders opposed this innovation because they sold their bulls on conformation rather than on the milk records of their female relatives. Understandably many small producers and those selling their milk direct to the housewife who did not keep a bull of their own thought that it was unnecessary.

Nevertheless, systematic recording of the milk yielded by each cow in a herd throughout the year determines its true capability as regards quantity and quality. This assists in economical feeding, identifies easily the low yielders and at the same time identifying the best animals for breeding. These records in turn are used for the selection of bulls especially for Artificial Insemination stations and provides useful information for research in the science and economic fields. Above all it removes guesswork and reliance on the memory and most importantly, increases the market value of the herd. As has been mentioned, good herdsmen can tell the good milkers from the bad, the difficulty is distinguishing between the moderately good and the slightly inferior animal. In effect the absence of milk recorded yields make efforts to achieve improved performance of little avail. It has to be done by 'breeding from a record of performance.'

The individual success of William Harley has already been noted. As far back as 1820, when he weekly recorded his dairy herd and had an ad hoc method of testing for butterfat, but combined efforts for recording did not take place until 1895. In the parish of Vegen in Jutland, Denmark, a group of farmers formed a society and engaged an expert to carry out the work. In the first two years after the formation of the Society in Vegen, the average yield of milk per cow was 670 gallons at 3.30% butterfat, eight yeras later the average was 730 gallons at 3.42% butterfat. Thereafter, numerous milk recording societies were rapidly formed in Denmark, Sweden, Norway and Holland.

Again as has been noted elsewhere, the controversy about show points in Ayrshire cattle dates back almost 150 years, when judges were putting great emphasis on upturned horns, teats not over 2.5 inches long, level sole to udder and to style, totally overlooking milking qualities. The Duke of Atholl believing that the milking ability of the cows was being neglected arranged the first public milking trial at the Ayrshire Show in 1860. The competition was for the cow which gave the most milk for ten consecutive milkings. Glen Gaur, a cow owned by Mr Wallace won, having averaged 26lbs 5.5 ounces per milking i.e. 263lbs. in five days.

An agricultural writer was moved to comment later, 'In fact the prize milk cow is like the masher of the period – she does not give much milk for fear of injuring the symmetry of her vessel...And all practical men who want to improve their herds stand aloof, because their object is milk and milk alone. They feel that they are more likely to injure than improve their stock by introducing prize strains.

Let breeders breed for milk, determine not to breed from a cow that does not yield a certain quantity of milk containing a given proportion of cream. Let them use as stock bulls those only which are the progeny of cows that comply with the above conditions.'

The ubiquitous John Speir who was so impressed by the Danish results on milk recording and its practicality demonstrated by the Duke of Atholl's milking trial, that he instigated with the assistance of the Highland and Agricultural Society the setting up of three milk recording societies, one each in Ayrshire, Dumfriesshire and Wigtownshire. As was reported, 'the object sought for and the main aim of the scheme was to obtain a means of comparing the cows of the same herd, calving at or near the same time, going on to the same pasture and subjected to the same climatic conditions, rather than to compare one herd with another.'

The details of the original scheme may be of interest.

The object is to encourage and assist the breeders and owners of dairy stock to keep records of the milk yield of their cows and the Highland

and Agricultural Society (referred hereafter as the "National Society") has adopted the following scheme:-

'It is intended that experts to be employed for the purpose, will visit certain herds in turn and take records of the weight and composition of each cow's milk.

Each herd will be visited at intervals of two weeks, so that one expert will overtake twelve herds.

The expert will arrive at the farm in time to be present at the milking in the evening and will stay overnight at the farm and will attend at the milking in the morning. Each cow's milk from the two milkings will be weighed and its composition tested by the expert.

Forms upon which to record the results of each test will be supplied by the National Society, one copy of the filled up form to be sent to the National Society and another to the Local Committee. A third copy will be retained by the expert until the end of the season and then delivered to the Local Committee.

Where practicable, particulars as to the liveweight of each cow and the kinds and quantities of the food given daily, apart from field pasture, should be entered upon the form.

It is intended that the test will begin as early as possible in the spring and continue till the end of October.

The assistance of the National Society is given on the condition that the Society is to receive and is to have the right to publish the records of all the tests made under the scheme.

The National Society will provide the appliances for weighing the milk and testing its composition and will pay half the costs of these appliances. The Local Committee will pay the other half and retain the appliances as their property.

The expert for the conducting of the tests will be appointed by the Local Committee, subject to the approval of the National Society. The expert will be paid a salary exclusive of his board and lodging and travelling expenses. Provided the conditions of this scheme are complied with and the National Society is satisfied with the manner in which the work is conducted, the National Society will contribute a sum equivalent to two thirds of the salary of the expert. The Local Committee will pay the other third and defray travelling and other local expenses and arrange for the conveyance of the expert from farm to farm.

All tests under this scheme must be arranged at the instance of the Local Committee or the Local Society approved and registered for this purpose with the National Society.

Local Societies desirous of conducting similar tests under arrangements differing from those detailed above, are invited to make their proposals known to the Secretary of the National Society. If the arrangements meet with its approval, the National Society may give a grant in aid of the expenses. In all cases such grant will be subject to the condition that detailed results of tests are supplied to the National Society with the right of publication.

For carrying out the foregoing scheme in the current year (1903), a sum not exceeding £200 has been voted by the National Society.

When applications were received they were administered in the three counties by the Ayrshire Farmers' Society, the Dumfries Farmers' Association and the Wigtown Dairy Farmers' Association respectively. To begin with there were 11 herds tested in Ayrshire in the parishes of Maybole, Monkton and Tarbolton; in Dumfriesshire likewise there were 11 herds tested around Sanquhar, Thornhill and Dumfries and in Wigtownshire, 12 herds around Stranraer were tested.

The first recorders in the three districts were, Thomas Howie, jun. Fairfield Mains, Monkton in Ayrshire; John Dunlop, Gree, Fenwick, in Dumfriesshire until he left to go to college when he was succeeded by Peder Rasmussen, a son of a Danish farmer who was in this country at the time; and in Wigtownshire there was also another Dane, Jacob Sear Trier.

Previous to this, a group of dairy farmers in Fenwick district had held competitions for the highest yielding cows. In 1905 a society was officially formed and received a grant from the National Society. In the same year due to the enthusiasm of A.W. Montgomery, Lessnessnock, the Cumnock District Milk Society was formed under the auspices of the Ayrshire Agricultural Association which paid the expenses of the society which were not met by the Highland and Agricultural Society.

The first recorder in the Fenwick Milk Record Association was William G. McLeary and the herds he visited were –

Mrs Mather, Thorn, Fenwick.
William Wilson, High Todhill, Fenwick.
John Lindsay, Moss-side, Fenwick.
James Howie, Hillhouse, Kilmarnock.
James Garven, Dalmusternock, Fenwick.
James Young, Marchbank, Fenwick
D & J Bicket, Raithmuir, Fenwick.
John Douglas, Langdyke, Fenwick

James Young, Hareshaw, Fenwick
A.B. Paton, Collarie, Fenwick.
James Lindsay, Blackbyre, Fenwick.
James Dunlop, Midland, Fenwick.
John Smith, Wylieland, Fenwick.
Robert Loudon, Harelaw,Fenwick.
James Dunlop, Gree, Fenwick.
David Murchland, Broadmoss, Fenwick.
Andrew Clement, Netherton, Newton Mearns.

The original members of the Cumnock Milk Record Association whose herds were tested by John H. Wyllie were :-

James Sloan, Dormiston, Ochiltree.
Robert Steele, M'Quittiston, Ochiltree.
Adam W. Montgomerie, Lessnessock, Ochiltree.
Messrs Wilson, Auchencloich, Ochiltree.
David Wardrop, Knockterra, Cumnock.
David Stevenson, Changue, Cumnock.
W. M'Lanachan, Loganhill, Cumnock.
W. M'Lanachan, Boreland, Cumnock.
A.M Baird, Garclaugh, New Cumnock.
John Lennox, Auchengee, New Cumnock.

In 1906 there were societies formed in Dumfriesshire, Wigtownshire and Kirkcudbrightshire. The five societies tested a total of 2688 cows. 353 in Cumnock; 742 in Dumfries; 455 in Fenwick; 601 in Kirkcudbright and 537 in Wigtownshire.

The Dumfriesshire Dairy Farmers' Association had 21 members whose herds were tested by R. Richardson.

William Lindsay, Cogries, Beattock.
William Mackie, Wamphray Gate, Wamphray.
Sir R.W. Buchanan-Jardine, Saughtrees, Lockerbie.
J.S. Paterson, Quhytewoolen, Lockerbie.
James Edgar, Castlehill, Lockerbie.
James Wyllie, Bankhead, Lochmaben.
John Paterson, Mouswald Grange, Ruthwell.
John Wilson, Boghead, Dumfries.
John Wilson, Tinwaldshaws, Dumfries

James Lamberton, Sandbed, Dumfries.
James Sloan, Carmaddie, Holywood.
Robert Millar, Lakehead, Closeburn.
W. Niven, Barnmuir, Closeburn.
William Sloan, Shawsmuir, Closeburn.
Robert Primose, Kirkland, Closeburn.
John Laidlaw, Glengar, Penpont.
J.R. Wallace, Auchenbainzie, Thornhill.
Thomas Brown, Drum, Thornhill.
A. Stevenson, Muiryhill, Thornhill.
James Moffat, Gateside, Sanquhar.
A.M. Dickie, Tower, Sanquhar.

In 1903 a 'milk record station' was set up in the Rhins of Galloway through which a number of herds were tested. This functioned for one year only and was reorganised in 1906 when 12 herds were visited by the recorder, James Woodburn. They were:-

John McCaig, Boreland, Stranraer.
W. H. Ralston, Dunragit, Stranraer.
W.H. Ralston, Boreland, Stranraer.
Miss McCaig, Drumdock, Dunragit.
Mrs McCaig, Barnultoch, Lochans.
Messrs Mc Caig, Barnchalloch, Lochans.
Andrew Murray, Port of Spittal, Lochans.
Miss Wither, Lagganmore, Portpatrick.
Robert Purdie, Craichmore, Stranraer.
Andrew Cochrane, Ardwell, Kirkcolm.
George Cochrane, North Cairn, Kirkcolm.
John Agnew, Balwherrie, Leswalt.

W.D. Vallance, in 1906 first recorded twelve herds for the Stewartry Dairy Farmers Association, situated around Castle Douglas. They belonged to:-

David McGill, Hillowton, Castle Douglas.
H.W.B. Crawford, Chapmanton, Castle Douglas.
John Hastings, Wheatcroft, Castle Douglas.
Hugh Parker, Boreland, Balmaghie, Castle Douglas.
Edward Gordon, Dunjop, Castle Douglas.

Thomas Douglas, Lochdougan Castle Douglas.
James McAdam, Craigley, Castle Douglas.
W.P. Gilmour, Balmanghan, Borgue, Kirkcudbright.
Sir Mark Stewart, Southwick Home Farm, Dumfries.
Captain Cochrane, Torrorie, Kirkbean, Dumfries.
Thomas Sloan, Newmains, Kirkbean, Dumfries.
Weir Bros. Brickhouse, New Abbey, Dumfries.

It is worthy of note that from these herds the 12 best cows averaged 1043 gallons at 4.16% butterfat in 214 days. A creditable performance considering the management of the time. This compares with the twelve best cows from the Fenwick Society which averaged 1054 gallons at 3.7% butterfat in 316 days. (Speir J. T.H.A.S.S. 1907)

The objective, as already mentioned was to ascertain the individual yield of each cow and compare that in the most equitable way possible with her contempories. The innovators of the scheme went further than that and tried to put a commercial value on this. They wanted a scheme that 'would authoritatively indicate the most profitable and least profitable cows in each herd, so that the owners might discard the latter and breed only from the former.'

A methodical costings system was adopted. The recorder in each district ascertained the cost of grazing and forage crops, allocated to each cow along with the amount of concentrates fed. The cost per ton of the homegrown foods in Kirkcudbrightshire and Wigtownshire was taken to be:–

Ryegrass hay and clover hay	£3-0-0.
Natural meadow hay.	£2-0-0.
Oat straw.	£1-11-0.
Turnips	£0-8s-0

The average cost of food in these two counties for the seasons 1907–1908 was 4.03d. per gallon. Added to this were the costs of rent, labour and depreciation. This was higher for farms supplying the town milk trade compared with those making cheese. Aside from the cost of the milkers, the return from the cow manure was estimated to be equivalent to the labour cost for feeding the cows. An allowance for depreciation on cows five years old and over was taken to be £1 per cow. Because the milk was mainly produced for butter and cheese making, in 1905 the average ruling was 5d. per gallon, which was lower than what was available for milk being sold into the liquid market. At that time it meant the profit margin was mainly from the value of the calf and the whey which was available for pig feeding.

Apart from the costings, other aspects associated with milk recording were looked at in some detail. The comparison of the quality of milk given by heavy and poor milkers; the effect of size on their yield of milk; the effect of age on the yield of milk; the effect of age on the percentage of fat in the milk; the effect of the period of lactation on the fat in the milk and the effect of cows being in season on the percentage of fat in the milk. (Speir J. T.H.A.S.S. 1905.)

The details studied are remarkable at such an early time in this newly established concept of milk recording. In this sophisticated scientific age many of these experiments may seem rather elementary, however, one must bear in mind the era in which they were carried out. They formed a basis for subsequent work. As the number of societies increased, at the end of 1907, the Highland Society while still giving grants and publishing results, devolved the administration to a new body 'The Ayrshire Cattle Records Committee.' under the chairmanship of Sir Hugh Shaw-Stewart, with John Hole, 58 Alloway Street, Ayr, as secretary. This was advantageous to the movement because it laid down uniform regulations for every local society and undertook printing and publishing results 'in a composite form.'

This organisation was later named the Scottish Milk Record Association responsible for milk recording throughout Scotland. To its governing body members from each society were elected together with representatives of the Highland and Agricultural Society of Scotland, Breed Societies and Agricultural Colleges.

Each local society had a degree of independence and each producer could be a member. Each society elected its own committee and engaged the necessary recorders.

In 1968 the head office staff moved into the Scottish Milk Marketing Headquarters in Paisley and the Board now operates the milk recording service under licence from the Scottish Milk Records Association.

In 1908 a society was started in England near Preston. The first official milk recording society which was based on the Scottish model began in 1914 at Cadbury, Somerset. This benefited from a grant from the Development Commission. In England it is under the aegis of the production division of the English Milk Marketing Board.

JOHN SPEIR 1850–1910

Sadly for milk recording it lost its greatest stalwart in 1910 by the death of John Speir, Newton. He really was its founding father. He first advocated the concept. In its early years he was very actively involved. 'He voluntarily took upon himself the duty of corresponding with the testers appointed by the local societies. He checked the sheets and the byre books of every herd tested, summarised the results and formed annual reports. He wrote pamphlets and delivered lectures on the subject, setting forth in statistical and convincing form the advantages to be derived from the regular testing of herds. The greater part of the success which the movement has attained must undoubtedly be attributed to him.' (Milk Record Report, 1909)

Time should perhaps be taken to note the achievements and effort John Speir had made in the interests of agriculture. From a perusal of agricultural history he does not seem to have been given due recognition. Although he did so much for British agriculture and was so well known in Europe and America, it was sometime after his death before a memorial was raised. That is the Speir Memorial Prize awarded annually to the best student in dairying at the West of Scotland Agricultural Society. Norway, however, saw fit to honour him with the Knighthood of the Order of St. Olaf.

In the 1950 Scottish Journal of Agriculture, J. A. Symon wrote a comprehensive article entitled *'Speir of Newton'* which summarises Speir's noteworthy career.

Born in 1850 in the parish of Dalry, where his father had a small property, John was educated at Dalry parish school, but what he acquired there must have been thoroughly imparted. He was taught to reason logically and to express himself clearly. Wide and intensive reading, extensive travel, keen powers of observation and a unique faculty for approaching subjects he tackled with an open mind, provided him with a store of knowledge remarkable for its breadth of vision and minuteness of detail. Nor did he keep his knowledge to himself: his life aim was to use it for the good of his fellows.

In 1876, he leased an extensive farm of Newton, Cambuslang, a big undertaking for a man of his years. One half of his farm was run as a dairy farm with an arable rotation, the other was devoted to market gardening and glass culture. There he found ample scope for carrying out trials with implements, crops, rotations, feeding-stuffs, milk production, etc., yet despite the work involved in this big enterprise he found time to give his services to many public bodies.

When in 1888 he was made a director of the then named Highland and Agricultural Society, it could not be said that he was received by the august Directorate with open arms. His comparative youth, his habits for independent thought and zeal for progress in his earlier years, not always matched with tact and discretion, caused him to be viewed at first somewhat in the light of an ugly duckling. In time, however, his great intellectual power and singleness of purpose were recognised at their true worth and his fame established, honours followed each other in quick succession.

In 1893, we find him serving on the Royal Commission on Agricultural Development; in 1897 he became a member of the Royal Commission on Tuberculosis and the following year saw him President of the Chamber of Agriculture. When in 1899 the West of Scotland College of Agriculture was founded, it was inevitable that his name should appear on the first roll of Governors. Always keenly interested in education, he did much to promote it in all three countries of the United Kingdom.

His most notable work, however, lay in conceiving and bringing into being systemised milk recording in Scotland. His visits to Denmark and other countries made him realise how advantageous milk recording was. Poor milkers could be discovered and weeded out; costs of production could be lowered; the advantages of food rationing could be exploited and a breeding policy be pursued aiming at the progressive advancement of milk yields as well as the butter percentage of a herd. Indeed, to Speir's enlightened mind, breeding in dairy cattle without access to the milk performances of the animal and its ancestors were largely groping in the dark. So well and so ably did he advocate milk recording that in 1903 he induced the Highland and Agricultural Society to give a grant of £200 to enable Milk Recording Societies, to be formed for the purpose to record over the first six months the milk yields and butterfat percentages of all cows belonging to their members. The object to confining the records to the summer six months, beginning May 1st. was to bring home mainly to cheese making farmers the fact that under nearly identical conditions of feeding, period of lactation etc., there could be wide differences in milk yields, butterfat percentages and the cheese output of different cows.

Today (1950) the relative merit of silage versus hay as a means of conserving grass for winter-feed is much discussed and so far a definite answer has not been obtained. More than sixty years ago Speir was seeking on his farm an answer to the same question. His method was as follows. To ensure that the material from which the hay and silage were made was the same, a field of aftermath was divided into two parts. In one part the grass was made into two kinds of silage, sweet and sour; in the other it was made into hay. The aim was to compare the feeding value of the processed material. This was done in two ways: (a) by chemical analysis; and (b) by feeding the silage and hay to two lots of as nearly as possible identical cows and recording the milk yields. Speir found from the analytical point of view both the sour and sweet silage compared favourably with hay. On a dry matter basis, the silage was higher in protein and lower in fibre than the hay. By experimenting he established that grass silage was a very suitable food for dairy cows which compared well with hay. Speir wisely did not claim more for it than that and indicated that more experimental work was needed before an authoritative statement could be justified. Incidentally, in this investigation he cast grave doubts upon the then prevalent idea that, somehow or other, the heat generated in the process of making sweet silage improved digestibility of the material. In the 1950's, it was the accepted practice to allow the temperature of the silage to rise to 100°F before completely filling the pit and rolling to prevent the development of butyric acid. By adding treacle with its sugars aided the production of lactic acid which dispensed with the need for "heating".

The dairy cow was to Speir not only an animal for producing milk which could be turned into cash; it was, under strictly comparable conditions, a suitable machine for comparing the values of different foods, systems of management, etc. The main conclusion arrived at was that the feeding value of different foods was determined mainly by their dry matter content and that the percentage of fat in the milk was little influenced by the food. This is now open to question.

The individuality of the cow, the period between milkings and the date since calving, were the main factors to influence the percentage of fat. In addition he made observations on the characters of the butters produced by the different foods. He found that when cows were getting green food, the butter had much more colour than when they were getting non-green food. Linseed oil cake and dried grains produced much softer butter than, say, cotton cake. Other trials determining the effect of cooking or steaming of foods given to cows exploded the popular idea that the food values were by these means considerably improved. Slight gains were recorded in favour of cooking, but so very slight not to warrant the extra costs involved. Another very important piece of research done by Speir was to show that byre temperatures of from 60°F. to 63°F. were not necessary to obtain optimum milk yields. These temperatures could only be obtained by restricting ventilation. Adequate ventilation coupled with considerably lower temperatures were reflected not by lower yields or discomfort of the cows but by an improvement in the health of the animals.

Speir had a great bent towards engineering. Had he followed it he might have become famous as an inventor. As it was he found considerable scope for both testing and advocating new ideas. In his twenties he was intrigued with the idea of inventing a milking machine. Nothing definite came of it, but after William Murchland of Kilmarnock applied for and was successful in getting a patent for his milking machine, one incorporating the principle of suction, it was Speir who tested it and reported on it. His report was that the cows did not take unkindly to it, that it did its work fairly well but that it did not milk altogether cleanly and was apt to interfere with the circulation of the blood in the udder.

In Speir's time well before the age of farm mechanisation, the urge to design new cultivation implements was less strong than it is today. Nevertheless his fertile brain found much scope in testing different types of implements. The American chilled plough, with its concave short board and wooden handles, had just been introduced and was being tried out against the old swing plough with its long cast iron convex board. In the years 1887–89 Speir did a considerable amount of work in testing the two types and found that both the American and English made ploughs reduced the draught very considerably, often as much as a quarter or a third. Speir also reported on such implements as the spring toothed cultivator or harrow, the combined drill and manure distributor, the dung spreader, grain drills manure sowers, sprayers, turnip and potato lifters and barn and food processing machinery. It is interesting to note that the principle of the modern hay and grass sweep was probably brought into this country by Speir.

In the 1902 Transactions of the Highland and Agricultural Society, an interesting article on boxing seed potatoes appeared under Speir's name. The system of sprouting early potatoes was practised in Jersey and Cheshire long before it became established in Scotland. Scottish farmers, however, came to hear about it and Mr Hunter of Maybole arranged for a sprouting box to be made for him in a wood yard in Aye. According to Speir another Scottish grower from the same area heard about this and resolved if possible to forestall Mr Hunter. Accordingly he made a special to Cheshire, visited a farm belonging to a Mr Marsh and finding him not at home cooly lifted a box, placed in the back of the gig in which he was travelling and telling the farmer's wife that he would pay for the box if he ever met Mr Marsh, drove off. After seeing the results of many trials conducted in Scotland, Speir concluded that sprouting of potatoes was well justified.

Another field of investigation which gave scope to Speir's experimental work was in testing new oat varieties. For a long time the old Sandy and Potato types had reigned supreme in Scotland, but towards the end of the nineteenth century new crossbred and foreign, largely Canadian, varieties were being introduced. Exhaustive trials of these new varieties were carried out by Speir and Dr Aitken, the chemist of the Highland and Agricultural Society. The grain yields, the length and standing power of the straw, the percentages of the kernel to husk in the grain and the overall feeding properties were determined.

His wide travels brought him into intimate contact with agriculturists in many countries. In Hungary he was surprised to find that agricultural and technical education was far in advance of anything of the kind in Britain. At the beginning of this century, Hungary had two flourishing agricultural colleges which had been developed from agricultural schools established in the 1840s. The country also had many agricultural schools for training young farmers, besides schools in dairying, poultry-keeping, agriculture, horticulture, viniculture, drainage and veterinary science, while itinerant instructors located throughout the country gave advice to and conducted classes for the farmers. Another feature of Hungary's agriculture was her Seed Testing Stations. In the aggregate, of 30,000 samples of seeds, including samples of hay and certain feeding-stuffs, were being examined yearly at the beginning of this century for purity and germination and in the case of hay and feeding-stuffs, for their botanical constituents.

In the light of history we can review dispassionately Speir's life and work. He was indeed a remarkable man. Some of his contemporaries, well qualified to judge, considered him to be the most remarkable man they had met. His intellectual superiority, broadmindedness, far-sightedness, courage, vitality and powers of inspiration set in motion movements which had a salutary and far reaching effect on Scottish agriculture. Our progress in such matters as milk recording, elimination of tuberculosis in cattle, byre ventilation, milking machines, farm implements, conservation of grass, new varieties of crops, not to mention agricultural education and research, owes much to Speir's dynamic energy. Tragic though his death seemed to be at the time it was fitting that such a man should die in harness before age had wearied him. He was cut off while preparing to receive yet another visit from the students of the West of Agricultural

College, but before death took him he had earned his place amongst the great farmers, not merely of Britain but of the world.

When one meets or reads about a man of the calibre of John Speir, Goldsmith's Schoolmaster in the *'Deserted Village'* springs to mind.

'And still they gazed and still the wonder grew,
That one small head could carry all he knew.'

In 1912 there were twenty four societies formed in Scotland, testing 18,356 cows in 438 herds. By this time pedigree breeders were seeing tangible benefits of milk recording with increasing prices for their cattle being sold into England and abroad. Both home and foreign purchasers were now placing considerable reliance on milk records, in some cases before cognizance of the pedigrees.

One of the societies formed at that time was the Strathendrick Milk Record Society. Some details from the original minute book are interesting.

'Within the Shepherd's Hall in Balfron on 24th February 1912 at a meeting of farmers called for the purpose of forming a Milk Record Society.'

Those present were:– Messrs. John Alston, George Campbell, W.H. Fleming, G.S. Gibb, Alex Hosie, Mathew Mitchell, A.B. Patterson.

John Alston was appointed chairman and John was appointed secretary.

Peter Bennet was proposed to be engaged as the milk tester at 15s. per week and it was agreed that he should bear his own expenses at Kilmarnock Dairy School.

The route for the tester was fixed as follows, beginning on 4th March 1912:– Monday night, Carbeth; Tuesday, Claylands; Wednesday, Home Farm; Thursday, Woodend; Friday, Carroquill. In the second the farms visited were:– Monday, Carbeth; Tuesday, Gartness; Wednesday, Blarnavaid; Thursday, Loaninghead; Friday, Ballaird.

At a later meeting it was recorded that Col. Ferguson Buchanan should be asked to give the tester a week's work 'as it was thought desirable to run a three weekly test.' It was also decided to ask the tester to collect £1 from each member every three months 'and no further call to be made for that reason unless required.'

'Mr Alston suggested that the tester should take note of all the heavy milking cows on each farm, with the quantity of milk given and the amount of feed received and to give the information regarding the same to those desiring it, but as the finding was not unanimous, it was decided by a few to leave it open to the tester in connection with the stock as suggested.'

Labour relations would appear to have been rather autocratic. 'The resignation of the tester, Mr Tom Gardiner was accepted. It was agreed to let him free one week before the 28th November, but if the outlay for a substitute before the end of the year would cost more than the average 15s. per week the present tester should pay part of the extra cost.'

In the T.H.A.S 1913 it is reported that 'the Strathendrick Milk Record Society was formed with a membership of 9 and marks the introduction of milk recording into Stirlingshire. The milk is entirely produced for direct sale and cows calve at all periods of the year. Of the 211 cows and heifers under test 64 cows and twelve heifers are classed as good and three as bad.'

Within the Loudon Arms Hotel, Duke Street Glasgow on 20th January, 1915, a meeting was held with representatives from Strathendrick, Kirkintilloch, Milngavie and Slamannan districts with a view to having a joint Milk Record Society. It was decided to name the new society Strathendrick, Kirkintilloch and district Milk Record Society. The pony and trap from the old Kirkintilloch Society was purchased for £20.

'This was due to the resignation of a number of members from each society who were milk selling farmers who did not breed or rear their own stock to any extent and were consequently not so deeply interested in their milk records.'

This has been par for the course throughout the history of milk recording.

As always the problem of costs prevailed. Compared with other costs in milk production milk recording has always been relatively cheap. Aided by grants from Milk Marketing Boards by upto 25% the cost per cow has been about the equivalent of 40 litres per cow. In earlier years when milk recording was being encouraged at the time when cows were hand milked and farm cheese prevailed it was pointed out to farmers that by paying attention to recording and cow selection 40 cows could be kept to yield the same quantity of milk as 60 cows therefore, the number of milkers would be reduced from 6 to 4 with an ongoing saving in feeding costs. Furthermore the yield of cheese made from a gallonage of milk was greater from that of a higher butterfat.

There were complaints and difficulties about the boarding of the milk testers. Farmers' wives resented their intrusion. The testers had to suffer at times hard or damp beds and the females objected at being asked to be unpaid baby sitters. There were brighter times when the latter were popular with the young farmers sometimes leading to matrimony.

Another bone of contention was the keeping of the milk tester's pony. When milk recording began, transport was very limited, trains were used wherever possible otherwise horse and cart was the main mode of travel. Later this was facilitated by the Societies supplying ponies and traps. This meant that the tester had to have the added skill of horsemanship which was of varying standards. Women were not considered capable for this job. In the winter time when the ponies were fed indoors because their only exercise was a short journey to the next farm they could be rather frisky and by travelling too fast over rough farm roads the traps were sometimes capsized. This could result in quite a mess spilling onto the road. There would be a suitcase with personal belongings plus 'the accoutrements of the trade' such as a spring balance, a weighing bucket, sampling dipper, boxes of sample bottles, a Winchester of sulphuric acid, a bottle amyl alcohol, a hand operated centrifuge, about a couple dozen of calibrated test- tubes, necessary stationery and byre record sheets.

On occasion the milk tester's pony was not so frisky. At Auchenhay, Borgue, William Parker was given a new bike for his birthday. When the milk tester arrived at the farm, he asked William for a 'shot' on his new bike. William reluctantly agreed. Being a good horseman, William in return asked for a gallop on tester's pony. Sadly the following morning the pony was found dead. It is to be assumed that no harm came to the bike.

In the winter testing the milk could be an unpleasant job during inclement weather when it had to be done in a draughty cart shed all 'muffled up' with overcoat, scarf and gloves. This was more unpleasant if the farmer had to drive his milk to the nearest station for a 6.30a.m. train which necessitated milking starting at 3.30a.m.

Occasionally in the summertime there was the problem of catching a perverse pony in the field, necessitating taking a quiet farmhorse out into the field and hoping that the infuriating pony would follow it into the stable to be harnessed. Tempers flared if after all this inconvenience the pony became really awkward and refused to back into the shafts of the trap to be yoked especially in the middle of haytime!

With the progress of mechanisation the testers were for many years transported from farm to farm by the farmers. In modern times the milk recorder is self transporting, there is no on farm testing, the milk recorder regularly visits the farms, twice daily takes samples from each cow milking and sends them for testing to the Central laboratory in Paisley.

The compositional results are computerised and returned quickly to the dairy farmer.

In spite of the enthusiasm of the pioneers of milk recording and their propaganda work, after twenty five years only 17% of the dairy cows in Scotland were milk recorded. At first sight this appears disappointing but at that time Denmark with 23% cows recorded was the only country with a greater number. Percentages in other countries were:- Netherlands 14%; Sweden 10%; England and Wales 8.5%; New Zealand 6%; Germany 5%; Canada 1.5%; United States 1%. In 1990, Netherlands 74%; Sweden 74.7%; England & Wales 51.4%; Scotland 40%; New Zealand 60.1%; Germany 55%; Canada 60.0%; United States 45.22%.

The progress of milk recording over the years tended to follow the fortunes of the dairy industry. For example in the 1960s progress was hindered when dairy cow numbers fell by almost 15%. Efforts to increase the numbers recording still continues. Making improvements to the service is ongoing. With computer programmes feeding into a computer bank each recorded herd owner is provided with a wealth of new data in a form which can directly help him in his herd management, such as estimations of predicated yields and a Breeding Index for selected pedigree cows.

Fig. 74 The benefits of "The Milk Recording Service"

When the Scottish Milk Record Association moved its headquarters from Ayr to Paisley the Scottish Milk Marketing Board operated the milk recording service under licence from the Scottish Milk Record Association which covered the whole of Scotland. Thereafter other services to producers were added. A Farm Costing Service was run in conjunction with the Advisory Divisions of the East and West of Scotland Agricultural Colleges.

With the statistical support from the Scottish Milk Record Association the Scottish Milk Marketing Board took over from the Department of Agriculture the running of the Livestock Records Bureau. This provides information to any producer even outwit the Scottish Board's area, on any dairy sire in which he is interested. The Bureau also provides information and advice to the Board's Cattle Breeding Department to assist in its constant search for better young bulls for proving in breeding ability and for proven sires of a high enough calibre to enter the Board' cattle stud.

CHAPTER 17

CHEESE

'Where fish is scant and fruit of trees,
Supply that want with butter and cheese.'
(Thomas Tusser.)

The history of cheese goes back probably further than any other prepared food, further back than when English was a spoken language. The Greeks were familiar with cheesemaking at the time of Homer. Hippocrates mentions cheese made from mare's milk and from goat's milk. Early Egyptians made cheese from the milk of asses, camels, goats and sheep. In the Bible David was sent by his father Jesse to 'carry these ten cheeses to the captain of their ten thousand and look how thy brethern fare.'

The Romans introduced their method of making a soft cheese. The milk in a tub kept at a certain by placing it near a fire until it curdled. The curd was then transferred into rush or osier baskets from which the whey drained off and became moulded into the shape of the basket. To facilitate this weights were placed on the filled baskets.

'The milk they obtain at dawn or
During the day, they cheese at night: the evening milk
They pack off at dawn in frails and the shepherd takes it to town,
Or sprinkle it lightly with salt and put it by for the winter.'
(Virgil, The Georgics.')

In more modern times the Church of Rome took a direct interest in cheese.

Many in Europe were taught various methods of making cheese by monks. 'Secret formulae for certain varieties were held as part of the wealth of monasteries.'

Thomas Tusser's book, *'Five Hundred Points of Good Husbandry and Housewifery'* in 1572 is one of the earliest handbooks on general farming and gives a number of do's and dont's on the making of butter and cheese. He gives instructions to his dairymaid which could be interpreted to be applicable today.

Too salty – 'Leave Lot with his pillar, good Cisley alone,
much saltiness in whitemeat is ill for the stone
White & dry – Gehezie his sickness was whitish and dry
Such cheeses, good Cisely ye floated to nie'
(skimmed too much)
Gassy – 'If cheese in dairy have Argus eyes
Tell Cisley the fault in her housewifery lies'
(dirty dairy and utensils)

'Thus Dairymaid Cisley rehearsed you see,
What faults with poor huswife in dairy-housebe,
At market abhorred, to household a grief
To master and mistress as ill a thiefe.'

Through the centuries in different parts of the world special methods of making cheese developed to suit local conditions and tastes there being about 2000 varieties available today. It is alleged that Napoleon on being presented with local cheese made by a peasant girl, Marie Marel, he kissed her and named the cheese Camembert, after the local town. Thereafter, he continued on his victorious journey and a statue honouring Marie was erected in the Normandy village.

In the U.K. there are quite a number of indigenous cheese varieties, 52 in England and 22 in Scotland. (British Food Facts & Figures, 1986.) Many are locally named. For a long time the recipes and methodology were handed down through the generations, the mysteries of which were unexplained by science. A simplistic definition to a very precise process is 'The development of acid in milk to take out the alkaline solution holding the case in, converting the latter into an insoluble curd, when collected and dried, forms cheese.' The principle of cheesemaking has always been to effectively control acidity, moisture and temperature.

Actually all cheese is made in much the same way. Special bacteria are added to warm milk as a 'starter' – these produce lactic acid which changes the flavour of the curds from being milky to cheesey. Rennet is then added to make the milk curdle so that within half an hour or so it forms junket which when cut separates into 'curds' and 'whey'. The 'whey' is then drained off.

The final quality of the cheese depends on a number of things: whether the milk has come from a cow, a goat or a ewe; the type of starter used – some starters make gas bubbles which leave holes in the cheese; whether the milk has been pasteurised; how much the junket has been cut up; whether the curds and whey are heated, to what temperature and for how long; how much salt is added; whether or not the cheese is pressed and if so how heavily, whether the curds are cut into small pieces before the cheese is pressed; how long it is kept to mature and how it is treated while it is maturing.

The principle difference between hard and soft cheeses is in the amount of moisture or whey that is left in the curd, the bacteria used to produce their characteristic flavour and their method of curing. Cream cheese is an 'unripened' soft cheese being marketed fresh without curing.

It is said that cheese stimulates the humane palate to a greater degree than any other food and among the various exotic and widely different flavours the need of the most discriminating taste is satisfied. It is amazing that so many varieties of cheese originate from the same raw material.

The 'starter' in cheesemaking is so named because it promotes (starts) acidity in milk by changing the milk sugar, lactose into lactic acid. The isolation of milk souring bacteria was done by Dr Lister in 1877 resulting in the development of the science, bacteriology. In about 1900 the first specially prepared liquid starter cultures, mainly varieties of Streptococcus lactis, were introduced. These were later supplied by colleges and other trade laboratories. From that period onwards the quality and uniformity of cheese improved enormously and the whole process was shortened because it no longer depended on natural acid development.

Until this time cheesemaking had been gradually developed mainly on empirical lines, as a result of practical experience. The evening's milk used to be allowed to sour naturally. This was caused by the milk's own acidity and any bacteria absorbed from the atmosphere. Various substances were used to accelerate this, – Muriatic acid, vinegar, tartaric acid, some salts of oxalic acid, or just soured skim milk and sour whey.

The study of bacteriology threw light on the causes of many unexplained fermentative changes in the milk and curd. 'Nature takes care, science explains', but 'the starter and control of acidity is everything for body and flavour.'

Experienced cheesemakers knew that starter cultures were very sensitive to careful handling, not realising that they were dealing with living organisms which could transmit their own characteristics like any other living being. The product would be well made if the starter had a pleasing flavour but if it 'had gone off' causing 'slow cheese' the product could be very undesirable. It was not until the 1930s when it was established that the main cause of a slow cheese was when the starter bacteria was destroyed by a virus, bacteriophage. This problem was eventually overcome when a system of asceptic starter propagation was devised.

In the old days every dairyman kept his own starter and there was much rivalry between them as to who had the best. Despite the 'friendly' rivalry there was always a great bond of comradeship which was useful in trouble. Whenever a starter 'was off' due to contamination there was always someone to help out. When a dairyman had a good starter he tried to keep it going as long as he could. Sometimes at the end of the season a sealed bottle would be buried in the garden and dug up in the spring ready to carry on.

Rennet, it used to be called 'yearning', is the other main agent used in cheesemaking which activatess a rapid curdling of milk. It used to be made from the juices of plants such as ladies bedstraw, thistles lessor spearwort, steepgrass i.e. butterwort. Rennet was also prepared from a stomach of a calf, lamb, hare, deer, sow or even a gizzard of a fowl. The most commonly used was the lining of the stomach of a suckling calf, called 'vell'. The production of the enzyme rennin was stimulated when an animal had just been fed on milk.

The action of rennet would be seen on the curdled milk in a calf's stomach from ancient times and this curd would be eaten as such or after it had been dried in the sun. A liquid extract from the fourth stomach contains the enzymes rennin and pepsin along with water, salt and some organic matter. In an acid medium this preparation coagulates the milk. When this extract became too costly to produce, it was mixed with a vegetable extract.

In the 1880s in Ayrshire, 'the rennet is the strained liquid in which the cut up salted stomachs of calves, called 'yearnings', is immersed for a few days, the water being usually boiled and allowed to cool again to milk heat ere the 'yearnin' is put in to steep. The stomach is emptied of its contents, which being cleaned and mixed with a handful or two of salt, is put back in again and being likewise well rubbed outside, the full stomachs are then hung up to dry in the kitchen and where they often hang for a year or more before using. It takes about one gill of rennet more or less, according to its strength, to properly thicken a day's milk of about about 20 cows.' (Sturrock, 1886.)

The coagulum of cheese so produced has to be of a uniform consistency free from whey and 'able to carry an egg.' The textbook says that the curds cut there from, should be 'Free from gasiness or frothiness;

should have a pleasing acid flavour and aroma and should in all aspects be pleasing to the eye and the palate.

Towards the end of the process salt is added. This brings out the flavour, influences the texture, controls bacterial fermentation and ensures the curing qualities of the cheese. Salt at one time was very scarce and was subjected to a penal tax. If the cheese became tainted by feeding too many turnips a litte saltpetre was added.

The appearance of the cheese can be altered by the addition of a colouring matter, annato. This is prepared from seeds from a sub-tropical plant mainly cultivated in The West Indies, India and Brazil. It is added about 10–15 minutes before the renneting. Contrary to what many think it has no effect on the making process nor on the taste and quality of the cheese.It is only added to please the market demand.

Formerly cheese was a basic food in Scotland along with porridge and kale. Little did the people know that cheese was composed of a third fat, a third protein and third water. Nor did they know that 1 lb. of cheese contained the equivalent protein of 1½ lb. beef steak and the equivalent in energy of 2 lbs. of beef steak.

Because of its value to the diet and its scarcity to most people, cheese was only considered as being either good or bad, new or old, hard or soft.That was all that was understood about quality. This was perhaps a blessing. Having stressed the importance of starters for quality cheese, it is difficult to see how much good cheese could have been made when sour milk or sour whey was all that was used in the early days to promote the production of acidity in the milk for cheesemaking.

About 1545 Skene of Hallyards told how butter and cheese were made from either from cow's or ewe's milk depending on the demand and the locality.'Kys milk is best for butter and yows milk best for cheiss, for kys milk will give both mor butter and better butter than yows milk and yoys milk will give mor cheiss and better cheiss than kys milk. They use in Cunninghame to make cheiss of kys milk, but it is not good.'

It has been noted elsewhere that when there was a surplus of milk in a household it was made into butter and sold nearby. Timothy Pont, a minister who came from Dunnet in Caithness to Dunlop in 1604, wrote in his *Topographical Account of Cunninghame* in 1608 : This part of the country yields a great deal of excellent butter, but especially in the parishes of Stewarton and Dunlop.

Practically every farm had a cow or cows, all dual purpose. When this trade expanded and there was a surplus of skim milk it was made into cheese. Cheese could be said to be the byproduct of butter making. The skim milk would be kept for a number of days to accumulate sufficient quantity to make into cheese by a 'rule of thumb method' resulting in very poor quality cheese. The importance of starter and rennet would then be unknown.

As time moved on dairying became more specialised with cows being bred towards single purpose. The result that any extra milk produced was made into whole milk cheese. This was the main farm economy of all the dairy farms out of reach of the liquid milk market.

In the days when dairy herds were small the tasks of milking, cheese and buttermaking were left to the 'gudwives' and 'dochters' 'who were much more at home in fingering a cow's paps (teats) than the keyboard of a piano, but were not on any account any less better women, less lovable, or less thoroughly useful members of society.... In addition they were expected to rear a large family, feed the hens and be at everyone's beck and call. They worked from 'cockcrow till noon and from noon till dewy eve.' (Sturrock, 1886.)

Often the farmer's wife had divided loyalties. She depended on the income from eggs and butter for financing the housekeeping. The return from these commodities went directly into the household's purse while the return from the cheese went into the farm account. There was some incentive for the housewife who was usually responsible for the cheesemaking to remove as much cream for the butter as possible without too obvious injury to the quality of the cheese.

They had to be fit and fairly strong. Originally before the curd was cut by knives it was manually broken up. When it was ready for moulding it had to be 'thumped' into the chissets. (from cheese – vat.) The resultant 40–60 lb. cheese had to scalded and pressed and thereafter, turned for a number of days, all heavy work.

Their attitude to cleanliness, good observation and keen sense of smell were all essential to the quality of the end product on which the whole economy of the family depended. They were endeavouring to make cheese in badly ventilated and for the most part unclean hovels. The surrounding contaminated air soured the milk without the aid of 'starters'. There were no thermometers or acidameters just a keen sense of smell, a fine touch and experience. As butter was more easily made and sold at a better price there was an incentive to remove as much cream as possible without detracting from the quality of the cheese.

History relates that it was Barbara Gilmour, Hillside, Dunlop, who pioneered the process of making cheese from whole milk. It has often been repeated that she learned this technique if there was one, when she fled to Ireland to avoid religious persecution during the Revolution in 1688. There is every possibility this happened as far as Miss Gilmour was concerned. It is more likely that she saw for the first time, Cheshire cheese made there which was always made from whole milk. This is a more full bodied cheese with a more pleasing taste than the skim-milk cheese she had been used to.

Cheshire cheese is probably the oldest of English cheeses with an origin lost in the mists of time. It was mentioned in the Doomsday Book in the 11th century and the 12th century writers appreciated this cheese. From very early times there was a shipping trade between Ireland, Isle of Man and the South West of Scotland. As cheese was very tradeable considerable volumes were transported. By the 1730's large quantities of Cheshire cheese and butter were being bought from two Aberdeen merchants, Farquharson and Leslie, for the estate of Grant of Honymusk. (Fenton, 1976).

Furthermore, it is highly unlikely that all the cheese made in Ayrshire was made from skim-milk. As William Aiton said in 1811– 'None who could make good cheese of skim-milk could be ignorant that more cream that was left to be made into cheese, the richer and more palatable it would be....I am not inclined to believe that the practice of making sweet-milk cheese, whoever it may have been that introduced it, could be of Irish origin.'

The Rev Thomas Brisbane, in O.S.A. for Dunlop perpetuated the Gilmour story but he admitted to the Rev. Mathew Dickie 'he only hazarded the theory that she learned the art of making sweet milk cheese in Ireland and introduced it into Ayrshire.

'In the late 19th century cheesemaking in Ireland was only a minority activity. Whey from cheese manufacture was not regarded as suitable for calf rearing and the rearing of young cattle and pigs was an important farming enterprise and relied on skimmed milk and buttermilk from butter manufacture.' (Foley, J. 1993)

Sometime before before 1732 Barbara Gilmour married John Dunlop of Overhill whose burial stone stands against the south wall of the church tower in Dunlop. Her husband is not to be confused with John Dunlop of Dunlop, a prominent 'improving' landowner of Ayrshire cattle fame and whose wife was a friend of Robert Burns.

When this method of cheesemaking became popular in the district, 'a sturdy body of independent cheese merchants soon sprang in the Kirktoun helping the growth of the former hamlet into a village. They purchased the cheese from farmers and conveyed them into Glasgow by road.' under the parish name of Dunlop. (Rev. Bayne, 1935.) Thereafter, as dairying spread out from Ayrshire, this was the common type of cheese made. It was also called 'laid' cheese.

There were areas where Cheshire cheese was preferred to Dunlop. In the 1790's an Annandale landlord encouraged people from Cheshire to settle on his estates and naturally introduced the long established make of cheese. There was also a quantity of Cheshire cheese made around Castle Douglas.

THE KANER & THE BOWER

As the herds of dairy cows grew in size more labour was required, especially in Dumfries and Galloway, where the farms were larger. The management of the dairying enterprises was devolved to professional dairymen. Ingenious systems of payment on results were evolved to encourage these men to become proficient in the precise process of cheesemaking. They were called Kaning and Bowing systems. If the rent was paid in cheese they were Kaners, if paid in cash they were Bowers. Confusingly the term Bower was later used for both systems.

Under these systems the farmer rented his cows annually to a dairyman and provided him with housing, the bulky homegrown food for the cows and certain quantities of concentrates per cow. The extra cheese made by the kaner or excess milk produced by the bower above the agreed rents was the profit of the respective parties.

In the Scottish National Dictionary kane is defined as: 'A payment in kind, especially of poultry, made by a tenant of land as part of his rent. It was frequently as kane – butter, – capons, – coal, – eggs, – fowls, –hens, – meal, – wedders, – labour.

In Burns' *"Twa Dogs,"* (1786).

Our laird gets his racked rents,
His coal, his kane and a' his stents.

James Biggar (1876) says: 'The kaner pays his rent on a fixed weight of cheese. In such cases the farmer has the power of sale and so by a species of hypothec secures his rent.' The weight of cheese which constituted the kane was fixed annually by mutual agreement between the farmer and the contracting dairyman.

Robert Raphael would formerly be described as a 'Kaner' because he paid a rent in cheese to manage the dairy herd at Ingleston of Borgue in Kirkcudbrightshire. Later, all those who did this were all called 'Bowers' irrespective of the terms of their contract. The following annual contract of 1922 between A & A Gray and Robert Raphael was fairly typical of the time.

It is **CONTRACTED, AGREED**and **ENDED**, between the Parties following, namely **ADAM GRAY**, Senior and **ADAM GRAY**, junior, both Farmers in Ingleston of Borgue, in the parish of Borgue and Stewartry of Kirkcudbright **THE FIRST PART**, (hereinafter called First Parties) and **ROBERT RAPHAEL**, dairyman, Ingleston of Borgue, **THE SECOND . PARTY.** That is to say the Parties have agreed as follows: **FIRST**. The First Parties agree that the said Robert Raphael shall have from them the Bowing of **EIGHTY COWS AND QUEYS** to be kept on the said Farm of Ingleston for one year from Twenty eighth day of November Nineteen hundred and twenty two to the Twenty eighth day of November Nineteen hundred and twenty three. **SECOND**. In respect of the said Bowing the said Robert Raphael binds and obliges himself to deliver to the First Parties and the survivor of them and their heirs **NINETEEN AND A HALF STONES** of Marketable Cheese of Twenty four pounds per stone for each Cow and **SIXTEEN STONES** of Marketable Cheese of the said weight for each Quey. The cheese shall be of first class quality fully matured and be delivered by the said Robert Raphael to the said First Parties or any person the latter may authorise out of the first cheese produced when ripe for the market. It is here specially agreed that the said First Parties or any person they shall appoint, shall have access to the Cheese Room at all times and no cheese shall be removed from the Cheese Room nor Swine from the premises by the said Robert Raphael without consent of the First Parties. The whole Cheese manufactured under this Bowing shall remain and shall be the exclusive property of the First Parties until the said Robert Raphael shall have fulfilled the whole obligations incumbent upon him under this Contract, but in so far as the said Robert Raphael may have or claim any property therein he hereby and assigns and makes over to the First Parties and their heirs the whole Cheese the produce of the said Cows and Queys and he also assigns... the Swine fed in connection with the said Dairy with power to the said First Parties and their heirs to take possession of and sell the same and uplift the price thereof and to pay themselves the value of the Cheese herein before undertaken to be delivered and without any process of the Law necessary for that purpose, it being sufficient that a demand for the delivery of the Cheese has been made without being complied with by the said Robert Raphael. **THIRD**. The cow and queys to have the following pasture the following fields, videlicet:- **BARNPARK, SOUTH END OF HOUSECROFT, WESTSIDE OF NORTH DRUM, FLICKIT CRAIGS, MEADOWFIELD, SOUTH CUBBOCKS** and **WEE DAM PARK**. (about 1 $^{1}/_{2}$ acres per cow.) **FOURTH**. the Cows and Queys to have for feeding Ten Imperial Acres of Swedish Turnips for the Winter and Spring use, (these were shawn by dairy and carted by farm staff) and Five Imperials Acres of Soft or Yellow Turnips for the Backend (these were carted by the dairy) and Eight hundred Stones of Bean Meal and Eight Hundred Stones of Bruised Oats. The whole Eighty Cows and Queys under this Bowing shall be fed off the said Turnips and Bean Meal and Oats.The Bower shall also feed off the said Turnips and Bean Meal and Oats two stock Bulls to be used for the Cows and Queys under this Bowing and which if it be thought necessary shall be kept in the house. The Second Party shall be bound to feed in the Wee Byre, next stable, any spare Cows or Queys kept for replacing Cows or Queys taken from the number included in this Bowing and in respect of his so doing the First parties shall be bound to supply for feeding said Cows and Queys the following quantities of feeding per head, videlicet:- Five carts of Turnips, Ten Stones Bean Meal, Ten Stones Oats. The Second Party is to receive Ten Stones of meal for his own and family use. **FIFTH**. The Bower shall have the usual allowance of straw for Winter and Spring and Meadow Hay from Tenth of April next. **SIXTH**. The Bower to have the use of the implements which belong to the First Parties and are at present in use in the Dairy. **SEVENTH**. The said reserve to themselves the privilege to keep a Mare and Foal also other horse on all or any of the Fields above mentioned and poultry, the latter to go at large, also his sheep to run on all or any of the fields from Martinmas to First March. **EIGHTH**. The Bower to supply and rear in a good and sufficient manner whatever calves the First Parties may desire to the number of Twenty and to keep the same until the first week in June, which said calves shall be delivered to the First Parties and for each of the said Calves so supplied the Bower shall be paid by the Setters the sum of Three Pounds. These calves to run on any of the above fields from Martinmas to the First week in February. **NINTH**. The Bower not to allow any of his stock to go at large but to be shut up in a house appointed them. The First Party to be allowed all the Dung made by the stock included in this Bowing but to give as much manure as will plant Eight Bushels of Potatoes for the Bower, the Bower supplying his own seed potatoes. **TENTH**. The Bower to keep the Dwelling-house, Dairy House and all Dairy Utensils in a clean and proper manner and in good repair and to leave them so; likewise to keep the Byres, Piggeries and all the Closes clean and to leave the implements and the houses in unexceptional repair and to cut the weeds in the pasture fields at least twice in the year, the first during the first week in June and the second time not later than the second week in August. The Bower shall also whitewash all the Byres and Piggeries once a year or oftener as may be required by the First Parties. The Bower binds and obliges himself that he and his family or servants shall gather all the eggs which shall be seen in, or about the premises occupied by him and give the same to the First Parties. **ELEVENTH**. The Bower binds and obliges himself that he and his familt or servants shall gather all the eggs which shall be seen in, or about the premises occupied bt him and give the same to the First Parties. **TWELTH**. The Bower to get a House and Garden and to have the use of a Horse and Cart, which the First Parties shall supply to do all the usual carting connected with the Dairy, except the carting of the Cheese, Bean Meal, Oats and Winter Turnips which the First Parties shall cart. (Carting the Swede turnips for the winter involved pitting 400 cartloads in the farmyard and covering them with straw to prevent frost damage) The Bower shall, however, himself cart the soft or yellow turnips for the Backend and also shall shaw all the Winter Turnips. **THIRTEENTH**. The Bower binds and obliges himself not to allow any of his family or servants to go into any of the premises not occupied by him and to leave the Stock and Houses on the Twenty eighth day of November, Nineteen hundred and twenty three without warning of removal. And the Bower shall be bound and hereby binds himself to keep a record of all Cows and Queys bulled prior to his waygoing and the dates of said bulling and to deliver said record to the First Parties not later than the Twentieth day of November Nineteenth hundred and twenty three. **FOURTEENTH**. The First Parties to have liberty to cut and finish any drains they may think fit to make in any of the said foresaid fields and to enter and go through the same for all farm purposes free of damages. **FIFTEENTH**. The Bower to give Security that the foresaid conditions shall be adhered to. **SIXTEENTH**. The Bower to supply the First Parties whatever new milk they may require during the year for which the Bower shall be paid at the rate of One Pound of Cheese for each Gallon of Milk. The Bower also to supply the First Parties and their work people with no less than the following quantities of butter, buttermilk and skim milk and at the prices, videlicet.– One Pound of Butter per week for each of the Cotmen at Ingleston and Five Pounds of Butter per week to said Adam Gray, Senior, at the price of **ONE**

SHILLING AND SIXPENCE PER POUND; also to supply the Cotmen at Ingleston with Two Quarts or One Half Gallon Skim Milk at the price of One penny per one half gallon and what Buttermilk they required at the price of One penny per gallon: The said Adam Gray also to be supplied with Skim and Buttermilk at the prices before stated for the supply to Cotmen. **SEVENTEENTH**. The First Parties reserve the right to themselves and family and others having their authority to go through the whole farm and Dairyhouses at their pleasure. **IN WITNESS WHEREOF** these presents typewritten on this and three preceding pages are subscribed by the said Adam Gray, Senior and Adam Gray, Junior and Robert Raphael, at Ingleston aforesaid, on the twenty eighth day of July, Nineteen hundred and twenty two, before these witnesses, Annie Jane Lyburn, Cook and Alexander Kirkpatrick, Farmhand, both at Ingleston foresaid.

This type of contract continued at Ingleston until 1936 when it was changed to a very simple form based on a cash payment.

BOWING.

The term Bowing originated from Steelbow which is defined in the *Scottish National Dictionary* (1976) as a condition of land-tenancy whereby a landlord provided a tenant with stock, growing grain, straw and implements under contract that the equivalent in quality and quantity should be returned at the end of the lease. Steelbow tenure was very prevalent in Scotland in the 14th and 15th centuries and continued down to recent times in some places.

Bowing, (1825), 'To tak a farm in a Bowin', i.e. to take a lease of a farm in grass, with livestock; this still remaining the property of the land-holder or person who lets it.

This was adopted widely in Dumfriesshire and Galloway by young immigrant Ayrshire farmers who had not yet found places of their own. These were followed by local farm workers becoming dairymen who found this a ladder to success. This continued into recent times where many of Galloway's most progressive farmers were at one time dairymen.

In the Bowing system the farmer was paid cash for the rent. The greater the yield from the cows, the greater was the profit for the bower. In the days before grassland improvement and the use of artificial fertilsers, the yields of herds was related to the quality of the land which was reflected in the bower's rent. James Biggar, (1876) said that the highest rents in Kirkcudbright and Wigtownshire were obtained on the good strong land of the Rhins of Galloway between Stranraer and the Mull of Galloway.

The earliest contract to hand was one drawn up in 1854 between John Campbell, Slagnaw, Castle Douglas and Charles Hastings, Dairyman. The format was similar to the one already noted except the reference to the payment of rent and does not contain so much detail.

'The Rent is to be seven pounds Sterling per cow when cheese is at eight shillings per stone and to rise and fall with the market tenpence Sterling for every penny above or below the said Eight shillings. Three queys in calf for the first time to be held as equal to two Cows.'

'The Rent to be paid as follows: The said Charles Hastings is to pay the said John Campbell the sum of Forty pounds Sterling, Rent upon the day of entry, viz. the twenty second of November, One thousand eight hundred and fifty four and upon the sale of any portion of the cheese or swine or other dairy produce, the whole price thereof is to be paid over to the said John Campbell the day after the said sale until the whole amount due be paid and that without prejudice to all rights of hypothec to which the said John Campbell is and may be entitled.'

'It is hereby specially agreed that should the said Charles Hastings fail to hand over the price of any of the cheese, swine or dairy produce aforesaid when sold as above stipulated to the said John Campbell there being any of the rent remaining unpaid then the said John Campbell is hereby empowered to take possession of all the said Cows, Dairy utensils, etc. from the said Charles Hastings and to make use of the same for his own behalf during the remaining portion of the term of this Agreement and to prevent the removal of any of the Produce of the said Dairy or the Swine, reserving all his title to any claims against the said Charles Hastings, however these claims may arise.'

'It is further hereby specially Agreed that the said John Campbell shall be entitled to the whole of the Dairy produce as his own property until the Rent herein stipulated be paid. That none of the said produce is to leave the farm of Slagnaw without the consent of the said John Campbell and any sale thereof is to be at the sight and mutual agreement of both parties.'

If there were any claims or disputes they were to be referred to arbitration procedures.

On this farm the rent per cow, which was £7 in 1854–55 rose to £12.15s. in 1880 and dropped to £11 in 1897–1898. This flexible payment system was continued until 1948.

Before there was electricity and milking machines, the farmers with large herds usually undertook to provide a number of milkers and pay them. In 1875 the current wage was 2s. 6d. per week.

Ian Mitchell was the West of Scotland Agricultural Adviser for Kirkcudbrightshire for a number of years after the Second World War. In the Journal of Scottish Agriculture in the 1952 Spring issue he wrote an interesting article on the various methods by which dairymen were paid in that area.

Until the 1939–45 War a dairyman could work under different systems and many did. For example, one on leaving school in 1886 worked as a byre boy, doing all the chores that no one else wanted to do. Having learnt to work hard he got his first 'place' as a single dairyman in 1891, where he received £16 plus board for a half-year to assist in looking after 45 cows. In 1893–4 this became £20 plus for 70 cows. In 1895 he contracted at £100 plus perquisites to be in charge of 70 cows. From 1914-1939 he took a Bowing contract then retired.

After the war when the liquid milk market expanded many farmers gave up cheesemaking and the payment systems changed. One of the commonest was to engage a dairyman to do all the work connected with the cows, byres and dairy premises at a fixed rate per cow, in 1952 about £10–13 per annum. Incentive payments were given to encourage high milk production. In some cases a bonus of d. to 1d. per gallon of milk sold was given and in others the bonus is applied over a certain gallonage per cow, for instance 2d. per gallon over 500 gallons per annum. These bonus payments were correlated with rates per cow, a relative rate being associated with a high bonus and vice versa. Clean milk production was also rewarded by a bonus. Payment for milk consumed by heifer calves was made at agreed rates such as 5–10s. a calf provided the animal at 12 weeks was healthy and thriving.

In 1944 the 'Sixth' system was introduced. A dairyman under annual contract had to provide all the labour to manage a liquid milk producing dairy. In return he received one-sixth of the income derived from milk, graded bull calves and an agreed sum for heifer calves reared to 12 weeks. The dairyman under this system handled the kale and roots required for the cows until usually 28th November. When feedingstuffs became more expensive the fractions were reduced to a seventh or eighth.

Another system which was used on some farms producing mainly winter milk was the 'Quarter' system. This was similar to the 'Sixth' system the main difference being that the dairyman received a quarter of the proceeds from milk sales and bull calves but he had to pay a quarter of the cost of concentrates, including market valued homegrown oats. He also had to maintain all the dairy equipment and pay for electricity and fuel.

As indicated earlier, with the advent of silage making and the changes in housing and milking of dairy cows there are few 'systems' remaining, other than cash wage with some bonuses and traditional perquisites.

Fig. 75 Robert Maxwell the last traditional farm cheesemaker operating a typical cheese press. c.1969

CHAPTER 18

FARM CHEESEMAKING

CHEESEMAKING at INGLESTON of BORGUE

In 1843 an Adam Gray (1799–1843) died at Barstibly, Kirkcudbright. He had moved from Carrick in Ayrshire sometime after 1802. This date is pinpointed because there is at Ingleston a medal awarded by the Highland and Agricultural Society to an Adam Gray for winning a ploughing match in Carrick. That year his son Adam II (1821–1894) moved to Ingleston of Borgue to take up dairy farming. Formerly, Galloway cattle were bred and reared and driven into England, later retained and sold locally as stores.

Ingleston farm was on St Mary's Isle Estate, owned by Captain John Hope. In 1897 it was bought by James Brown along with the farms Muncraig, Chapelton, Rattra, Barlocco, Corseyard to constitute Knoxbrex Estate.

In the North British Agriculturist, 5th June 1885 there appeared a letter,

Sir – In your issue of May 15th in a communication entitled 'Transactions of the Highland Society' you make some extracts from a paper on Scottish cheesemaking by John McMaster, Culhorn, Stranraer. These extracts as they appear in your paper are calculated to convey a wrong impression in so far as they relate to the place at which the cheese which took highest premium at Edinburgh Highland and Agricultural Show in 1848 was manufactured. As a matter of fact James McAdam came as dairyman to Ingleston of Borgue, Kirkcudbright, in 1847, being the only dairy of Ayrshire cows either in the parishes of Borgue, Twynholm or Girthon. The prize cheese was made in Kirkcudbrightshire not Wigtownshire and was generally believed at the time to have been the first occasion on which Ayrshire cheesemakers had suffered defeat. James McAdam was also in the prize list with his Ingleston of Borgue cheese at the Glasgow Highland and Agricultural Society Show in 1850. These successes, as may be imagined created a sensation among Ayrshire cheesemakers, but to their credit be it spoken they profited by the lesson and they sent a deputation from Ayrshire Society to study the Cheddar system in Somerset. (1854) This was followed by Mrs Robert McAdam setting out from Wigtownshire for a like purpose and to this rivalry between Ayrshire and Galloway may be ascribed the great advance of cheese manufacture in the latter district.

Trusting you may find space for my letter.

I am &c. Adam Gray, (III) Senior. (1852–1935.)

This letter was a reaction to an article on Scottish cheesemaking by John McMaster, Culhorn, Stranraer, which is printed in the 1885 Transactions of the Highland and Agricultural Society of Scotland. In it he states that James McAdam had adopted the Cheshire system while at Balterson near Newton Stewart, Wigtownshire. It had been introduced by Mr Caird in 1844 had sent his dairyman Robert McAdam into England for instructions on the new method. When James, his brother, showed the 'imitation Cheshire' cheese (sometimes called 'wrought cheese') at the Dumfries Highland and Agricultural Society Show in 1845 'the judges withheld a premium, which they thought his sample deserved, on the supposition that such ripe cheese could only be of the previous year's make.' In 1848 he won the championship.

A further discussion on the McAdam family's contribution to Scottish cheesemaking comes later. They were succeeded by Andrew Veitch in 1860's and John Plunkett in the 1870's.

To date there is no information about dairymen at Ingleston before 1910 other than that David Gibson made cheese from 1899–1909, thereafter he rented the farm of Spittal, near Creetown in Kirkcudbrightshire. He had two mischievous younger sons. Robert and Richard, probably aided and abetted by their boss's son Adam (IV), Junior. (1895–1971) They all attended Borgue Academy. Because of some misdeeds Mr Munro, the headmaster, would not allow them to take part in the annual concert and prize giving. Thereupon Richard, who was the smallest climbed up a tree in the churchyard and collected a full bonnet of crow eggs and hid behind the school dyke. When Mr Munro, dressed in his morning coat walked down the street to the concert they pelted him with the eggs.

Richard became a farmer in his own right in the south of England. When I was showing Knockbrex Belted Galloways at the Oxford Royal Show in 1951 Richard stopped me in the cattle lines he asked me if I knew an Adam Gray. It was then a family secret came to light!

David, Junior along with John Gordon the joiner's son from Chapelton Row, Borgue, emigrated to America in 1910. David became manager of the world renowned Ayrshire dairy herd at Strathglass farm, New York. It was brought to eminence by the outstanding breeding ability of a bull Lyonston Douglas. David practised in-breeding with success unlike many of his contemporaries. His only son, David, became secretary of the American Ayrshire Cattle Society.

Robert, after the First World War joined David in America, becoming the manager of a large Guernsey herd also in New York State. Robert came back to Creetown to retire but David and his wife Agnes also from Borgue remained in America. He told me on a visit there he always yearned for Scotland because he could never trust the Americans like the Scots.

John Gordon became a successful businessman in New York.

From 1910–1960 a number of cheese records have been kept. The dairying year ran from Martinmas to Martinmas (28th November) the traditional day dairymen flitted. Whereas all other farmworkers moved from a farm on the 28th May.

In the byre at Ingleston there were 76 stalls. On average the herd comprised of 61 cows and 15 queys. (heifers). The 25% replacement rate has nor altered much in the past ninety years.

Note: One gallon of milk is required to make one pound of cheese. Therefore, 100 gallons of average quality will make 100 lbs. of cheese. If the milk is of a higher quality i.e. containing more butterfat and protein, the 100 gallons of milk might yield as much as 105 lbs. of cheese. On the other hand if it is of a poorer quality it may yield 95 lbs. of cheese. This is an important factor in the profitability of cheesemaking be it done on the farm or in a creamery.

Fodder cheese, which is cheese made before cows went out to grass in the springtime yielded better than that which was made from spring grass, as did cheese made from milk produced off grass in the autumn. The prices varied from month to month according to market demand and also varied for red or white cheese. The prices quoted are average for the cheesemaking season. If prices were poor in the autumn the cheese was held over in the cheese loft till January or February, where the temperature was controlled by heating via steam pipes. When that happened the final settlement for the year was made on the 28th May

In 1910 the total weight of the season's cheesemake was 16tons 6cwt. 1qr. 25lbs. The rent to be paid by John Milroy was 15tons 7cwt. 0qr. 17lbs. The difference 1ton 5cwt. 1qr. 17lbs. at 56s. per cwt. was his profit. In the interests of simplicity the weights have been rounded into hundred-weights. One hundredweight being approximately 50 kilos.

JOHN MILROY 1910–1916.

YEAR	MAKE cwts.	RENT cwts.	EXCESS cwts.	PRICE	PROFIT
1910	332	307	25	56s.	£70
1911	305	310	-5	65s.4d.	-£19 12s.
1912	330	308	22	66s.6d.	£73 3s.
1913	336	310	26	66s.	£86 18s.
1914	316	310	6	70s.	£21
1915	313	303	10	88s.	£44
1916	336	308	28	104s.	£145 12s.

John received income for milk used elsewhere e.g. in 1912 –

Butter supplied to farmhouse	£10 8s.
Butter supplied to farmstaff	£10 0s.
Milk supplied to farmstaff	£5 6s. 2d.
Skim milk to to farmstaff	3s.11d.
Milk for quey calves	£50 0s. 0d.
Total	£75 18s.0d.

In later years his son James was awarded an M.B.E. for services to cheesemaking while at Chapelton dairy, Borgue, working for Captain John M. Gilmour.

JOHN HOGG 1917–1920

YEAR	MAKE cwts.	RENT cwts.	EXCESS cwts.	PRICE	PROFIT
1917	312	310	1	145s.	£7 5s.
1918	323	311	12	171s.	£102.12s.
1919	NO RECORD				

It would appear that John Hogg was not a successful cheesemaker at Ingleston and reflects what was said by an old cheesemaker – "Want of knowledge in or inattention to this particular point, i.e. adding starter, has caused many bad 'kanes' of cheese and even by good makers – nothing being more frequent than the complaint that while they could make good cheese on one farm they could not do it on another."

However, when he left Ingleston he went to Lennox Plunton where he was more successful and thereafter farmed a small farm at Brigend of Kildarroch near Borgue.

When John Hogg was engaged as dairyman he was supplied with 9 large chissets, 5 small chissets, 7 milking pails, 4 carrying milk cans, and 3 milk plates. At that time Adam Gray enquired from a friend on his suitability. He was told that he had a big family that would be suitable for the milking, 'I don't know how good they will be but there is enough of them that they could sook the coo's.'

His brothers, Alex and Sam were also cheesemakers in Borgue. Alex with the assistance of his wife and his daughters, Kate, Nell, Nettie, Ruby and Winnie were at Upper Senwick, Borgue. When James Williamson moved from Upper Senwick to Alex Hogg took over the tenancy. Sam made cheese at the Ross, Borgue and later farmed Kirkland, Gelston, near Castle Douglas. Another brother Duncan made cheese at Barstibly for a time before farming Midtown which is also near Castle Douglas.

ROBERT RAPHAEL 1920–29

YEAR	MAKE cwts.	RENT cwts.	EXCESS cwts.	PRICE	PROFIT
1920	374	311	63	162	£510 6s.
1921	371	311	61	168	£512 8s.
1922	380	308	73	100s.4d.	£366.4s.4d.
1923	410	320	90	115s.10d.	£516 5s.
1924	405	318	87	98s.	£426 6s.
1925	404	319	85	108s.6d.	£461.2s.6d.
1926	407	321	86	86s.	£369.16s.
1927	411	322	89	100s.4d.	£446.9s.8d.
1928	396	320	76	107s.10d.	£409.15s.4d.
1929	380	321	59	89s.	£262.11s.

Over this period Robert Raphael received about £50–54 annually for 'extras' plus a plentiful supply of free whey for pig feeding.

From the increased weight of excess cheese produced above the rent agreement gives a good indication how Robert Raphael was a much more successful cheesemaker compared with John Hogg. This was borne out by the many successes he had at cheese shows at Dumfries and

Kirkcudbright. As mentioned earlier, the Raphael family accumulated sufficient capital to take over Carco Mains farm in Dumfriesshire. Minimal income tax would be a help.

WILLIAM FERGUSON 1929–36.

William Ferguson came to Ingleston from Muirside, Dumfriesshire. The rent for cheesemaking was raised to 21 stones per cow and 17 stone per heifer. The increase in rent was possibly because the previous dairyman was able to rent a farm after making cheese at Ingleston for only ten years! This is the first time in the contracts that queys are referred to as heifers. The remainder of the contract was similar to that for Robert Raphael.

YEAR	MAKE	RENT	EXCESS	PRICE	PROFIT
	cwts.	cwts.	cwts.		
1930	336	332	4	77s.	£15 8s.
1931	350	340	10	70s.	£35
1932	365	334	21	70s.4d.	£73 8s.
1933	357	345	12	62s.	£37 4s.
1934	374	353	21	90s.	£94 10s.
1935	370	354	16	87s.	£69 12s.

As the figures show William Ferguson did not make much money from cheesemaking. His income unlike previous cheesemakers was augmented by sales of liquid milk to Kirkcudbright Creamery owned by the Stewartry Dairy Association. This began in April 1930 when 1475 gallons were sold for 9½d. less ½d. for haulage. In October of the same year 66 gallons were sold for 10d. and in November 1657 gallons for 10½d. less ½d. for haulage. This gallonage was computed into a cheese weight for the sake of the cheese rent amounted to £126 7s. 8d.

In the dairy records for the Ferguson era any milk produced between December and February inclusive was made into cheese and this totally belonged him. It is only to be assumed that this happened previously, though not recorded.

In 1933 the dairyman's contract was amended so that the farmer reserved the right to sell milk or make cheese throughout the season. This was an insurance against future bad makes and also gave an option to sell to the liquid market if prices were favourable.

In 1934 the Scottish Milk Marketing Board gave 1d. per lb. for making cheese. This was the beginning of giving cheesemaking allowances for farm house cheesemaking. These allowances were given for the actual cost such as bandages, rennet, salt, cheese cloths, bandages and extra coal.

Maybe William Ferguson was not a very good cheesemaker but he had no problem in getting assistants to manage the dairy and to supply hand milkers. A milking machine was not installed until June 1938. He had six boys and six girls, William, Andrew, James, Alexander, Tom, Robert, George, Ian, Margaret, Nan, Jenny, Jessie, Dorothy, Edith, Betty and Sheila. The older members of the family brought up and taught the younger ones!

It was alleged that one night while his wife was attending a W.R.I. meeting on his baby sitting duties he found all the children asleep except one. Much to his consternation the child persisted in crying, because he was a strict disciplinarian, adopting the philosophy that provided the child was alright 'top and bottom', if it girned it was given something to girn about. When Mrs Ferguson arrived home he told her about this child. On 'looking in ' on the family she discovered that the child was Jim Glover, the ploughman's son.

When William Ferguson left Ingleston in 1936 he was followed by William McCreadie from Killumpha, Port Logan, Wigtownshire. The kaning system ceased and the new contracts were based on cash and in a simpler from.

Minute of Agreement
between
Adam Gray, Farmer, Ingleston,
in the parish of Borgue and Stewartry of Kirkcudbright,
herein after referred to as the First Party.
and
William McCreadie, Killumpha, Port Logan, Wigtownshire,
herein after referred to as the Second Party.

(FIRST)The Second Party has agreed to manage Ingleston Dairy in the Parish of Borgue for the First Party and to keep all the dairy premises clean and to do all the work connected with the stock indoors, to rear heifer calves and to make first class cheese during the season for a period of one year from Martinmas, twenty eighth November, nineteen hundred and thirty six to Martinmas twenty eighth nineteen hundred and thirty seven, for the total sum of two hundred and fifty pounds to be paid by the First Party.

(SECOND)The First Party undertakes to provide the Second Party during the year with light, coal, milk, and cheese for his use only, two tons of potatoes and four stones of meal.

(THIRD)The First Party agrees to pay in full the National Health and Unemployment Insurance Contributions payable on behalf the Second Party only, it being declared that the First Party does not undertake to make any contribution in respect of National Health and Unemployment Insurance in respect of persons employed by the Second Party in connection with the working of the dairy.

(FOURTH)The First Party undertake to pay the Second Party two shillings and sixpence for each calf reared and brought to grass.

(FIFTH)The First Party allow the Second Party all whey produced in the dairy and the use of the piggeries to breed and rear pigs for his own use.

(SIXTH)The First Party agrees that if and when required by him he will employ one lad for summer work on the farm of Ingleston at the rate of five shillings per day: IN WITNESS WHEREOF these presents typewritten on this and the preceding page are subscribed by us the parties hereto at Stranraer on the twenty second July nineteen hundred and thirty six before these witnesses, James Henderson, Road Foreman, Eighteen Queen Street Stranraer and William T. Allan, Cheese Merchant, Barloan, Stranraer.

Wages						
	1937	£280	1938	£300	1939	£320
	1940	£400	1941	£420	1942	£504
	1943	£574	1944	£590	1945	£664
	1946	£690				

The cheese was made by William McCreadie's daughter, Marion, who was excellent as proved by the many prizes she won at the cheese shows.

The cheesemaking season was traditionally from 1st March until the 30th September, later it did not begin until 1st April. As dairy and grassland management improved more milk was produced in May and June than the cheese vat could hold. This surplus milk was sent in 10 gallon cans to the Scottish Milk Marketing Board.

Dairying was revolutionised with the advent of electricity into Borgue in 1936 and the installation of the milking machine in 1938. This changed everyone's attitude to living and working.

In 1946 the McCreadie family, like some of their predecessors left Ingleston to rent a farm. They went to Culcaigrie, Twynholm, Kirkcudbrightshire.

DONALD McCLYMONT 1946–1954

When William McCreadie left Ingleston in 1954 it was more difficult to engage a farm cheesemaker. As the older cheesemakers retired, few young men and women wanted to undertake the long hours associated with cheesemaking, some five hours outside normal milking times. The McClymont family was an exception. Donald with his six sons, Tom, Andrew, Donald, Billy, Stewart, and Jim went to Ingleston in November 1946. Prior to that, the eldest son Tom attended a cheesemaking course at Auchencruive and became a proficient cheesemaker.

The arrangements for their employment were similar to that for the McCreadie family. Over this period the increase in wages was not in line with the increased output. This was partly compensated by an increase in the number of pigs and hens that the dairyman was allowed to keep.

When the McClymont family left Ingleston, Donald and Donald Junior went to a liquid milk producing dairy at Borgue House, Tom moved to a cheesemaking farm at Milton near Kirkcudbright and the other sons found jobs on farms elsewhere.

JAMES BATEMAN 1954–55

James Bateman had been a cheesemaker but while his family were growing up had been employed in liquid milk producing dairies. He came to Ingleston with two sons. Unfortunately, his sons who were very proficient became disenchanted with cheesemaking as was the wont of many young people because of the long hours involved and the family left after one season. James Bateman was employed on the 'sixth system' which proved expensive.

THE SNEDDON FAMILY 1955–

When Jim Sneddon a retired policeman from Liverpool heard that there was vacancy at Ingleston for a dairyman, he approached Adam Gray IV one Sunday morning at Borgue church and expressed the opinion that his younger brother David, who was in Norfolk, would be interested in applying for the position. Whereupon Adam Gray replied 'Tell David to be at Ingleston on 28th November and I will engage him then' Such was the confidence between the two men, that this came to pass.

David's grandfather left the Isle of Skye at the end of the 19th century. According to his family it was either because he was suspected of sheep stealing or as a result of a runaway marriage. He somehow arrived in Borgue. He was employed by Adam Gray III at Muncraig where he brought up a family and died.

Prior to the demise of his father, the eldest son John, when he became married, worked at Culgruff and at later High Borgue before returning to Muncraig. There he stayed for thirty years and also brought up a large family.

When James Brown, the landlord of Knockbrex estate gave Adam Gray III notice to quit Muncraig farm because he wanted a resident tenant, John Sneddon rented the nearby farm of Barlocco. Because the farm could not sustain all the sons David worked at Carleton and Barmagachan before moving to England where he married and had a family of six sons and three daughters – Tom, John, Bob, Douglas, Gerald, Ken, Edna, Brenda and Bess.

Like Tom McClymont, David attended the course for cheesemakers at Auchencruive. Unfortunately he was not so successful at it as Tom. He made cheese until his retiral in 1960. Tom and John Sneddon who were assisting him were not interested in continuing, thus ended an era of cheesemaking at Ingleston from 1843–1960.

Tom and John assumed the management of the dairy at Ingleston on the retiral of their father. This coincided with the most radical changes in dairy farming to date. The pigs were sold and the steading was converted into the present day system with milking parlour, cow cubicles, and self-feeding silage. The dairy herd was expanded to 200 cows but was cut back to 180 on the introduction of quotas.

Tom and John are unique in both being bachelors and rarely go on holiday. John enjoys curling in the winter time and used to referee football matches during the summer. Tom on the other hand has only gone away on holiday for two weeks in thirty five years. His relaxation is going to a few shows and sales and usually he is participating. He used to take an active part in dart competitions. It has been said that if he had played in modern times he would have made more money at it than milking cows.

CHEDDAR CHEESE

As noted James McAdam's achievement in beating theAyrshire cheesemakers at Kilmarnock cheese show in 1848 motivated the Ayrshire Agricultural Association to send a deputation of agriculturists to study cheesemaking in Somerset, Wiltshire and Gloucestershire in 1854. Those deputed were Messrs. James Drennan, Holmston, Ayr and David Cunninghame, Chapelton, Ardrossan, – 'to visit and inspect various of the best dairy districts in England and afterwards to report to the Association which of the English modes in their opinion was the best adapted for introduction into this county, granting of course, if a better method could be found than the old Ayrshire or 'Dunlop'.

The deputation thought the Cheddar system in Somerset was the best. The decision would not be too difficult because the cheese made in Wiltshire and Gloucester was not 'full milk cheese'. (Greenshields, 1859) Acting on the recommendation of the deputation they asked the most renowned cheesemaker there, John Harding and his wife to come to Scotland where they gave public demonstrations on Cheddar cheesemaking on seven or eight farms in Ayrshire and Wigtownshire. Their audiences had difficulty in understanding their dialect but understood what they were doing.

In 1859 Joseph Harding published his 'Practical Aspects of Cheesemaking' in the *Ayrshire Advertiser*. There was actually a dairymaid, so far unamed from Somerset who made Cheddar cheese near Castle Douglas before the Cheddar system was adopted. Nevertheless, a number of other instructors came north to Ayrshire and a number of farmers, their wives and dairymen went to Somerset to gain and spread knowledge of a method of making cheese.

In 1855 Robert McAdam, who was the cheesemaker at the 100 cow unit at Baldoon dispatched his wife to visit Joseph Harding in Somerset. On her return the McAdam brothers, Robert, James and William from Barmagachan, Borgue, Kirkcudbrightshire, all successful at cheese shows gave a great lead to the spread of the Cheddar system in Scotland. Robert emigrated to America, more about that later. James moved eventually from Ingleston of Borgue to Craigraploch and William in 1866 took over the tenancy of Whitepark, near Castle Douglas, where a great grandson Robert, still farms.

Encouraged by the results of the McAdams, in 1862 John McMaster from Culhorn, made a tour of the cheesemaking farms in Somerset and 'found fine dairies few; irregular and poor much more numerous'....and he introduced to Wigtownshire the steam-heating of water in double-walled cheese vats – thus making uneccessary the crude method of adding hot whey to heat the milk.' He kept a record of his study tour regarding the construction of dairies and cheeserooms.

In acknowledgement of the benefit the landlords and farmers had gained from his teachings he was given a presentation in 1868. He was supported by other well known families of the day – McLelland, McCulloch, Garner, Hannay, Harcomb, Sawer, Baird, Hastings and Smith.

They must have had a measure of success because in 1885 John McMaster was wont to say that 'In 1869 a challenge for £200 aside, sent by the Galloway to the Somerset makers was declined. The general opinion among the dealers most conversant by both was that one or two of the best prizes would have gone to Somerset but the greater number to Galloway.' This rivalry continued for many years. In 1913, 'and many were the rejoicings we heard at the news just come to hand that the Scottish cheesemakers had carried off the bulk of the prizes at the London Dairy Show.'

In later days the well known farm cheesemakers were, the already mentioned Messrs Hoggs, Milroy, Raphael, Milroy, plus Cruickshanks, Hastings, Hyslop, McHarg, McMinn, Deans, Donley, McCarlie, Morrison and Robert Maxwell who was the last of the farmhouse cheddar cheesemakers in Scotland.

Robert Maxwell retired in 1973 from making cheese for 34 years, at the Ross farm, Borgue, which is still farmed by J. Brian Finlay. Robert Maxwell had an outstanding career winning Farmhouse Cheesemaking Competitions at the London Dairy Show, Royal Show, Royal Highland Show and many local shows. His proudest achievement was winning The Company of Scottish Cheesemakers farmhouse cheese grading trophy for six times.

He has now retired and lives in Kirkcudbright where he makes first class cheese in a large biscuit tin for himself, giving any surplus to his friends, or to his seven sons and three daughters.

It has been said of those professional farmhouse cheesemakers that they 'took as much pride in their production as a painter in his picture or

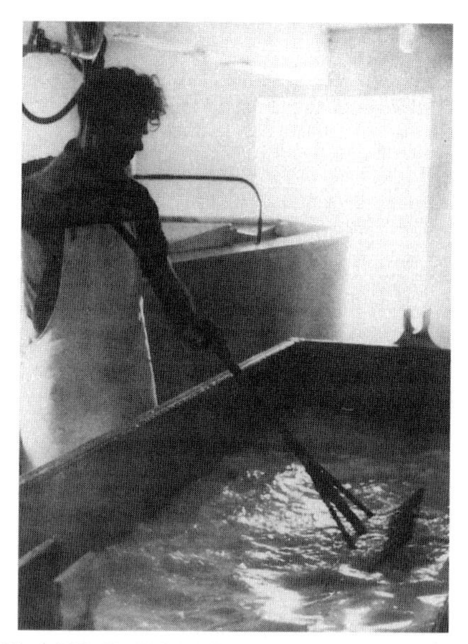

Fig. 76 Cooking & stirring the curds.
John McCarlie, Rainton Farm, Gatehouse

Fig. 77 Cutting the curds into blocks on the drying rack after running the whey.

Fig. 78 Stacking the blocks for cheddaring

Fig. 79 John McCarlie and family punching curds into "chissets".

a musician in his rendering of a world famous piece of music.'

'Cheddar cheese so called because it was partaken by visitors who went to nearby cliffs and caves in the Cheddar Gorge Somerset.' It originated in the 15th century and proved so popular that 16th-century travellers in England would go especially to the district to sample the cheese.

In those days the Cheddar was immature and mild in flavour because it had to be made quickly to meet the demand. Gradually things changed and the actual size of the cheese was increased, which meant a stronger flavour developed. This would be the case when a 270cm (9 foot) wide Cheddar Cheese weighing 11 cwt. was made by Mendip farmers for Queen Victoria's wedding celebrations in 1840.

One of the early advantages the Somerset cheddar makers had over the Scottish was their commitment to cooperation, an early indication of the factory system. Communal cheesemaking had been practised in the Cheddar gorge since about 1635. As else where in the country there were many small milk producers. their milk was 'bulked' at one farm. Each owner's amount was logged and all the milk was made into one cheese. the size of the cheese made depended on the amount of the milk available. They could be a hundredweight or more. It was recommended that the larger cheeses should be kept for 2–5 years according to their size. This reduced variations in quality of cheese being made from milk being collected and stored on individual farms until there was sufficient quantity to make a cheese, whichwould often be too acidic. (Defoe, 1724.)

Joseph Harding of Marksbridge (1805–1876) progressed methods of taking out other variables in cheesemaking in the quest for better quality cheese. He thought that the method of making Dunlop cheese was too 'rule of thumb' and not flexible enough in reacting to changing conditions. One of the major improvements he made was the introduction of cheese vats made of tin with a convex bottom and a tap at the end to facilitate the 'running' of the whey. This was vastly better than the old 'wooden boyen' commonly used by the makers of Dunlop cheese.

His successful methods for which he acquired an undisputed high reputation, were propagated by members of his family comprising of seven sons and six daughters. John, his son, and a Mr Norton furthered his advice to cheesemakers in Scotland. Henry introduced the new methods of Cheddar making in Bodella, Australia, which eventually had far reaching effects on the cheese market in this country. His daughter also won many prizes including a gold medal at the 1865 French Exhibition.

Joseph Harding pioneered new equipment into the process, a revolving breaker for cutting curd, which saved doing it laboriously by hand. He introduced a water-heating apparatus whereby hot water from a boiler passed into a false bottom of the cheese tub to warm the contents and also into pipes that ran around the cheese making room and the curing room. This enabled the cheesemaking process to proceed at the optimum temperatures in the winter. For the first time the the curds and whey could be steadily heated up to an average temperature of about 100°F to cook the curds sufficiently to drain them of whey and firm up quickly instead of the haphazard method of heating by adding hot whey. The combination of temperature and acidity being so important in the correct formation of the curd. In addition abundant quantities of hot water were made available. In those days many did not realise the importance of cleanliness.

He encouraged the use of thermometers which were frowned upon. However, it eliminated an area of judgement in favour of accuracy, which was further assisted later by the use of litmus paper and acidimeters to check the acidity.

In the old days the acidity was gauged by 'drawing the crud'. the local blacksmith put a wooden handle onto a flat piece of iron and this was heated in the dairy fire. When it was red hot, a small piece of cheese was pressed against it, just above the red-hot part and drawn away in a fine thread. the length of the 'draw', its elasticity and appearance told the dairyman how the process was progressing in acid development.

During the "steerin' of the vat he would draw the curd several times and from the length and thickness of the 'hair' and the way it broke he knew whether he had a fast or slow cheese and how much he needed to heat it or cool it and stir it. This was the prefered method of testing for acidity development long after the introduction of acidameters.

The stirring of the vat was a boring task taking about an hour using a wooden rake. To pass the time the women used to sing. Sam Hyslop at Cairniehill used to whistle, Alex Hogg at Upper Senwick sang Psalms and AndyMc Harg at Cairnhandy used to make up poems.

Joseph Harding insisted, that in the dairy there should be separate areas cut off for making, pressing and curing the cheese to prevent contamination particularly of the starter. Usually if a gallon of starter was used in a day it was propagated by keeping back a cupful for the next day.

In 1875 Harding used the first commercial 'Standard Rennet' to be imported into this country and 'by so doing placed another milestone on the road of progress in cheesemaking. It was first produced by the Danish

Fig. 80 Turning the cheese on the "dale" in the cheese loft. Regular turning is essntial if the cheese is to mature evenly

Fig. 81 The finished product maturing in the cheese loft before sale.

chemist, Christian Hansen in Denmark. In 1878 he set up a factory at Little Falls, New York and standardised rennets became universally used so that the 'use of vells is well-nigh discarded by the best cheesemakers.' From about 1960 microbial rennet extracts have been marketed; they were developed because of the shortage of animal rennets.

As a result of the pioneering of the 'Harding method' of making cheese Scottish Cheddar became acclaimed quickly throughout Scotland usurping Dunlop cheese almost completely.

There must have been a lot of bad cheese made before milk marketing became organised. It would be soul destroying for a milk producer living from day to day, or week to week, or month to month, not knowing whether his milk would suddenly be unwanted. His only recourse was to feed it to animals or make it into butter or cheese. Having only small quantities of souring milk available was not conducive to making good quality cheese. It was at that time made into small Dunlop cheese.

It was considered that for economic farm cheesemaking the herd size should be at least 40 cows in number. On the otherhand if the size was more then 100 the utensils of the day could not cope. 'there are as yet no public dairies.' (creameries) (McLelland, 1875.)

These supplies were unsatisfactory for buyers who were wanting large volumes of cheese of a standard quality to satisfy an increasing demand.True there had been a great improvement due the efforts of John Harding et al. but not good enough to prevent buyers going abroad for their supplies.

'Within twenty years from 1850, the imports of butter and cheese had trebled, leaving out of account imports of butter from Ireland into Britain. Holland were the main foreign suppliers of butter and they sent steadily increasing quantities. In the 1850's Holland sent threequarters of the cheese imports, but by 1865 American factories were the largest source of British supplies; a decade later, they were putting one million cwts. of cheese on to the British market and were setting the level of both prices and quality for the trade in the home produced commodity.' (Orwin & Wetham, 1964.)

'The extent to which American cheese is being imported into Ayrshire and retailed at prices greatly under the cost of the home produced is beginning to tell in a way that was hardly anticipated by the dairy farmers in the county. Many of these farmers it appears are still themselves in possession of the bulk of the cheese manufactured last season with little prospect of getting it disposed of at anything like the price that they have been in the habit of realising. The price was 62–64s.

per cwt. in Glasgow. (*Kirkcudbright Advertiser* 4th July 1879.)

Professor Sheldon in his book *'Dairy Farming'* c.1880 decries the lack of attention to detail and cleanliness as the main reasons causing the home product being not up to the standard of the overseas competitors. 'Because they attended to these matters, the American and French cheese superseded the U.K. cheese in the market place – they had a much more scientific attitude to the whole process...'

'While it is true that several eminent men have devoted much scientific investigation to cheese and buttermaking, the teaching of science in these industries has not by any means been generally accepted and the great bulk of cheese and butter makers are working still in their forefathers groove. They seem as if they thought that they could succeed well enough with their sheer physical force without paying attention to the delicacy of details, looking upon the care that the French buttermakers and American cheesemakers as puerile and on the whole necessary and are amiable infatuations..'

'Then they thought that it was the very wet seasons, the lack of sun, the changing herbage, new artificial manures and feedingstuffs, not knowing that they were unable to cope with the sensitive process.' They did not believe that the poorest land can produce good cheese and good cheese is always made in the cheese room.

The influence of imports reduced the price of cheese lower than it had been for twenty years which was aggravated by the failure of the City of Glasgow Bank in 1878. The decline was equal to the entire rent paid for many good dairy farms in Wigtownshire.

In 1884 the Scottish Dairy Association was formed. It formed branches in the counties of Ayr, Kirkcudbright, Wigtown, Argyll and Lanarkshire.

Andrew Clement, a prominent Glasgow cheese merchant, imported large quantities of Canadian and American cheese, the first of which came from Robert McAdam, who had emigrated to U.S.A. from Wigtownshire to set up a small cheese factory.

Following on the success of John Harding et. al. and in order to combat the criticisms of so much inferior cheese being made in Scotland, he encouraged the Scottish Dairy Association to induce Canadians, Messrs. Harris and Drummond to come to Scotland and lecture on American methods.

The American cheese was made in factories as early as 1851, by 1904 there were over 3000 factories making cheese. Like the producers in Somerset they realised the benefit of cooperation. In 1867 the American

Dairyman's Association sent Mr X. A. Willard to study cheesemaking in England. This Association had as its aim the 'mutual improvement in the Science of Cheesemaking and more efficient action in promoting the general interest of the dairy Community.' This showed that competition is the life of trade and one can learn from competitors.

The Scottish Dairy Association organised classes of instruction in various areas. Although Mr R. Harris stayed only one season, his method of making cheese became universally adopted in Scotland. He was succeeded by Mr R.J.Drummond as itinerant instructor. He devoted his time mainly in Ayrshire, Lanarkshire and Argyllshire whereas Mr John McMaster Culhorn, Stranraer gave instructions in Dumfriesshire Henry McFadzean in Wigtownshire and South Ayrshire and James Smith, Standingstone, Borgue, attended to the cheesemakers in Kirkcudbrightshire. The plan was to hold a 'dairy school' at selected centres for a period of about a week and then move on from farm to farm and monitor the progress following the instruction.

The importance of cheese starters was well understood. In 1897 the Stewartry Dairy Association in conjunction with J.R. Campbell, Professor of Agriculture at the Yorkshire College, Leeds undertook to test the value of pure cultures of bacteria for cheesemaking. When the initial experiments proved satisfactory, they were extended on to cheesemaking farms. Several well known cheesemakers were involved – James Robertson, Twynholm Mains; Alexander Kirk, Craigraploch; William Devlin, Boreland of Balmaghie; James Smith, Slagnaw. James McAdam, Craigley. James Kerr, Culdoch and D.Connell, Chapmanton. Over a hundred tons of cheese were made from milk inoculated with a pure starter.

The cheeses made from these starters were assessed and judged by Mr John Robertson of Andrew Clement & Sons and Mr Henry Mc Fadzean, the cheese instructor to the Wigtownshire Dairy Association. Although the use of pure starters was proven, 'there is no royal road to the acquisition to the skill of the eye and hand'. the results of these experiments were reported in the 1899 Transactions of the Highland and Agricultural Society for Scotland.

At this juncture it is worthy of note the important role that the Highland and Agricultural Society took in the advancement of dairying. It formed a Dairy Committee to assist progress in the dairy industry.

In the long history of the Society the list of awards given is extensive. Medals were given for essays on a wide range of subjects – on enclosing land, cultivation of grasses and green crops, on the management of 'black cattle, (this term included any colour including horses until it was dropped in 1829,) for the farmer getting the highest price for a threeyear-old bullock not housed for the previous two years, on linen and woollen manufactures, on planning roads, bridges, and villages. Still being awarded are medals for new implements and ploughing matches.(Ramsay, 1879)

Premiums were offered to encourage better quality butter and cheese. In 1796, the Society awarded a gold medal or a piece of plate of the value of ten guineas to the person, in the counties of Bute and Dumbarton, who made for sale the greatest quantity of cheese of the best quality in a dairy of twelve cows and upwards, the quantity being not less than 36 stones in weight. Mrs Campbell of Stonfield won this 'as well as on account of the quality and quantity of her cheese as that she was the only competitor.' these premiums were understandably not given again for nearly thirty years

They were then given annually on a regional basis. These regions, peripatetically arranged, extended from as far south as the Border counties, (1823) to as far north as Lerwick in the Shetlands (1837), the award in the latter case being for butter.

On 31st October 1832 there was a regional cheese show held at Dumfries under the auspices of the Highland and Agricultural Society. there were classes for 'Immitation English' – Double Gloucester, Stilton, North Wiltshire and Cheshire. For cheese made with skimmed milk, 'the milk had to stand for at least 12 hours'. 'Each competitor brought a cartload of cheese.' The judges were Messrs Thomas Orr, Rosehall, McHarg and Robertson, Dumfries. The winners were – Mrs Janet Mackay, Dinwoodie Green; William Niven, Barnmuir, Closeburn; and John Rodan, Foregirth, Kirkmahoe.

The first Society show was held in Edinburgh on 22nd December 1824. It was at the show at Aberdeen in 1834 where first premiums were awarded for dairy produce. there were twenty one competitors with exhibits of Dunlop cheese and a type of Double Gloucester. Two years later this list had grown to include imitation forms of North Wiltshire, Cheshire and Stilton. It was a number of years before Cheddar was shown as such. For a considerable time this variety was described as 'imitation' i.e. imitation of English Cheddar!

The Highland and Agricultural Society was sufficiently interested in dairying that there was a working dairy, demonstrating on butter and cheesemaking at the Edinburgh Show in 1884, at Aberdeen in 1885 and at Dumfries in 1886.

These efforts to improve the dairy industry were brought to the attention of Parliament emphasising how far the U.K. dairy was behind its overseas competitors. There were privately owned residential courses available at Munster and Glasnevin schools in Ireland. Most European countries had State-aided dairy schools. There were no dairy schools in America as such, but dairying was taught at a number of the State Colleges of Agriculture The Ontario Agricultural College at Guelph had by this time developed a special dairy section.

Parliament, as was their wont, appointed a Commission under the chairmanship of Sir Richard Paget, M.P. 'to enquire into and report upon Agriculture and Dairy Schools in Great Britain which may properly receive Government Grants.' A wide range of evidence was canvassed including that from the Highland and Agricultural Society. It recommended the establishment of one agricultural college, with experimental farm, near Edinburgh and this proving successful, an addition of two more- one near Aberdeen and the other near Glasgow. It also recommended that the colleges be supplemented by one or more dairy schools not necessarily affiliated to them.

Other Scottish views recommended that a dairy training centre should be located near Glasgow and a school for buttermaking not only be located there, but that there be two cheesemaking schools in the South West – one for Ayrshire and Dumfriesshire and one for Wigtownshire and Kirkcudbrightshire. There was general agreement as to the desirability of continuing the itinerant system of instruction in cheesemaking and all pressed the need for Government assistance if centralised training was to be brought within the reach of the poorer members of the agricultural community.

The result of this report culminated in 1889 in the founding of the Scottish Dairy Institute on an acre of land rented from Lord Howard de Walden, the owner of Holmes Farm, Kilmarnock, 'having with gratifying public spirit, agreed to give a site of one acre on that farm, at the nominal feu duty of 5s. per annum'. The first director appointed was Mr R.J. Drummond, formerly the itinerant instructor in cheesemaking. This was funded by student fees at 2s. per day, subscriptions, County Council grants and grants from the landowners in the South West of Scotland and 'whisky money'. This was money about £750,000 a year originally collected in the U.K. for the purpose of compensating dispossessed publicans and subsequently largely applied by local authorities for promotion of technical education. Funds were made available at this time to finance full time instructors. (Symon, 1959.)

In 1899 the West of Scotland Agricultural College was established at 6 Blythswood Square Glasgow. In conjunction with this and the generous financial support from the Highland and Agricultural Society plus an annual grant, a new Dairy School was opened near Kilmarnock in 1904. In 1927 it moved to the 272 hectare estate at Auchencruive near Ayr, which was donated by John Hannah, Girvan Mains.

On completion of the short courses at the Dairy School certificates were awarded. In 1897 the Highland and Agricultural Society in association with the Royal Agricultural Society of England introduced the National Diploma in Dairying and for Agriculture. This ceased in 1973. It was not until 1902 that the Scottish Agricultural Colleges were given powers to grant diplomas.

THE DEMISE OF FARM CHEESEMAKING.

The zenith in farmhouse cheesemaking was from 1840–1870. From then till 1973 it imperceptibly disappeared. Unlike Somerset and other parts of England there was no concentration of production because as one dairyman admitted, 'I wouldn't care to trust another man's milk. I know the standard of my own cows.'

Until the advent of the boards there were thousands of small farmhouse cheesemakers. From 1930–35 the numbers fell from 1000–318 in the S.M.M.B area, to 40 in 1951, to 18 in 1960 and none after 1973. there has been a renewed interest in cheese being made from ewes' milk with several now being in production, while there also has been a re-emergence of successful farm cheesemaking.

Initially the Scottish Milk Marketing Board encouraged producers to continue making cheese on the farms. Any producer, if he so desired, could enter into an agreement with the Board to manufacture his milk into Cheddar or Dunlop cheese. The producer had to provide all the labour, utensils, etc. and supervise all operations in accordance with the direction of the Board. The average price of the cheese was determined by the sales notes submitted to the Board by the cheese merchants and the cheese price was made up to the average wholesale milk price less standard haulage rate plus any premiums in respect of graded milk to which the producer was entitled. The gallonage of milk was reckoned as 100 gallons milk equivalent to 95 lbs. of sold cheese and addition to these prices an allowance of so much a gallon was allowed as expenses of manufacture. There was the added bonus of a good supply of whey on which pigs fattened well. One gallon of whey was equivalent in feeding value to one pound of barley meal. It would appear that the producers had no cause to cease making cheese on the grounds that it was uneconomic. This did not endear them to the producer-retailers who were paying levies.

There were various other reasons for the demise of farmhouse cheesemakers. Skilled people were scarce. Because of the long hours involved without adequate remuneration, the younger people generally were not interested.Sons of experienced makers who were interested were given jobs in the creameries, such as John Donley and Joe McHarg. Instead of investing in new machinery the farmers turned to the expanding liquid market where there was less time, trouble and labour required. 'Wherever there was a contiguous railway, the cheesemaking succumbed to the milk trade.' The advent of railways, motor transport, creameries and milk boards, all mitigated against the survival of farm cheesemaking. For sometime farm made cheese commanded a premium in local shops over that which was produced in creameries because it was more desirable to the palate. Sadly in the dying throes of this farmhouse industry this conception faded largely because bacteriophage which killed off starters became more difficult to control. Eventually creamery made cheese improved in quality and was more economical to produce thus bringing to an end a challenging and interesting part of the agricultural scene.

CHAPTER 19

BUTTER

Butter, like cheese, has a long history. Both have been consumed for thousands of years. Butter is mentioned in the Hindu Vedas about 1400 B.C. It was probably similar to the traditional ghee (clarified butter) of modern India, or the samn of Arabia. The Old Testament mentions butter several times, 'surely the churning of milk bringeth forth butter.' (Proverbs 30: 33) The Ancients Greeks and Romans had butter, but seldom used it as food. They often put it on their hair as brilliantine or for skin injuries. Soot from burnt butter was 'thought good for sore eyes'. Nero's wife Poppaea used butter to cure pimples on her face.

In Scotland until the last century it was used as lamp-oil. In the 19th century butter was used for 'smearing' sheep. This was done to protect them from maggots, other vermin, skin disease and the cold. The ewes were milked for a time after weaning and the cream therefrom was made into butter. This was mixed with tar and palm oil into a salve. The salve was applied at the beginning of the winter by parting the wool into rows from head to tail and spreading it with the finger on the skin. It was difficult to prevent the wool being contaminated which meant that it made less money than the unsmeared wool. Lard, tobacco juice or soap were sometimes substituted for tar. In Annandale, Dumfriesshire where little butter was made, it was imported from England for this purpose.

It is worthy of note that before Ayrshire cattle were known as Dunlop or Cunningham, the district of Cunningham was famous for its butter. In his Topographical Account of the district of Cunningham; Timothy Pont writing c. 1600 says: 'The 2d. degree and parte of this countrey, being a grate deall louer then the former and for the most pairt 3 or 4 mylles bredth, is much more fertile in corne and store, being of a deipe, fatt clayeish soyle, much enriched by the industrious inhabitants lymeing of their grounds, quherby the pastures heir, since this experiment ves practised, is become much more luxuriant than befor; quence it was that pairt of the countrey yeilds a great deal of excellent butter, as all the countrye besyde, but especially the parishes of Steuartone and Dunloppe. The butter of this country in effecte serves a grate pairt of the kingdome, one aker of ground heir yeilding more butter than three akers of ground in any of the next adjacent countreyes'

It is interesting to note that for all practical purposes butter remains the same in all districts, whereas cheese has any number of varieties named after the districts in which they were first made.

One of the advantages of making butter compared with cheese is that it is a less complicated process and yet a more consistent product can be made from small quantities of milk even if the milk is kept for a time and made into butter perhaps twice a week. Time is not such a controlling factor and there is no curing period before the product is ready for consumption. There was an added advantage in earlier days that the skimmed-milk could be kept for a number of days to accumulate to a sufficient quantity before making into cheese.

Before the advent of refrigeration it was difficult to keep butter fresh until it was sold. To aid this it was well salted. If it was not salted it was wrapped in a rhubarb to keep it cool or wrapped and kept in a well. If it had to be stored for any length of time, it was wrapped, put in a wooden container and sunk in a boggy pool hence the name 'bog butter'.

'He in his house great plenty had
Of burnt oat bread and butter found
With garlic mixed, in boggy ground,
So strong, a dog with help of wind,
By scenting out with ease might find.
And this they count the bravest meat
That hungry mortals e'er did eat.'
(Trans. Dumfries & Galloway Antiquarian Society, 1966 Vol. 43.)

The basic idea of making butter has been the same throughout history. The cream is taken off the milk and churned. This coagulates the butterfat which rises to the surface and is collected. By manipulation of this mixture of fat and water, butter results which by law must only contain 16% water. The quality of the butter can vary according to the time of year and the diet of the cow. Being a delicate product it is affected by light and readily picks up odours or flavours from other foods. It was not until modern methods of production were speeded up that large quantities of a quality butter became available.

Variability in quality was unavoidable because 'butter was made in a hundred different farm dairies, taken to villages and towns in a hundred different baskets full of pound and half pound lumps done up in a hundred different ways and patterns.' At one time wherever there were cows butter was made. It was seen as a basic food and necessary to supplement the family income.

The milk was poured into 'setting pans' which were large shallow

Fig. 82 The method of impressing the designs onto the butter blocks.

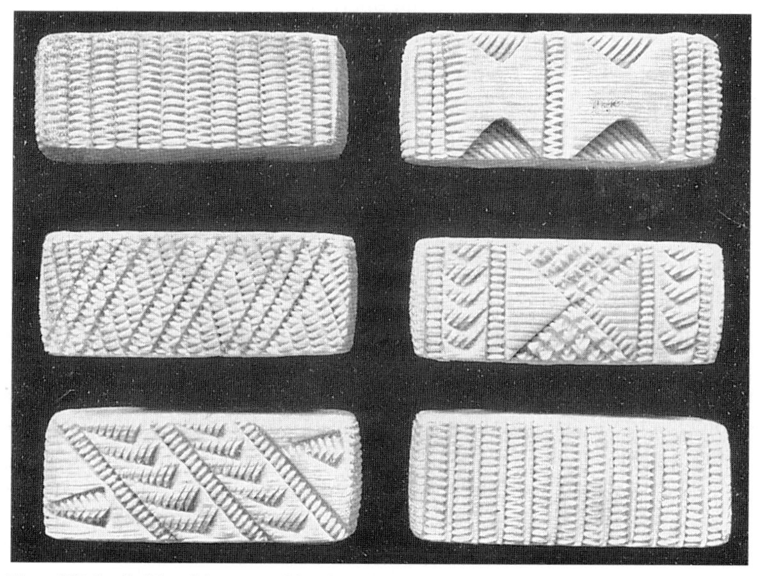

Fig. 83 Individual butter blocks, impressed with decoration. 1924

pans made of either earthenware or tin and left overnight, by which time the cream had separated from the milk. This operation was known as 'setting the milk'. The cream was skimmed off by using a 'skimmer or a fleeter' which resembled a shallow perforated saucer with a handle. The cream was covered usually with a muslin and kept for forty eight hours to ripen i.e. a souring process, once called loppering. In earlier times this process was aided by adding a little buttermilk or 'lapper-milk'. (soured whole milk.) In the 'back kitchens' of farm houses there were long stone or slate shelves on which the 'setting pans' were put full of cream.

The ripening of the cream increases the churnability of the fat, produced the aroma and flavour which is always associated with butter and improved its keeping quality. As in cheesemaking the souring process creates an acidity. If this is allowed to be done naturally as in setting pans, the milk can be contaminated by bacteria which can produce bitterness and bad flavours. This is overcome by adding a starter of a culture containing lactic acid producing organisms (Bacillus lactis), which is of paramount importance to the buttermaking process similar to that which has been noted in cheesemaking. It determines the flavour and keeping qualities of the butter and without flavour, butter is nothing.

The risk of contamination of the milk was largely overcome with the divising of a cream separator by Laval which was first exhibited at Kilburn show in 1879 under the auspices of the Royal Agricultural Show.. This replaced the overnight setting of the milk. The centrifugal force created in a fast revolving chamber causes the heavier skim milk to fly to the outside while the lighter cream remained near the centre. These machines could be hand cranked, horse-geared or power driven. Their price was for quite a time beyond many buttermakers, who in any case were suspicious of their capabilities. Their use was not in demand for those who made butter from whole milk instead of cream, because this resulted in a greater amount of buttermilk being available for sale in low income areas where the demand was high, giving a return of £4–5 per cow. Nevertheless, this invention was to turn buttermaking from a farm craft into a factory trade.

In the churning process which follows ripening; the cream is subjected to violent agitation which causes the fat globules to unite into butter grains sufficiently large to facilitate their removal from buttermilk. Over the years and in different parts of the country there were many types of churns – plunger churn, rocker churn, barrel churn, rectangular box churn, rounded box churn, triangular-type horizontal barrel churn, etc. In the late nineteenth century there were 50–80 churns of distinct types exhibited at the National Dairy Show. In 1907 it was estimated that there were 150 enumerated by German authors. (Green & Young, 1907.)

In South West Scotland small glass churns, varying in size and capable of churning up to rather more than half a gallon were available. A larger wooden churn usually made of oak of a stationary cylindrical type with an internal dasher was commonly used. In late nineteenth century the most popular was the end-over-end barrel churn.

For example in the county of Renfrew at the beginning of the nineteenth century 'the churns consisted of vertical boxes and the end of a lever, by which the churn was worked after the fashion of a hand pump. This was greatly improved by the introduction of a large horizontal churn, driven by water or horse power.' (T.H.A.S. 1887.) In Orkney windmills were used c.1822.

After churning, the butter was washed and 'worked' to expel moisture, consolidate the texture and if necessary to distribute the salt. For larger quantities a wooden butter worker was used which had a wooden roller on it. Before its advent the butter was kneaded by hand or by using 'butter beaters' which resembled very large heavy butter pats.

By using butter pats, which were two pieces of thin bat shaped wood about nine inches long, the butter was made into pound or half pound bricks or rolls. These were decorated on top with designs ranging from flowers and birds to abstract shapes ready for market. It was felt that decorated butter 'was pleasing to the eye and enhanced the pleasure that fine quality affords' The main mode of transport for many years was the basket.

Despite the simplicity of the method of manufacture, the amount of first class butter reaching the market was small. The main reasons for so much poor farm made butter was firstly, because of its perishability. Unless special care was taken it quickly became tainted or rancid, especially fresh unsalted butter. To minimise the tainted flavour a little saltpetre was added. Secondly, the average buttermaker did not appreciate the fundamental principles which determine the production of a high grade article. Finally, buttermaking was usually less remunerative than milk selling or cheesemaking therefore, therefore, there was no incentive for improvement.

The production of quality was almost impossible because 'so contemptuous were the people of cleanliness that it was considered unlucky to wash the kirns; they were so given up to superstition that sometimes that a frog was put in the tubs to make the milk churn and they were so full of experimental wisdom that they maintained that the

Fig. 84 "The Old Way". David Morrison "Kirning" butter at Garthland Mains. Stranraer.

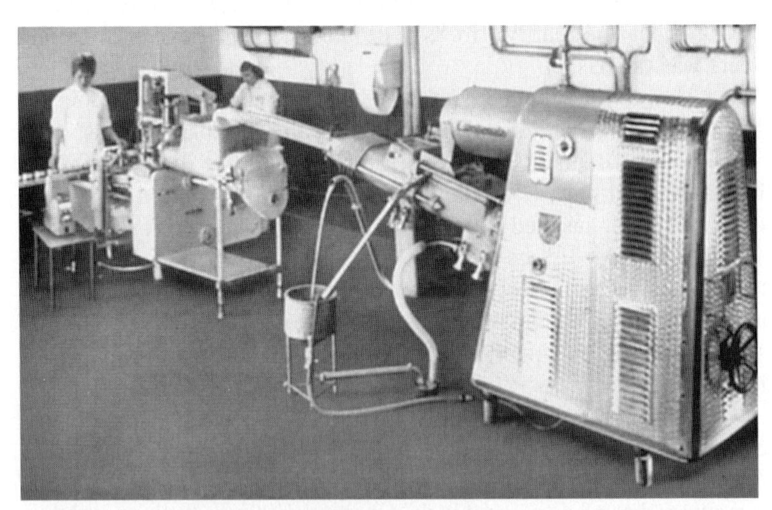

Fig. 85 "The New". Continuous buttermaking machine at Mauchline. 1964

consistency of the butter depended on the number of hairs it contained.' (Graham, 1906.) A number of premiums were awarded by the Highland and Agricultural Society for improving various processes in dairy management. These appear to have had a very great educational value. By 1829, the Society was able to congratulate itself on the fact that a 'remarkable progressive improvement in dairying had taken place under their encouragement.' (Orr J.B. T.H.A.S. 1931)

It would be wrong to be repetitive but the efforts to make butter which was able to compete with imports followed closely to what was done for cheese. In 1827, 211,000 cwt. of butter was imported from Holland. By 1862 this had increased to over a million cwt. a proportion coming from Germany. Thereafter, more than half the imports came from Scandinavia, comprising of all the butter made in Denmark. Other supplies came from France and Siberia and when ships were refrigerated more came from the Americas and Australasia.

Although this industry never attained the importance of farm cheesemaking especially in the South West of Scotland, it was of local importance near cities and towns where it had to compete with imports. As noted elsewhere the Highland and Agricultural Society took an interest in butter production. Following on the success of appointing cheesemaking instructors, in 1884 the Scottish Dairy Association appointed a buttermaking instructor Mr Chilton from London who was not a success. It was thought at the time that as Denmark had become the leader in the production of butter on scientific principles, it would be right to appoint in 1885 a Dane, Mr Segelcke. Due to language difficulties 'little profit was derived from the latter's instruction and as a consequence the effort in this direction was allowed to lapse.' Fortunately the opening of the Dairy School and the appointing of butter instructors in various parts of the country remedied the situation.

The Scottish Farmer ran a column which gave answers to queries on the samples of butter sent to it by dairymaids and farmers' wives. These were replied to by the pseudonym of Butterman. They could also be point scored by the following standard:– on flavour 45; colour, 3; grain and texture, 25; dryness, 15; style and neatness, 7. Those who scored the top score at or about 100 points were later invited to send a portrait photograph to the Scottish Farmer. These would then appear in page after page of the ensuing annual album. There could be up to a hundred and thirty dairymaids' pictures' at one time. Apart for the pleasure and interest of these high scores, dairymaids used such publicity to secure jobs. This was facilitated if they were members of the British Dairymaids' Association.

The entrants who also used pseudonyms, eagerly opened the Scottish Farmer each week to see their score and what advice or criticism Butterman had to offer.

X.Y.Z.- A wee bit insipid. Try to improve the flavour. Score,42, 8, 23, 15, 7.-95. Class I
A Beginner.—The flavour is not nearly sweet enough. Are you using a pure culture starter or a good buttermilk starter? It tastes as if you allowed it to ripen too long. Score, 41, 8, 23, 15, 7.-94. Class I.
A.L.M.L.– Better this time, but still 1 off texture. Score 99. Class, choicest

Butterman sometimes gave a poetical reply to a competitor-

I like weel and fain would steal
A march upon my thinking,
But if I try, you're far too fly
To fail to see I'm winking
I only fix it ninety-six
And that you ken is plenty
The month of May may mak the hay
But never butter dainty.

The production of quality butter for which a premium could be obtained was hindered by the amount of adulteration that it was subjected to. Before 1907 there were no regulations governing butter standards. Butter was adulterated in several ways to increase its weight after it was bought from the producer by cadgers before it was sold on to the consumer. The most common method was to 'load freshly churned butter with water or milk, the latter being either fluid or solid' There was also a lot of blending of butter done in creameries which came from a variety of sources.

A large amount of imported butter was also adulterated by the addition of vegetable oil or animal fat. Oleomargarine, mainly beef suet, was exported to Denmark from America, mixed with butterfat and re-exported to the U.K. as butterine and often as Danish butter, which was confusing. After a lot of pressure from the British Dairy Farmers' Association legislation under the Margarine Act of 1887 changed the name from butterine to margarine which in a modern form has subsequently overtaken butter in the market place.

Margarine was originally prepared by a French chemist named

Mege-Mouries, at the instance of Napoleon III, with the object of obtaining a wholesome cheap substitute for butter for the poorer inhabitants of Paris. Its production was stimulated by the Franco-Prussian War (1870–71). It was originally made from churning oil from kidney fat with milk and sliced cows' udders. Later towards the end of the nineteenth century, coconut and palm-kernal oil from West Africa became the dominant ingredient. Margarine has subsequently overtaken butter in the market place as a result of modern production methods and various opinions on health habits.

Like cheese, the butter industry changed dramatically when it moved from the farm to the factory. This was assisted by pasteurisation, large centrifugal separators, continuous buttermaking and packaging machines and the introduction of the Babcock test for the determining of butterfat content in milk and cream. Big advances in dairy chemistry enable the manufacture of butter to be so standardised that quality butter can be produced from milk no matter what the butterfat content or its acidity may be.

The butter industry in Scotland never was large. To date 43% of the milk going into the dairies in Europe is made into butter and a third of the world's milk is used to make butter.

BUTTER INFORMATION COUNCIL.

This Council was formed in 1954 to promote the consumption of butter in the U.K. on behalf of home and overseas suppliers. With the entry of the U.K. into the E.E.C. and the cessation of imports into the U.K. from outside the E.E.C. (other than New Zealand), the membership of the Council was restricted to the current suppliers i.e. Denmark, the Irish Republic, England and Wales, Holland, France, New Zealand, Northern Ireland and Scotland. The Council's work is funded by contributions of members and from the Community's Co-responsibility Fund. Its activities include generic advertising for butter, consumer promotions and an extensive public relations campaign.

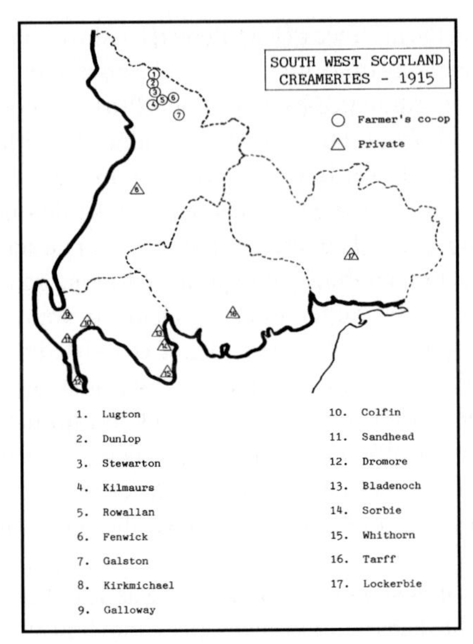

Fig. 86 The Creameries in S.W. Scotland - 1915

Fig. 87 The Creameries in S.W. Scotland - 1959

CHAPTER 20

THE CREAMERY MOVEMENT

In the U.K. the introduction of factory manufactured cheese developed slowly compared to America where it spread rapidly in a short space of time. In 1870 the first cheese making creamery was set up in England at Longford, Derby, to which an American cheese maker was invited to advise in the methodology. By 1876 there were 10 factories operating in making cheese in five counties.

For a time there were discussions in Wigtownshire to establish a creamery which never materialised, 'as most farmers had good dairy accommodation at home the project was never carried out.' Eventually a number of private cheese factories were established mostly away from the areas with a large demand for liquid milk. Later as more milk was produced a larger number of farmer dairy cooperatives came into being closer to urban areas, mainly to utilise milk surplus to liquid milk requirements.

DUNRAGIT CREAMERY

In 1882 Andrew Clement, a cheese factor in Glasgow, in partnership with Robert McCracken, the son of A.E. McCracken, Gillespie, bought a disused farina factory from a Mr Cunningham at Dunragit in Wigtownshire and set up 'The Creamery Company'. Andrew Clement was responsible for the selling of the products, Robert McCracken was the general manager and a butter expert from Denmark was responsible for the buttermaking.

Robert McAdam who was in the same business in Rome, New York State, was consulted regularly by correspondence and wrote: "The manufacture of 1000 cows' milk into butter is a big job and the arrangements necessary to perform such nice work in a satisfactory manner would require considerable thought and giving of details more fully than the mere writing a letter. But presuming it has to be done at Dunragit, I will endeavour to indicate somewhat about the method of proceeding that I would attempt, (taking an imperfect remembrance of the building into account.)"

This creamery developed to employ 300 staff most of whom travelled in a 'Special' workers' train running between Stranraer and Dunragit. By about 1879 there was a railway link between Portpatrick,

Colfin, Stranraer, Castle Kennedy, Dunragit, Glenluce, Kirkcowan, and Newton Stewart, linking up with the Glasgow and South Western at Castle Douglas.

Milk was stored in 800 gallon vats from where it passed to the newly introduced centrifugal cream separators. Part of the resulting cream was made into butter and part was well chilled and put into earthenware jars, carefully sealed and despatched to the cities every afternoon or sent in 17 gallon churns. The skim milk was made into cheese.

The Creamery Company later became known as United Creameries Limited when it was amalgamated with Valleyfield Dairy Company near Kirkcudbright, known locally as Tarff Creamery, along with Sorbie and Colfin in Wigtownshire; Kirkmichael in Ayrshire and Campbeltown.

A report in the Galloway News in December 1888 commented that- 'A company of gentlemen interested in dairy matters have taken over the premises at Valleyfield near Tarff Station, occupied some years ago by the Largs Cattle Food and Manure Company, for the purpose of establishing a butter and cheese creamery. The contract for the engineering work has been carried by J & R Wallace, the Foundry Castle Douglas.'

At the end of the First World War the Dunragit creamery changed over to margarine production which was then in great demand because of the scarcity and high price of butter and the low price for low quality cheese.

If there was any surplus of buttermilk, skim-milk or whey they were fed to 3–500 pigs. The company also owned West Challoch farm where a herd of 120 cows were kept.

About 1921 Dunragit Creamery was sold to the English Margarine Company which was a subsidiary of Levers Brothers of Liverpool. In 1940 the Nestle Milk Company bought the creamery and changed to milk condensing. In the mid 1960's milk intake ceased and Non-milk foods were extensively manufactured.

TARFF CREAMERY

Tarff Creamery shipped a lot of whole milk and cream by rail to Edinburgh, Newcastle and Manchester. Any surplus was made into butter. The butter was sold in $^1/_2$lb. rolls and packed into trays and fitted into special boxes. The churns in the early days were open top and known as Butt and Ben type designed for churning acid cream. Rolled dried skim milk powder was also produced.

From about 1927 Lactic Acid Casein was made in normal cheese vats. From about 1929 Rennet Casein was also made for export to Africa and the Middle East.

In 1938 the creamery was converted to a whey condensery and was supplied with whey from cheese making creameries in Galloway. By 1958 the condensery was handling on average 20,000 gallons per day over its eight month operating period. The site was also used to feed about 1000 pigs for fattening in a large piggery which were for a time bred at Sorbie Creamery. Tarff Creamery closed in 1974.

SORBIE CREAMERY

Sorbie Creamery was built by United Creameries Ltd. as a small cheese unit in 1891. The first factory had two farms, Kilsture and Creech, totalling about 200 acres. On the farms there was a large pig unit with breeding sows whose progeny were all fattened, numbering about 2,500 head. It also had an extensive cream trade with skimmed milk either being dried or fed to pigs.

The United Creameries became part of Wiltshire United Dairies in the 1940's. When in the 1950's United Dairies and Cow and Gate merged into Unigate, the factories at Sorbie and Colfin became part of the United Foods Division.

In 1974, Sorbie Cheese Co. Ltd. was established by a consortium between Unigate and the Cooperative Wholesale Society, having 51% and 49% of the shareholding respectively. It built a new factory on a green field site. The re-routed A746 passed over the site of the old Creamery. This Creamery had a capacity of 270,000 litres per day, producing 6,000 tonnes of cheddar per annum. This was in 20kg. blocks. Resulting from the cheese production, a whey screening and separation plant was installed. About 250 tonnes of whey butter per annum was made from the separated whey cream.

This resulted in the closing down of Tarff, Colfin and Bladnoch processing plants.

Henry Christie of Dourie Farming Company and Robert Robinson of Culbae, Whauphill, fed between them 55 million litres in their large pig producing units from Sorbie and other cheesemaking creameries in the Scottish Milk Marketing Board Area.

WIGTOWNSHIRE CREAMERY.

This creamery was built at Sheuchan at the west end of Stranraer, on the shore of Lochryan c. 1886 by James McHarrie, Duchra and Provost Young of Stranraer. They formed the Wigtownshire Creamery Company. These enterprising men also built creameries at Dromore, Sandhead in Wigtownshire and Ballymoney in Northern Ireland. This Company continued in business until after the First World War, Provost Young having died in 1914. The Wigtownshire and Ballymoney Creameries were sold to the Cooperative Wholesale Society, while the Dromore and Sandhead Creameries were sold to the Galloway Creamery Company.

In the 1930s the C.W.S. demolished the old Creamery and on the same site built the most modern of the time. When this was closed in 1974 the site was converted into a charming picnic area.

In 1974 Sorbie Cheese Co. Ltd. was established by a consortium between C.W.S 49% and Unigate 51%. Unigate and C.W.S. having 51% and 49% of the shareholding respectively. It built a new factory on a green field site. The re-routed A746 passed over the site of the old Creamery. This Creamery had a capacity of 270,000 litres per day producing 6,000 tonnes of cheddar per annum. This was in 20kg. blocks. Resulting from the cheese production a whey screening and separation plant was installed. About 250 tonnes of whey butter per annum was made from the separated whey cream.

Previously in 1916 the C.W.S. took over the privately owned Sheuchan Creamery at Stranraer and closed it in 1974. They also owned a butter and cheese making creamery at Whithorn which was closed in 1939 and one at Bladnoch, which was changed to margarine production and later to cutting and packing cheese.

In the late nineteenth century there was a was a small private creamery established at Sorn, Ayrshire, owned by by Mr Sommervell. This was used to make his tenants' summer milk from 150 cows into butter. A large proportion of this butter commanded a premium price in London. He had benefited from the advice of Mr Chilton, the travelling butter instructor of the Scottish Dairy Association for 1884 in the use of the best utensils to use. He was the first to pay for the milk on a quality basis. 'The standard here is fixed at 12% of cream by the test-tube and for every percent up or down, the prices rises or falls one farthing on the price of each gallon.' (Speir, 1886.)

DAIRY COOPERATIVES

It has been noted elsewhere that there were a number of dairy cooperative associations set up before and after the First World War, most which were associated with milk depots or manufacturing creameries. Very often both functions were carried out. There were too many of them in number and too many carrying out the same functions in competition with one another. The necessity for rationalisation became very evident which continues to the present time.

By purchasing nineteen of these units the Milk Marketing Board quickly gained control of the problem of surpluses and the experience of running commercial enterprises, which was useful in future price negotiations. It had control of 50–60% of the manufacturing milk. It is noteworthy that nine of them had piggeries. The disposal of whey was a problem until whey driers were installed.

The functions and subsequent changes of the Boards purchases summarised in Robert Urquhart's book. (1979) have been added to.

BRAND'S DAIRIES was a retail and wholesale bottling dairy and a milk depot, which was unsatisfactory and inconvenient and was replaced in 1936 by Hogganfield Creamery, Glasgow, when the Board took a most important decision to cease participation in the liquid milk trade. Hogganfield was subsequently used for the innovative installation of U.H.T. longlife milk. This was transferred to Kirkcudbright in 1976.

CRAIGIE was a cheese factory with a large piggery adjoining where the whey was used for pig feeding. Cheese making was discounted in 1934 and the building was used as a cheese store. Thereafter, it was sold to A. McLelland & Sons Ltd. in 1944, who utilised it as a grain store in conjuntion with their grain and animal foods business in Kilmarnock.

DALRY also had a cheese factory and the whey was later transferred to Stewarton for drying. Cheesemaking was discontinued in 1943 but the cheese store remained in use until the buildings were sold in the 1960's.

DRUMMORE was a cheese factory, the whey being fed to pigs. It was managed from and regarded as part of the Galloway Creamery, separate accounts were then not kept. Manufacturing was discontinued in 1936 and for a time the premises were on lease and eventually sold in 1941 to A. McLelland's as a cheese and grain store.

DUNLOP CREAMERY was also used for cheesemaking but the bulk of the milk supplied the liquid market. These operations ceased in 1934 and the building sold in 1941.

GALSTON CREAMERY was originally used for cheesemaking and later for sterilised cream. In 1935 the canning of cream was discontinued but fresh cream and skim were sold. This stopped in 1940 and the creamery was sold in 1945.

LESMAHAGOW had a cheese factory. Operations ceased in 1936 and the creamery was sold in 1946.

KIRKMICHAEL had been used as a condensery but was sold to Wiltshire United Dairies in 1936 and continued in the same use until closed.

PINWHERRY had a cheesefactory managed from Kirkmichael. Manufacturing was discontinued in 1935 and the premises sold in 1941.

PORT WILLIAM CREAMERY made cheese and had roller driers installed about 1939 for the whey. It was sold in 1971 to Dourie Farming Company.

RESTALRIG CREAMERY was a milk depot for Edinburgh. It was equipped for the production of fresh cream and butter. The skim milk was originally sold to bakers but later was treated with acid and the curd sent to Hogganfield for processing into casein. Ultimately it was used only for liquid milk and the operations were discontinued in 1949 when the lease was given up.

ROWALLAN CREAMERY, Fenwick, was a cheese factory, the whey being used for feeding. Operations discontinued in 1938 when the premises were let and eventually sold in 1941.

SANDHEAD was always a cheese factory and for many years the adjoining piggery was operated by the Board. This provided an outlet for some of the whey. Until 1939 Sandhead like Drummore was regarded as part of Galloway Creamery and no separate accounts were kept. It was sold in 1972.

STEWARTON CREAMERY was used initially for condensing, canning cream and fresh cream, but, as in the case of Galston, the Board went out of this market in favour of the proprietary condenseries in 1937.

THANKERTON CREAMERY Association was formed in 1911 to carry on a creamery business in Lanarkshire. The milk was supplied by 38 members having 30–40 cow herds on 300 acres. Most of the milk was delivered by the suppliers, for those more distant arrangements were made with the creamery who owned a motor lorry. All the milk was water cooled and despatched to St Cuthbert's Cooperative Society in Edinburgh. Payment was made on a butterfat basis. There were no contracts with St Cuthbert's for a definite amount but they reserved the right to reject milk in excess of its requirements. If this milk was made into cheese by the Association it was compensated by St Cuthbert's for any loss sustained. The Association was a member of the Scottish Milk Agency when it received good prices but resigned when its prices fell below that of St Cuthbert's Cooperative. In 1931 the turnover was £21, 933, the running costs were 13% of the turnover which resulted in a small loss.

KIRKCUDBRIGHT CREAMERY

The Stewartry Dairy Association was formed in 1919 and erected a creamery in 1921. The milk was drawn from a radius 20 to 25 miles covering the south of the county. There were 180 members and 200 suppliers most of whom had dairy herds of 40 to 80 cows. A number of the suppliers sent milk to the creamery all the year round while others only in the winter, making cheese in the summer. The milk was collected by creamery lorries daily in winter and twice daily in the summer. The members nearby delivered their own milk. When hired lorries were used they were paid on a gallonage basis. The quantity handled varied between 1500 in December and 6,500 in June. Payment for the milk was made monthly on a butterfat basis.

Milk was pasteurised and sold liquid wholesale to surrounding towns and some to Glasgow, Edinburgh and into England. Two two-horse waggons hauled the milk and cream from the creamery to the station which were for a long time more economical method of haulage over short distances. When the new bridge was being built over the river Dee, the road was very rough causing a wheel to come off a cart resulting in a load of cans and milk disappearing down the river.

The Association had a retail rounds and seven shops locally. There were two shops in Newton Stewart, one in Dumfries, Castle Douglas, Dalbeattie, Gatehouse and Kirkcudbright. The bottles had a logo of Mickey Mouse.

For Mickey's strength
Let's thank the fairy,
Who sends him milk
From the Stewartry Dairy.

Butter and cheese were both made and trade in cream and butter-milk. Ice-cream, bakery and confectionery products were supplied and the creamery was the first to make crustless (processed) cheese. The bakery and crustless factory were situated on the opposite of the Dee from the Creamery. There was a piggery where 500 pigs were fattened. Dairy requirements were sold to farmers. On the other hand butter cheese and eggs were bought from them.

This was the largest cooperative creamery in Scotland by 1931, with a turnover £181,503 and shares at £11 each. About 2,823,490 gallons annually was purchased at an average price of 8.12d. per gallon. The average received for produce in all forms was 11.5d. per gallon. Running costs were 15% of turnover. (Plunkett, 1932)

Its success was largely due to the endeavours of a number of leading farmers under the chairmanship of Mr Hugh Baird of Kirkchrist and having the foresight to appoint James K. Murdoch as manager who became a very shrewd businessman.

'J.K.' was succeeded as manager of the Stewartry Dairy Association by Thomas Murdoch who came from Hapland, Dunlop.

The Milk Marketing Board bought Kirkcudbright Creamery in 1933, from then more emphasis was put on butter making. The skim milk from this operation was sold to the Scottish Milk Powder Company which had set up a drying plant on the same site in 1934. In 1961 the Board took over the Company combining the two operations under one manager.

After the Creamery was bought by the S.M.M.B. Stewartry Dairy Association carried on trading until it went into liquidation in the 1950's.

In 1976 the UHT processing and packaging of long life milk products which had been carried out at Hogganfield, was updated to meet the current increasing demand and installed at Kirkcudbright and can handle 60 million litres per annum. Shortly afterwards the butter/powder unit was closed.

In 1967 when this process was originally set up at Hogganfield was one of the first of its kind in the U.K. market. By 1983 there was a range

Fig. 88 The original Creamery at Kirkcudbright c.1920's

Fig. 89 The new Creamery at Kirkcudbright. c.1960's

Fig. 90 Road transport of cans between the wars

Fig. 91 J. K. Murdoch - Manager
Hugh Baird - Chairman of Stewartry Dairy Association. c.1930

of twelve products being sold incorporating over forty labels, ten years later there over a hundred separate forty labels, ten years later there were over a hundred separate labels going to all the major national and regional supermarket groups as well as cash and carry outlets.

DALBEATTIE CREAMERY

Dalbeattie and District Farmers' Association was formed in 1920 to carry on a creamery to handle the milk available in the eastern part of Kirkcudbrightshire. Initially there were 140 members and 133 suppliers. The milk was collected once a day by creamery lorries, 'the members being requested to bring their milk to platforms on main roads.' They were bound by the rules of the society to sell to it the whole of their output except cheesemakers, for which they were paid monthly on a butterfat basis. Most of this milk and cream was sold to Newcastle and Lancashire industrial districts. (Plunkett, 1932) Cheese was made with the surplus milk , no butter being made. Skim milk from the cream separation and whey was sold for pig and calf feeding at 1d. per gallon. A number of pigs were fattened at the creamery.

In 1931 the sales were 823,409 gallons of milk, 14,716 gallons of cream and 66,738 gallons of skim milk and whey, being £48,527 in value plus £2,627 for cheese sales. The society was a member of the Scottish Milk Agency for three years selling to many of its customers through the Agency. It had competition from a proprietary creamery in the town which eventually went into liquidation. The society had a retail in shop in Dalbeattie and also attempted to sell dairy requirements to its members but this failed due to the lack of support.

In 1955 two 2,500 gallon cheesemaking vats were bought from New Zealand equipped with overhead traversing gears operating spade like stirring paddles making this creamery one of the larger belonging to the Board with a capacity of handling 15000 gallons daily.

Like many cheesemaking plants and especially on farm cheese making dairies Dalbeattie Creamery had problems with starter failures due to bacteriophage contamination leading to too much poor quality cheese being made. These were finally resolved in 1956 by the introduction of single strain starters assisted by Dr. Crawford from the Dairy School at Auchencruive. By this innovation the texture and body of the cheddar cheese vastly improved resulting in the cheese from this creamery under the control of dedicated managers, Jim Crawley and Bob Stewart winning many honours at national shows and creating a country wide demand for it. This success proved to many that creamery cheese could be equal and better than farm cheese and thus hastened its demise. It was with regret that this well run creamery had to be closed in 1974 because of the large amount of capital which was necessary to renovate the building.

GALLOWAY CREAMERY.

The following is extracted from unpublished notes written by Jim Crawley, a former manager of Port William, Dalbeattie and Galloway Creameries.

When a number of farmers became aware of the success of the privately owned creameries at Dunragit and Sheuchan paying better prices for products made from milk sold collectively to them compared with cheese made on individual farms they decided to build and run their own creamery at a meeting held on 22 June 1899. The Galloway Creamery Cooperative Farmers Ltd. was formed under the chairmanship of Mr McMaster Jr. Culmore Mains and the producers throughout the Rhins were canvassed for their support.

The shareholding was to be raised by a levy per cow and an annual dividend paid to the shareholders in addition to the price paid for their milk.

As a result of many meetings it was decided that:–

1. Farmers who became members 'to sign allegiance for 2½ years.
2. Milk price was to be based on previous year's trading.
3. Butterfat standard to be 3.6% and a bonus would be paid for overs and a penalty applied for unders.
4. It was decided that the committee would appoint a responsible person to weigh and test the milk. It was recommended that this person should be Neutral.

On the 7th September plans for the erection of the Creamery on the site of the present Creamery were passed by the Town Dean of Guild.

The contractors involved were:–

Architects	Caird & McFarlane
Builders	Mr Purdie, Stranraer
Joiner	Mr McLauchan, Stranraer
Plumber	Mr John Forsyth, Stranraer
Slater, Slabs and Tiler	Mr McCormack, Stranraer
Dairy Plant & Machinery Suppliers	Mr J. Gray, Stranraer

15 H.P. Robey Engine & 20 H.P. Boiler	A. Lamb
Iron Work	David King & Sons, Glasgow
Electric Lighting	Mr W. Gourlay

(This type of lighting was used to avoid objectionable fumes.)

'The Creamery was open for Traffic on 1st November 1899, only eight weeks after the first sod was cut.' At the time it was intended that an extension would be built for a Margarine department and to provide a railway siding.

Initially the Creamery was used mainly for buttermaking.
'From the weighing can the milk passes into large receiving vats. It is then conducted to a 'warmer' (a heated vat), the temperature raised to 88°F and separated in an Alfa Laval machine at the rate of 400 gallons per hour. Cream for butter passes over an Alfa Laval cooler into ripening vats, then conveyed to the churn. Butter is washed with pure spring water and then manipulated on slabs, weighed and made up in rolls and prints. The milk or the product is never touched by hand. A cold storage chamber for butter was placed underneath the ground.

Double cream was filled into jars and sold locally and elsewhere throughout the country. The skim milk from it intended for consumption was heated and cooled to improve its keeping quality and the surplus was mixed with some whole milk and made into cheese.

This Creamery was reported to be the 'best equipped in the U.K.' and was successful for a time but for some reason not reported by Crawley, it went into liquidation. 'Little or nothing is known to me of the reason for this. It may have been due to the stresses of the war years but I prefer to think that it was due to a new and younger band of enthusiastic farmers and businessman seeking to control the destinies of the Creamery in a bright new world.' However, the creditors were paid out in full.

The first manager of the Creamery until 1903 was Mr H. Kelly. When he moved to the Sheuchan he was succeeded by Mr Todd followed by Mr Clauchie.

'The affairs of the Galloway Creamery Cooperative Farmers Ltd. were wound up at a meeting held on 30th April 1920 and the business was transferred to the newly constituted Galloway Creamery Ltd. Mr W. Ferguson was appointed chairman with Mr John Gibson as secretary. Mr Henry Fletcher was appointed as manager and proved to be very successful in developing a progressive and profitable company. He was supported by an energetic committee comprising of Messrs. J. Rutherford, J.P. Hunter, A. Cochrane, A. McCaig and R. Watson.

In 1926 a new refrigerator plant and boiler were installed at the

The Galloway Creamery Co., Ltd.

STRANRAER, N.B.

CHOICEST QUALITY

Unsalted and Slightly-Salted Butter,

CHURNED DAILY FROM FRESH PURE CREAM.

WARRANTED ABSOLUTELY PURE.

Prints, Rolls, and Squares, and in Bulk Packages.

Pure Fresh Double-thick Cream,

IN JARS AND IN BULK.

OUR CREAM IS FAMED FOR ITS HIGH-CLASS QUALITY AND RARE DELICACY OF FLAVOUR.

☞ Special Terms to large Buyers in Bulk. ☜

NEW MILK. ***SEPARATED MILK.***
ACCOMMODATION SUPPLIES.

All Orders despatched same day as received.

SEND FOR PRICE LIST.

Telegraphic Address—"Galloway Creamery, Stranraer."

CITY DEPOTS:

EDINBURGH, ... 24, Lochrin Buildings, Gilmore Place.
GLASGOW, ... 157, North Street.
DUNDEE,... ... ... 15, West Dock Street.
INVERNESS, ... 4, Falcon Square.

Fig. 92 Advertisement for the products of the Galloway Creamery, Stranraer.

Creamery for a costof £2,400. This enabled milk and its products to be transported further afield out of Scotland into the Midlands of England. Milk was sent by railway tankers to London. There was an annual throughput of 2,236,448 gallons with a turnover of £150,464 and a profit of £24,000. The average paid to the farmers was 10¼d. per gallon.

This Company did not join the Scottish Milk Agency because it was thought that if the price fell it would be changed to a cheese factory which indeed happened eventually. By 1933 the average price paid by the Company fell to 7.19d. per gallon when the price for cheese milk 4d. per gallon, in some places less.

In 1934 Mr Roberts, manager of Dalbeattie succeeded Mr Fletcher on his retiral. This coincided with necessary changes at the Creamery. Milk production was expanding and there were more producers giving up farm cheese making resulting in this milk being made into cheese at the Creamery and thus throwing up a problem about whey disposal. Fortunately more markets were becoming available for whey butter and whey powder.

In 1935 new buildings were erected and a roller drying plant from Galston was installed for drying skim milk and whey. At this juncture Sandhead and Drummore creameries were linked with Galloway to the extent that no separate accounts were kept for them.

The production of milk in Wigtownshire was traditionally geared to summer time to take advantage of the locality's grass growing potential. It was therefore not until 1953 that cheesemaking was made all the year round at the Galloway, when 1000 gallon vats were put in with stirring paddles driven by electric motors through a gear-box fixed on the end of each vat. This was a great advance from the drudgery of manually stirring the vats.

Again due to the necessity for increased capacity and streamlining production which was benefiting from the handling of milk in bulk, 2,500 gallon vats were installed. These were U.K. replicas of the New Zealand vats which were a success at Dalbeattie. This led to the whole process being improved by changing from producing the large traditional round 80lb. cheese to 40lb. rindless blocks which were wrapped in a wax film and heat sealed.

There is no doubt that the 'old stagers' viewed these changes with some apprehension, voicing the oft quoted 'it'll naw work'. The same doubts are around with today's modern machinery!

It is said that to stand still is to stagnate. It has been well illustrated at the Galloway Creamery. Between 1964–66 a large new creamery was built on the existing site and the surrounding land extending to some $7^1/_2$ acres. This became necessary because of other Board creameries were unable to cope with the increasing supplies. It was built to handle 350,000 gallons of milk weekly and three times that if necessary. The approximate cost was £1 million pounds a third of which was met by development and investment incentive grants.

This investment was the initial stage of the complete mechanisation of cheesemaking by the introduction of the Bell Siro cheesemaker from New Zealand. This plant milled the curd, added salt electronically controlled and filled chissets weighed out at a predetermined amount ready to go into new type of horizontal cheese presses.

There was also erected 8 x 12,500 gallon storage tanks, milk and whey pasteurisers and separators. The continuous 'Contimab' process was installed for the preparation of cream for buttermaking and the manufacture of skim milk products such as casein.

Storage space is always a vital necessity and this was improved by providing a 2000 ton cheese store and two stores of each 1000 ton capacity for butter and skim milk powder.

With the challenges from the European Common Market on the horizon and the cheese vats being old and below the necessary capacity it was decided in 1973 to have a further re-equipping programme which reflected the world wide changes in trading habits and dairy technology.

This involved the installation of totally enclosed vats in which the cheese was made followed by curd draining and cheddaring in mechanised equipment manufactured by Bell Bryant Proprietary Ltd. in Australia. The totally enclosed cheesemaking cycle was programmed and monitored from an independently automated panel for each vat.

The importance of starters has always been paramount in cheesemaking and more so in this technological age. This was catered for by adopting modern techniques in a new Starter Laboratory and Tank Room which incorporated a flow meter and batch counter system to provide automatic and accurate dosing of the starter into the milk flow line on its way to the cheese vats.

Modern techniques were also introduced in this capital investment programme to the pressing, wrapping, storing of cheese and the handling of whey, all resulting in the cheesemaking process being able to handle 60,000 gallons per day.

The programme costing some £12m. involved stopping cheesemaking at Mauchline and Sorbie Creameries and re-furbishing the Galloway Creamery enabling it to have a throughput of some 150m. litres per annum. As part of a major rationalisation programme within the cheese industry in Scotland, Scottish Pride, together with the Cooperative Wholesale Society and Unigate established the Galloway Cheese Company once more, as a joint venture in 1990.

The milk throughput of the Creamery was 150 million litres per annum, the equivalent of some 330 farms. The daily throughput peaked at 900,000 litres in the spring and reduced to 225,00 litres in the autumn trough period. The cheese production was in excess of 15,000 tonnes per annum of the cheddar variety including some low fat hard cheese. In terms of daily production capacity the Creamery is one of the largest cheddar operations in the world.

More than 2000 tonnes of butter were produced annually, almost half of which was in packet form for Scottish Pride. As a by-product of the cheese operation, some 7,000 tonnes of whey powder was produced annually. The creamery had also the capability to produce skimmed milk powder and casein and was a supplier of skimmed milk to a number of liquid dairies in Scotland for use in low fat milks.

When this investment programme was completed Adam McCartney, Managing Director of Scottish Pride said 'The new plant will provide much needed economy of scale and consequently will ensure that the cheese industry in the South West Scotland is well placed to maintain and develop its competitive advantage, particularly in premium markets.' Sadly this did not reach fruition which was outwith Adam McCartney's control. On 1st November 1993 the Galloway went into liquidation. Therein lies another story.

MAUCHLINE CREAMERY

Mauchline Creamery was strategically built in 1937 on a new site surrounded by many milk producing farms and was well placed to supply the main centre of demand as and when required. It replaced a number of the smaller and economic units in Ayrshire.

Similar to Kirkcudbright the Scottish Milk Powder Company had a skim milk powder factory there alongside the Board's cheese and butter producing units to utilise the skim milk and whey. This too was bought by the S.M.M.B. in 1961.

In 1963 the first continuous butter-making in Britain was installed. This was followed in 1972 by an extensive scheme of reconstruction and re-equipment in 1972 as a result of visits to modern plants in Australasia and leading European countries.

Alfa-Laval O.S.T. enclosed vats and the New Cheddarmaster cheddaring and curd draining conveyor were installed. This was the first occasion on which the Cheddarmaster system was operated outside Australasia. To cope with increasing volumes of whey and skim milk an evaporator of a much greater capacity was also installed.

The imposition of milk quotas in April 1994 had a dramatic effect on the structure of the manufacturing facilities due to the supplies being reduced by almost 20%. Cost-saving campaigns had to be introduced necessitating the centralisation of the butter activities at Mauchline along with the introduction of a high speed cheese pre-packing line. Except for Arran, Rothesay and Campbelton, cheddar cheesemaking was centralised at the Galloway Creamery and the spray drying operation at Kirkcudbright ceased.

TORRYLIN CREAMERY

Torrylin Creamery on the island of Arran was established by the S.M.M.B. in 1945. The creamery was subject to a refurbishment in terms of fabric as well as plant and equipment in 1992 at a cost of £30,000. The new facility still has the traditional hand-made approach to cheesemaking which has served it well over many years.

Milk intake is approximately 2.75 million litres per annum and is supplied exclusively from twelve producers, all of whom are based on the southern half of the island.

Output is approximately 270 tonnes per annum of a hard-pressed cheese somewhat more akin to a Dunlop rather than a typical cheddar type. Whereas much of the cheese produced at the creamery is in 20 kilogram blocks, a growing proportion is made into a wide range of traditional truckles and wheels in an effort to generate additional added value in respect of the output. The small 1 kilogram mini cheese sold under the Arran brand remains at the forefront of the specialist concept, but the round waxed truckles are gaining ground in both home and export markets. Arran cheese can be found in shops in France Belgium, Germany as well as in the U.S.A.

ROTHESAY CREAMERY

The S.M.M.B. first established a creamery in Rothesay in 1954. This was replaced a new one on a greenfield site which was completed in 1991 fora cost of £2.5 million. The new building provides modern, attractive, yet functional design features. The plant and equipment embraces state of the art technology but incorporates a traditional approach which enables the cheesemakers to utilise their skill and experience during the daily production cycles

Rothesay Creamery is supplied by the 32 milk suppliers on the Isle of Bute and has further supplies from eight producers on the Cowal peninsula.

Annual cheese productionis approximately 1,600 tonnes with some 36 tonnes of whey butter produced as a by-product. Cheddar is the dominant variety, but Drumleish, launched by Scottish Pride is also produced at Rothesay.

A proportion of the cheese here is utilised through the Scottish Pride pre-pack operation at Mauchline in Ayrshire.

GLENROTHES CREAMERY

This Creamery was opened in 1958 to absorb growing milk supplies in the Fife and Angus areas. It produced butter and milk powder and was later changed to a liquid milk depot only.

CAMPBELTOWN CREAMERY

At the time of writing, Campbeltown Creamery is operated by Kintyre Creameries Limited, a company in which Scottish Pride has a 67% shareholding in partnerwhip with a venture capital company 3i.

A creamery was first established on the site of an old distillery in 1919 by United Creameries and for many years a range of products from cheese and condensed milk to butter and industrial casein were manufactured. In 1974 Unigate sold the creamery to a family business jointly owned by the family holdings of Rupert Cooper and George Marwick and Campbeltown Creamery Ltd. was established. The new owners converted the operation to cheddar cheese production and established the modern facilities which exist today. In 1990 Campbeltown Creamery Ltd. was acquired by Scottish Pride.

The ‘milk field’ supplying the creamery is based on the Kintyre peninsula south of Tarbert and includes milk produced on the Isle of Gigha. In total 83 producers consign milk daily to Campbeltown. These supplies, together with some additional milk purchased from the North of Scotland M.M.B., provide an annual intake of some 38 million litres for the creamery.

White and coloured cheese is produced at the creamery, with whey butter produced as a by-product. Annual cheese production amounts to some 4,000 tonnes, with whey butter producing around 200 tonnes.

Cheddar is predominately marketed under the Campbeltown brand along with minor brands of Highland and Kilbrannan.

An interesting value added development with good growth potential is reflected in increasing sales of matured waxed truckled cheese under the Mull of Kintyre label. These are becoming established on the home market and are seen as having an important role to play in the Scottish Pride export programme.

Operating as a division of Campbeltown Creamery, Argyll Creameries are involved in processing and distributing fresh pasteurised milk and a range of dairy products throughout the Kintyre peninsula up the west coast to Oban, where the division operates a separate distribution depot. Argyll Creameries' service also covers the islands off the west coast and extends from Barra to Islay.

In the early years of the 1939-45 war the Ministry of Food instigated the setting up of creameries in the West Highlands and Islands- Gigha, Coll, Islay and Lochgilphead. Only Islay is still operating as a private venture.

EXPRESS CREAMERIES

Upper Nithsdale Dairy Farmers' Association was formed in 1919 owned and managed a creamery at Sanquar, which made the locality's summer surplus milk into cheese. The milk was collected by hired lorries organised by the creamery. Previously it was lifted by the creamery's own lorries which proved unsatisfactory. 'Payment was made monthly on a butterfat basis, prices being fixed with regard to those received during the previous month.' The Society had its own retail round where the bulk of the milk was sold. A little milk was sold wholesale and some butter was made and sold locally.

The wholesale milk was sold to the Independent Milk Suppliers in Marylebone, London. This company began in 1919 through the initiative of a newly demobbed Sergeant Allan Mercer using his £17 war pension to buy a churn and a barrow to sell his milk from door to door in London. Its subsidiary, Northern Wholesale Dairies leased the Sanquhar Creamery in 1940 and bought it in 1943. Milk was sent to London from here.

At Lockerbie in the 1930s a group of farmers formed the Dumfries Dairy Company to set up a creamery and milk selling business at Well

Road from where milk cans were conveyed in two hand operated trucks to a railway siding for dispatch to the cities. The Creamery was subsequently operated by the Edinburgh and Dumfriesshire Dairy Company which were also bought over by Northern Wholesale Dairies in 1944. The first pasteurising plant was borrowed from the S.M.M.B. and from 1947 the liquid milk was despatched to St Cuthbert' Cooperative in Edinburgh in 3100 gallon bulk tankers.

In the 1950s there was a considerable increase in milk production in excess of the liquid market demand necessitating the S.M.M.B. to have more manufacturing facilities. It encouraged the establishing of a new cheesemaking creamery on the old wartime R.E.M.E. site at Park Place, Lockerbie in 1954. Unfortunately with a daily output of 22,000 gallons the unwanted excess whey had to be dumped in local quarries and flushed down I.C.I. drains into the Solway Firth until 1956 when a new condensing and drying facility enabled the company to sell the whey powder for animal food.

The Express Dairy Company, who also owned Kilmaurs Creamery in Ayrshire, bought the Sanquhar and Lockerbie Creameries in 1960. In the interests of rationalisation these three smaller plants were replaced in 1975 by Priestdykes Creamery at Lockerbie capable of handling 700,000 litres per day. It was opened by Her Majesty the Queen. The production was concentrated on either cheese and whey powder or butter and skimmed milk powder depending on market reqqirements. As the Company had by this time entered the Food and Catering industry, the organisation became known as the Express Dairy Foods Company Limited.

In 1969 the Company was acquired by Grand Metropolitan who in 1992 hived it off to a management buy-out organised by a group of senior managers and backed by leading investors and international bankers.

CONDENSED MILK PRODUCTS

Condensed milk products were first brought into the UK. by the Anglo-Swiss Company in 1867. Basically sugar was added to milk which made it sweet and appealing. Importantly, a high concentration of sugar inhibited bacterial growth thus giving it a better keeping quality. It was largely consumed in the towns, mainly by the poorer sections of the townspeople. There was a heavy demand for it by the Armed Forces during the First World War, thereafter the demand decreased and prices fell. It has already been noted the a number creameries such as Dunragit and Stewarton were involved in condensed milk products many years ago.

Mr A.H. Philpot formed the Scottish Milk Powder Company and built a drying plant next to the S.M.M.B. Butter Creamery at Kirkcudbright. This was opened on the 27th July 1935 by the Minister of Agriculture, Sir Walter Elliot. Most of the milk powder was then shipped south to companies such as Van den Berg and Jurgens for margarine manufacture and to British Extracting Company for animal feeds.

At that time the only other Milk Powder produced in the U.K. was by Cow & Gate for baby foods. Later roller skim milk powder was produced by Aplin & Barratt and Wilts United Dairies, in an attempt to dispose of their residual skim milk resulting from butter production. The U.K. market for milk by-products e.g. dried whey, skimmed milk, butter milk etc. was largely for the food processing industries. Large importations of skim milk powder from New Zealand and sweetened condensed milk from the Condensed Milk Company in Ireland continued. Thus Company developed from the enterprise of the Cleeve Bros. who came from Canada to Ireland and started a factory for the manufacture of prepared coffee at Landsdowne in Limerick in 1881.

At the outbreak of the war in 1939 A.H. Philpot was asked to join the Minister of Food and be the Chairman of the Milk Powder Pool which was responsible for the distribution of all the milk powder in the U.K. much of which was imported. When the Scottish Milk Powder Company factories at Kirkcudbright and Mauchline were sold to the S.M.M.B. in 1961 he became the sales agent and after the decontrol of food the agent for the other Boards. This led to the formation of the Milk Powder Marketing Company involving three Milk Marketing Boards, Cooperative Wholesale Society and other independent producers.

This company had to be dissolved on the advice of the Monopolies Commission when the Restrictive Trade Practices Act was brought in. The company of A.H. Philpot & Sons (Milk Powders) Ltd. retained the agencies and carried on marketing milk powder.

The Carnation Company was founded in the United States in 1899 by a Stewart family who retained the business until it was sold to Nestle in 1985. It built a factory in Dumfries in 1935 and took over milk condensing which had previously been undertaken in other creameries in South West Scotland. The site was chosen because of the large volume of high quality milk produced in the area, the availablity of river and subterranean water and the proximity of a railway.

Earlier this factory produced a number of products and later concentrated on evaporated milk producing up to 3.2 million cans in 1990, utilising a fifth of the milk allocated for manufacturing by the Scottish Milk Marketing Board. The Carnation factory was closed in 1992 because of a depression in the export market which absorbed most of its production and as a result of an expansion of the Nestle factory at Girvan.

As far back as 1725 Mary Tuke, a Quaker, opened a grocer's shop in York. Her business developed as Wm. Tuke and Sons Ltd. who described themselves as tea dealers but who also roasted coffee and made chocolate. The cocoa and chocolate side of the business was further developed when Henry Isaac Rowantree acquired it in 1862.

Rowntree's introduced their first confectionery line – Fruit Gums and Fruit Pastilles in the 1889s about the same time that a manufacturing business for Mackintosh's Celebrated Toffee was established in Halifax. After beginning as separated companies in the North of England, Rowntree & Co. Ltd. and John Mackintosh & Sons Ltd. grew simultaneously until merging in 1969 into one of the world's major confectionery businesses- Rowantree & Mackintosh.

Its subsidiary Rowntree Mackintosh Confectionery Ltd. opened a chocolate crumb factory on a greenfield site at Grangestone Industrial Girvan in January 1980. This was done after looking at alternative sites in Europe. The Company was encouraged in their decision by the Scottish Milk Marketing Board which was farsighted enough to see the need that the avilable supply of high quality milk should be diversified away from the commodity products, butter and cheese, into a wider range of those with a higher value.

The factory had subsequently undergone an expansion programme when it was bought over by the Nestlé Company in 1985. This made it one of the most modern and hygienic plants of its kind in Europe which can process 125 million litres per annum. The crumb produced is the principal ingredient in the manufacture of milk chocolate which contains 35% milk, 55% sugar and 10% cocoa. It is used for block chocolate, coatings for biscuits, or chocolate assortments in well known products such as Aero, Kit-Kat and Dairy Box. Also in 1985, Nestlé bought the Carnation Foods Creamery at Dumfries.

Henri Nestlé established in Switzerland his first factory producing full cream condensed milk in the late 1860s and it was this product more than any other that Nestle founded its world wide success. The company's first condensery was opened in Aylesbury, Bucks. in 1880.

THE COMPANY OF SCOTTISH CHEESE MAKERS
127, CANDLERIGGS GLASGOW, C.1.
TELEPHONE: BEL 0844

NO. 1 3 2

MAKER John McColm,
ADDRESS Garthland,
Stranraer.

FACTOR A. McLelland & Son,
ADDRESS Cheese Market,
Glasgow.

ALLOTMENT ADVICE NO 3 7 0 2

DATE OF SALE 18.6/3.8.65.

ACCOUNT SALES

IDENTITY MARK	NO. OF CHEESE	GRADE	GRADING CERT. NO.	MONTH OF MAKE	TYPE	WHITE COLOURED OR DUNLOP
1271	43	1	1952	Apr./May.	Cheddar	White
"	8	N.S.	1953	Apr./May.	Cheddar	White

I/We certify that this Account Sales is a true record of the Cheese shown hereon, and I/We enclose cheque for the amount shown in full and final settlement of this transaction.

	£	s.	d.	Price	CWTS.	QTRS.	LBS.
Weight per Allotment Advice					27	1	8
Weight Sold							
43 W/C	334	5	10	275/-	24	1	7
PROCESSING. 8 W/C	47	12	6	210/-	4	2	4
TOTAL WEIGHT SOLD					28	3	11
Price Realised per Cwt.							

Date ... G 1965
For A. McLelland & Son Ltd
Signed [signature]
Factor

FOR C.S.C. USE ONLY	
Check Allotment	
" Calculations	
" Charges Rates	
Recorded Offers Register	
" Day Book	
Shrinkage %	
Recorded Statistics	

	£	s.	d.
TOTAL VALUE	381	18	4
Deduct Commission @ 2%	7	12	9
Discount	3	3	8
Handling 8/- ton 49Cheese	2	10	6
3/- each 2Cheese	-	17	1
TOTAL CHARGES	14	4	-
Net Realisation	367	14	4
Deduct Amount Advanced on Allotment	[illegible]	[illegible]	[illegible]
AMOUNT NOW PAID	[illegible]	[illegible]	[illegible]
C.S.C. USE			
Deduct Company Levy @ 1/3 Cwt	1	16	1
Storage (Invoice Attached) 7550	6	14	6
Freight (Invoice Attached) 7272	1	1	0
TOTAL DEDUCTIONS	9	11	7
Net Realisation To Maker	358	2	9
Deduct Amount Advanced on Acceptance	289	7	10
Net Amount Due By/Due to Company	68	14	11

I certify that the above is a true Account of the sale of the Cheese. A cheque for the amount due by the Company is enclosed.

Date
Signed [signature]
Manager

THE COMPANY OF SCOTTISH CHEESEMAKERS LTD.

Fig. 93 Statement of account for cheese supplied to the Company of Scottish Cheesemakers. 1965

CHAPTER 21

SHOW & SALE

Butter and cheesemaking on the farms were the beginning of commercialism of dairy farming. What was not consumed was bartered for other comforts of life. As towns and villages grew they had their weekly markets to which the farmers' wives and daughters took their butter, cheese, eggs, poultry and honey and sold them direct to the housewives or whoever would buy them.The goods would be carried on their back, paniers on an old pony or in a pony trap along footpaths or rough drove roads.

The main streets must have been scenes of pandemonium. There would be bad tempered cows with calves who were muzzled to prevent the cows from being suckled, noisy bullocks, bleating sheep, the odd kicking horse and noisy bargaining farmers and dealers, many of whom would have too much to drink.

When farms and and cattle numbers increased butchers and dealers went on to the farms and bought the cattle and sheep. there were also cheese buyers interestingly called 'cadgers', who resold into the urban areas. From early days butter and cheese moved over quite long distances. In the 1790s Cheshire cheese was sent from England to the North of Scotland, Berwickshire butter was sold in Edinburgh. In 1812 Mr Traill of Hobbister was making Dunlop cheese for sale in Edinburgh. (Fenton, 1976) Large quantities of butter and cheese moved from Ayrshire into Glasgow.

There was little emphasis on quality when the 'cadgers' were buying dairy produce. there were no grading standards. It was based on personal personal judgement. Initially there were no premises for storing. The cadgers just gave a service by visiting the farms and buying the cheese on the spot at whatever price was decided after a lot of haggling about the amount of the 'indrink' i.e. the loss of weight in cheese between the time of make and deliver to the stores. the custom in the 1860s was to sell the whole season's make in June or July and delivery into the merchants' stores in two or three times a year so that a share of the 'indrink' fell to the factors.

Factors, as the merchants came to be known, established centres for the marketing of farm produce at city Corn Exchanges or the Glasgow Bazaar which was erected in the Candleriggs in 1817 on the site of the old Glasgow Bowling Green.

At the Glasgow Bazaar there were a number of wholesalers, e.g. Andrew Clement & Sons, A. McLelland & Son, Lovell & Christmas, Cooperative Wholesale Society, John Templeton & Sons, J. Hamilton, et al. to whom the 'cheese-cadgers' and local farmers brought their cheese. the Bazaar was open Tuesdays, Wednsdays and Saturdays. 'Cheese bought by provision merchants and others was inspected on the spot and owing to its wide variety of flavour it was sold without any obligation for delivery.'

The farmers were obliged to deliver their cheese to the factors' stores or to the nearest railway station. Some farms had long carts specially made for the transport of cheese e.g. F. R. Evans of Penkiln Farm, Garlieston. At Ingleston of Borgue the cheese and bull calves were carted seven miles to Kirkcudbright station. On the return Journey coal, fertiliser, flour and oatmeal were brought back. In the era of Adam Gray III, the foreman who drove the lead cart had a two gallon jar of whisky which his master consumed with great regularity with his cronies. In Adam's later years he had a piercing whistle which he blew at the window once in the morning to summon the foreman to give him insructions and twice if he wanted to have a discussion with the dairyman.

Probably the oldest cheese factoring business in Scotland is A McLelland & Sons, Ltd. It was founded in Kilmarnock by Provost McLelland and William McFadzean in 1849. For the first ninety years it was in business this company traded only with butter and cheese which was made in Scotland which it sold all over Britain. Complementary to this business which was oparational mainly in the summer months, there was also an animal feeding business which traded mostly in the winter time. Many farmers ran a contra-account which stabilished the cash flow.

When the Minister of Food took control of the distribution food and the Milk Boards acted as agents, the cheesemaking farms and creameries had to nominate the factors they wished to handle their produce. Later it was decided the proportion of this to be traded by each factor was to be according to the volume purchased by the various factors during the years 1937–38–39. The allocation to A. McLelland & Sons was 60–70% of the Scottish cheese made, the remainder being divided between the other factors.

This company still has a large trade in Scottish cheese. It has had for some time a controlling interest in the Islay Creamery and recently acquired a controlling interest in the newly formed Caledonian Cheese Company, Ltd at Stranrarer.

Islay Creamery has long held a good reputation for making

excellent cheese. It once however, bamboozled John McFadzean, who became a director of A. McLelland & Sons. Early in his career John was sent to Islay before his company's corporate involvement to buy the cheese. He was very impreesed by the high quality of the cheese on offer but could not understand the unusually pleasant flavour which he had not experienced before. When it was pointed to him that there were five whisky distilleries on the island and most of the cows were fed on wet draff therefrom, he understood.

Andrew Clement & Sons another important factor moved his business to the Glasgow Bazaar in 1868. The father of Andrew Clement the founder of this business died at an early age his mother had a grocer's shop in Ochiltree, Ayrshire. She specialised in selling butter and cheese which she bought from the local farmers. In a history of Ochiltree – 'old Mrs Clement kept a small shop in the village famous for the quality of the cheese she sold.'

Son Andrew, after shepherding on the Fenwick moor for six or seven years, worked for John Wilson a provision merchant in Glasgow. Thereafter he began a provision retailing business on his own in 1861 at 80, South Wellington Street. In order to enter the wholesale butter and cheese business he moved to the Glasgow Bazaar.

The McAdam brothers, who have already been mentioned, sold all their cheese to Andrew Clement. James married his cousin Mary Clement and became known as 'the King of Dairymen'. When Robert emigrated to Rome, New York State to start a small cheese factory, Andrew Clement imported his cheese.

Another friend of Andrew Clement, Thomas Ballantyne emigrated to Stratford, Ontario, and exported his branded 'Black Creek' cheese to George Bowles, a wholesale merchant at Smithfield, who was the main importer of American and Canadian cheese. In 1875 Andrew Clement visited Canada and America to check on the prospects of developing the importing side of the business. Parallel to this his eldest son, Thomas, was sent to study cheese industry in Canada under the supervision of Dr. J.W. Robertson from Stranraer, yet another friend of Andrew Clement. Dr. Robertson ultimately became the Dairy Commissioner for Canada and he had a strong influence on thomas Clement with regard to the importance of scientific knowledge for cheesemaking in relation to quality.

Andrew Clement's thoughts about the future of his business was to take on a new dimension by the growth in production of Canadian and American Cheese coupled with the personal connections he had with that

ANDREW CLEMENT & SONS, LTD.

(FOUNDED 1861)

BUTTER & CHEESE IMPORTERS & MERCHANTS

Head Office:
64 ALBION STREET,
GLASGOW, C. 1.
Telegrams:
"Clementine, Glasgow."

Managing Directors:
Sir THOMAS CLEMENT, K.B.E.
JAMES CLEMENT.

London Office:
29 TOOLEY STREET,
LONDON, S.E. 1.
Telegrams:
"Oxtall, Boro, London."

Branches in
Manchester, Liverpool, Newcastle, Leith, New Zealand, Australia, Canada, and Argentine.

A VIEW OF PART OF OUR STORE

FINEST SCOTCH CHEDDARS AND DUNLOPS

Importers of the Best Brands of New Zealand, Australian, and Irish Butter, and New Zealand and Canadian Cheese.

CONSIGNMENTS SOLICITED—
WE HAVE THE GENUINE OUTLETS

ALL GOODS HANDLED BY EXPERIENCED STAFF AND SOLD TO BEST ADVANTAGE

Fig. 94 Advertisment from Glasgow Herald 1934

Fig. 95 Andrew Clement & Sons Ltd, Head Office, 64 Albion Street, Glasgow.

Fig. 96 Staff at Andrew Clement & Sons Ltd, Glasgow.

industry. He also saw the vast potential that was becoming available with Australia and New Zealand emerging as large exporters of butter and cheese. Furthermore, for many years Liverpool held first place as port of entry for American and Canadian produce, followed by Glasgow and Bristol, London being fourth.This meant that many London merchants had to travel to Liverpool each week to attend the market. They stipulated their requirements to brokers who took them round the various importers where the produce was examined. For these services, including forwarding, the brokers received half a percent commission. All this motivated Andrew Clement to expand his business in London.

To progress this he financed a company, Andrew Cruickshank and Company, American Cheese Agents at Sun Wharf, Tooley Street. Andrew Cruickshank had spent some time in America. Later Andrew Clement became concerned about the risks that Andrew Cruickshank was taking and instigated a son of Robert McAdam to join the firm as a partner. The firm became known as C. McAdam and company. Disputes arose between the partners and Andrew Cruickshank left the Company. He persuaded a Somerset cheesemaker to join him in a business. This ultimately became Lovell & Christmas a well known cheese factoring company in the U.K.

In 1890 Andrew Clement and his wife visited Australia and New Zealand and found that the butter made in Australia of a superior quality to that produced in the U.K. He was encouraged to buy some as the Australian Government were offering 4d. per pound subsidy for all that was exported in the ships fitted with refrigerators. The first consignment he shipped made 4d. per pound profit in London, the same as the export subsidy.

This led to an extensive importing trade between Australia and New Zealand and Andrew Clement & Sons under the management of Andrew's son Thomas, later Sir Thomas Clement. Sir Thomas also travelled extensively in Russia, Italy and Argentine persuading under-developed areas to adapt themselves to expand milk production for the manufacture of butter and cheese for the U.K. markets to sustain this country's growing industrial population. With this vast experience he was an obvious choice to be appointed Chairman of the Cheese and Butter Imports Committee of the Ministry of Food, during the First World War.

Since the beginning of the twentieth century there have been changes in the source of cheese supplies. Before 1939 65% of the cheese was imported from canada and about 3% from New Zealand whereas, after that New Zealand supplied 68% and Canada only 4%. Australia, Denmark, the Netherlands Germany and Ireland have been the other main suppliers. (Houston, 1961.)

After the war, Sir Thomas became a strong supporter of 'Empire Preference' and of Lord Beaverbrook's 'Empire Crusade', who said that. 'The Empire Crusade is a movement to weld the British Empire into a single economic whole enjoying complete freedom of trade between its component parts and protected against the rest of the world by tariff walls. It is founded on the belief that the British Empire is already able to supply its own needs of food and raw materials; it aims to create a new era of prosperity and a high standard of living for all who dwell under the British flag. In the new order which it seeks to bring into being the British farmer must play a vitally important part.' Sir Thomas supported this by saying in 1929 that:–

'I am convinced that a great expansion of employment in British agriculture would readily take place if only the farmer were guaranteed a fair market for his produce.'

Andrew Clement took a keen interest in promoting good cheese at home although he had a rapidly increasing trade from overseas. At a Cheesemaker' conference held at Castle Douglas in 1901 he said that:–

'Although various experiments have been made within the last few years with the object of turning out a perfect cheese, we are still a long way from producing an article such as the public demand. These experiments have not proved altogether a success and will be required to be continued until some better results can be obtained. Our cheese shows should be used more and more for this purpose.'

In 1894 at the second annual open dairy produce show held in the Castle Douglas Town Hall there were 1300 cheeses entered. 'It was noted that a number were inclined to be plain and hard and a few were fiery.' This show continued at the annual county show until farm cheesemaking ceased. Similar local cheese shows were held in other parts of the country such as Stranraer and Dumfries.

In 1900 Fullwood & Bland, Ellesmere, presented a handsome trophy to the Castle Douglas Cheese Show. It was enclosed in a glass dome making the overall height 29 inches. It was valued at £1,000. In 1917–19 it was won outright by William McLean, Arwick, Ardwell. Fullwood, Ltd. acquired it from his daughter, Miss Jessie McLean, Balgowan, in 1994.

These local shows also acted like the hiring fairs of old, where farmers in need of a dairymen sought information of their availabilty or engaged them if found suitable. The cheese factors played a part in introductions. They were in a strong position, because being buyers they knew how good or bad the dairymen were at making cheese.

The part that the Royal Highland and Agricultural Society of Scotland has played over the years in organising butter and cheese shows as well as having classes at the Highland Shows as has already been noted. There were butter and cheese classes at many of the local shows throughout the country until the demise of the farm cheesemaking. the competition and rivalry was keen. No more so than in the county of Ayr, where it was said that "Every one of the 46 parishes had its local 'society' besides 'estate clubs'." Lord Palmerston once remarked that, 'Agriculture, like every other industry, is promoted by the interchange of ideas, by mutual intercommication of knowledge by one man telling others what he has done, how he has succeeded and how he has failed.' The 'Kilmarnock Farmers' is the oldest society being established in 1786.

Following the Ayrshire Association's success in its promoting the making of Cheddar cheese throughout Scotland, it further stimulated interest in it by holding the first public exhibition of Scotch Cheddar cheese at Ayr in 1855, at which Mr and Mrs Harding exhibited. In the following year and annually thereafter it was held at Kilmarnock. For a time there were three cheese fairs held annually at Kilmarnock, the principal being held in October. This exhibition later drew entries from many other dairying countries. In addition to cheese there was a large number of exhibits of butter, grain and roots.

There was a report in the *Kirkcudbright Advertiser* of a show held on 31st October 1879. 'In all the departments there was a decrease in the number of entries; but the depressed state of agriculture and the unseasonable weather during the past year no doubt sufficiently account for the falling off.'

Year	Cheese	Butter	Grain	Roots
1876	362	354	52	122
1877	478	354	42	90
1878	485	282	61	182
1879	409	263	38	114

'In looking over the prize list it will be seen that in Class I with the extraordinary number of 85 entries, Mr William Smith, dairyman, Slagnaw, Castle Douglas, was awarded the first prize with very fine samples full of meat and well flavoured.

Sweet milk cheese according to any method – 85 entries –
1, William Smith, Slagnaw, Kelton, Castle Douglas; 2, William Master, Challoch, Dunragit; 3, James Smith, Balgreddan, Kirkcudbright; 4,

Daniel Kirkland, Airdrie, Kirkbean; 5, William and Thomas Allen, Crockwood, Erchfont, Davies, Wilts.; 6, James Lauder, Clapton Farm, Cucklington, Wincanton, Somerset; 7, Alexander Plunkett, Ingleston Borgue, Kirkcudbright; 8, James Hoddinott, Hillhouse, Lipyet, Bath, Somerset; 9, James McAdam, Brough, Southwick; 10, Mathew Stewart, Shawsholm, Dumfries; 11, George McKerrow, Conchieton, Kirkcudbright; 12, Bryce Nairn, East Welton, Mauchline; 13, David Roger, Drumoral, Isle of Whithorn.

Sweet milk cheese made according to the Cheddar method – 76 entries– 1, Robert Gibson, Valleyfield, Kirkcudbright; 2, William Smith, Slagnaw, Kelton, Castle Douglas; 3, George McKerrow, Conchieton, Kirkcudbright; Nairn, High Landslide, Craigie; 5, James Smith, Balgreddan Kirkcudbright; James Whyte, Kirkmabreck, Sandhead Stranraer.

There was a class for a ton of cheese of any kind or shape, shown in bulk at the fair and entered in the name of the maker. The cheese to be made in the present season. – 1, James Smith, Balgreddan, Kirkcudbright; 2, John Kirk, Muncraig, Borgue, Kirkcudbright; 3, Daniel Kirkland, Airdrie, Kirkbean; 4, Alexander Dunlop, Curragh, Girvan; 5, James Wylie, Mossgiel, Mauchline; 6, Alexander Plunkett, Ingleston, Borgue, Kirkcudbright.

There were other classes for – Two cheese made strictly according to the Dunlop method, 13 entries; Loaf cheese, Cheddar, or any other imitation English, 44 entries; Uncoloured cheese made according to any method, 48 entries. There were also special classes for cheese made which were coloured by Nicholl's annatto or by Mitchell's annatto and a class confined to Ayrshire cheesemakers.

The judges for cheese were, Messrs George Gibbons, Tunley Farm, Bath; Thomas Gibson, Edinburgh; Alex. Osborne, Glasgow; James Allan, Jr. Glasgow. John Burn, Edinburgh; James Weir, Glasgow and John MacLelland, Glasgow.

Many of the exhibits were sold and the buyer of them often contracted to buy the season's make of the owner. At this particular show the cheddar cheese averaged 60–65s. per cwt. and the Dunlop 55–58s. per cwt. the first prize ton of cheese made 71s 6d. per cwt.

After the event a large number of members of the Association dined in the George Hotel, Kilmarnock, which was chaired by the Earl of Eglinton. M.P.s, landlords and local dignitaries also attended. The toast list was extensive. There were toasts and replies to the Houses of Parliament, the army, the navy, the Lord-Lieutenant of the county, the Ayrshire Agricultural Association, the Judges, the Clergy, the Provost and Magistrates and Exhibitors and Visitors from other Counties. It can be well understood why this occasion began in the afternoon!

The premier cheese show in the world was held for many years in conjunction with the London Dairy Show at Olympia. Towards the end of each year varieties of cheese from all over the world were exhibited there.

There was a magnificent Lonsdale cup for the champion farmhouse cheese of any variety in England, Scotland and Wales. Galloway cheesemakers won this coveted cup many times over the years – Sam McColm, Garrochtree, Port Logan; Gavin Love, Killumpha, Port Logan; John Whyte, Kirmabreck, Sandhead; George McDowall, Boreland, Glenluce; John Niven, Mahaar, Kirkcolm and James Donley, Kirkeoch, Twynholm and J.A. Houston, Overlaw, near Kirkcudbright.

These men won this cup at least once but Willie Rodger who was the cheesemaker for John Niven, Mahaar, had a unique record. In 1949 he won the reserve championship, in the years 1950–1952 inclusive, he won the championship. He followed this in 1953 by again winning the reserve championship.

At this show there was also a cup for the best cheese made in a creamery. Here again, Galloway cheesemakers were prominent. For a period of ten years this cup came into the Galloway area being won at various times by Dalbeattie, Sandhead, Galloway and the Cooperative Wholesale Society Creameries. The latter Creamery under the manager, James Lorimer, won this cup three years in succession.

Judging cheese at this event must have been a daunting task. John McFadzean previously mentioned, related how he once judged a class of cheddar cheese at Olympia along with an English colleague in which there were 160 entries of pairs of cheese. John started judging at one end of the class and his colleague at the other. On completion of this, they compared notes. Without consultation they both selected the same best ten cheese and placed them in the same order except they differed which entry was to be sixth and seventh.

The introduction of grading standards changed the whole status of showing and selling of cheese. the original grading system was introduced in New Zealand by Dr Ruddick, a Canadian, with whom Sir Thomas Clement became friendly when he was in Canada as young man studying cheesemaking. Cheese thereafter was classified to standards of quality.

This meant that the factors financed the holding of the cheese, supervised its further maturing period, graded the cheese according to market needs and acted as first-hand wholesalers.

From 1940 to 1945 the Ministry of Food purchased all the cheese and controlled its distribution to such an extent that during the war it ordered maximum cheddar production in place of many regional varieties because of its better keeping qualities. It also insisted that the factors weighed all the cheese before it was allocated out to the shops. There was one month during the war there was no home produced cheese available in the South and West Scotland only very poor cheese from New Zealand.

In 1954 the Ministry gave the industry only six months notice of its intention to relinquish this control and that the manufacturers would have to market the products themselves. Thereupon the Scottish Cheese Factors Association intimated that its members were unable to finance the purchase cheese on the old system as it would take seven times as much money as before the war.

The five main manufacturers at the time, the Scottish Milk Marketing Board, Scottish Wholesale Cooperative Society, United Creameries, Northern Wholesale Dairies and East Kilbride Dairy Farmers decided to form the Company of Scottish Cheesemakers, a non-profit-making concern limited by guarantee. In due time every Scottish Cheddar creamery maker and farm cheesemaker became a member of the Company.

The Company came into operation on the 6th December 1954. the Management Committee comprised of John G. Inglis, chairman and Messrs. A.F.H. Briscoe, A. McBride, George P. Ross and W.D. Smith. Its main objectives were,–

(1) to improve the quality of Scottish Cheddar by organising an independent grading system and mark cheese by grade and Scottish origin.

2) to promote more efficient marketing of cheese produced in Scotland by buying, financing, selling cheese and arranging advertising.

The procedure was for cheesemakers to offer cheese for grading about four weeks after manufacture; the Company graded the cheese and was obliged to buy it from the makers paying 80% of its estimated current value. the Company stored the cheese in its own stores or arranged to leave it in the creamery stores. When the Company considered that the cheese should be marketed it was offered to the factors who could accept or reject the offers. If the factors accepted, the were liable to pay 80% of the estimated value to the Company. When the factors sold the cheese they paid the Company the difference between this and the full market value after deducting factors' commission and other expenses. the Company in turn settled with the cheesemaker after deducting a levy for its services.

To grade the cheese into the categories of Choicest, First Grade, Graded and No Stamp, two cheese experts were appointed in 1954. Mr John Gardner, who had made cheese on farms and creameries and lectured at Auchencruive and Mr Gilbert Brine, from New Zealand with wide cheesemaking experience who later worked for the Minister of Food.

In the mid 50's the Company bought two buildings which were converted into cheese stores, one at Gelston and one at Castle Kennedy near Stranraer. These stores proved of value to the Company members in supplying additional storage at very competitive rates which created income for the Company of Scottish Cheesemakers and savings in storage costs for members using them.

To maintain the long time established showing of dairy produce, the Company of Scottish Cheesemakers staged their inaugural Trade Show in the Trades House, Glasgow in 1966. A similar trade show for butter was held in the nearby premises of Andrew Clement & Sons Ltd.

In welcoming some two hundred guests John G. Inglis, Chairman of the Company, said that Scottish would make a greater impact on the market if it were marketed under a single brand name instead of a variety of individual trade brand names.

The various winners of the butter and cheese contests were:-

The McLelland Perpetual Challenge Cup (for the best exhibit in the cheese section) – ScottishMilk Marketing Board, Dalbeattie.

The Lovell and Christmas Perpetual Challenge Cup (for the best exhibit of cheddar)- ScottishMilk Marketing Board, Dalbeattie.

The Gilmour Perpetual Challenge Cup (for the best exhibit of home produced rindless cheese) – Express Dairy Co. Ltd., Appleby.

The Clare Cup (for the best truckle exhibit) – Scottish Milk Marketing Board Torryinn.

The Andrew Clement Trophy (for the best exhibit in the butter section)– New Zealand Dairy Co. Ltd., Taupiri, New Zealand. Reserve – Scottish Milk Marketing Board, Kirkcudbright.

The Company of scottish Cheesemakers' cheese grading trophy for the best creamery-made cheese was won by Sorbie Creamery.

The Company of Scottish Cheesemakers' cheese grading trophy for the best farmhouse cheese section was won by Mr Robert Maxwell, Ross Farm, Borgue, Kirkcudbright.

In 1968, the Company appointed an advertising Agency to widen the scope and promotion of Scottish Cheese. Over the years since then advertising for Scottish cheese progressed and introduced new themes to suit the requirements of a changing industry and changes in the population's buying habits and tastes. These became indentified with the development of 'Own label' brands in the supermarkets which sprang up all over the country.

In order to compete with other own brand labels the Scottish Milk Marketing launched the Scottish Pride logo in 1957. This covers a range of over fifty product lines which can be found in most of the major outlets throughout the country.

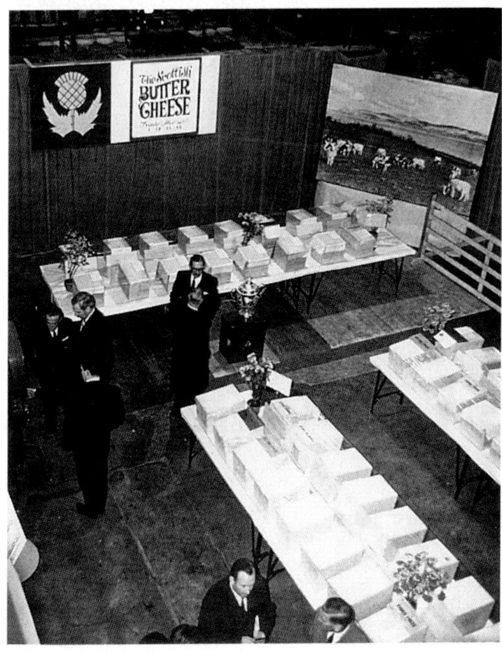

Fig. 97 The Scottish Cheese & Butter Trade Show, 1966

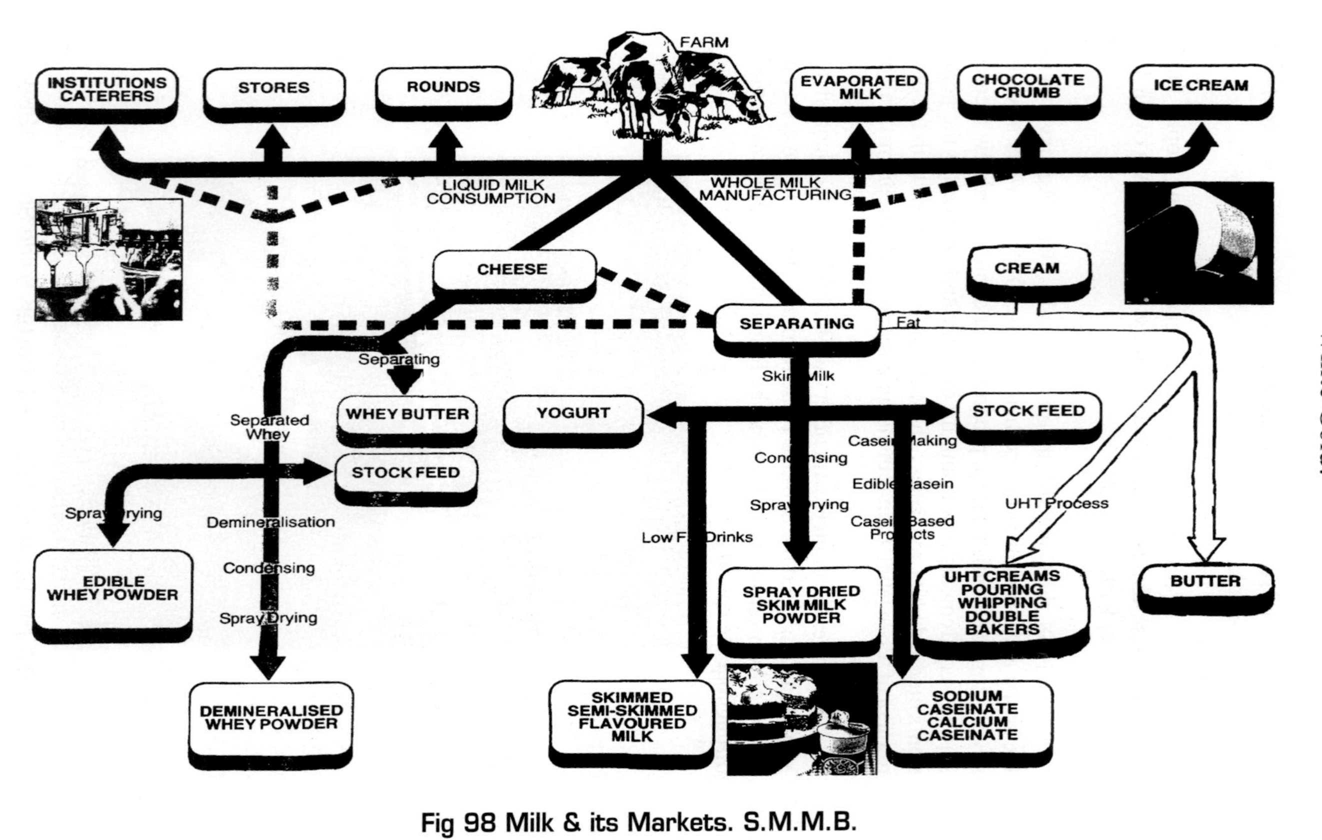

Fig 98 Milk & its Markets. S.M.M.B.

APPENDICES

APPENDIX 1

CHAIRMEN OF THE SCOTTISH MILK MARKETING BOARD.

Earl of Stair,	1933–1935.
Sir George Wilson,	1935–1950.
Sir James B. Douglas,	1950–1962.
Sir William Young,	1962–1980.
Mr Robert Lammie,	1980–1982.
Mr Andrew Howie,	1982–1994.

BOARD MEMBERS 1934–1994.

G.A. ANDERSON, 7 Edgehill Road, Bearsden, Glasgow. 1978–84.
(Appointed Member.)
Mrs J. BEATTIE, J.P. 22 Townhead Street, Bearsden, Glasgow. 1975–81.
(Appointed Member.)
HUGH BAIRD, Silvercraigs, Kirkcudbright. 1934.
ALEXANDER BATCHELOR, Craigie Home Farm, Dundee.1934.
F.A. BELL, Chapelbank, Auchterarder. 1934–38.
ALEXANDER BUCHANAN, Garscadden Mains, Bearsden,
Glasgow. 1940–44
GEORGE BUCHANNAN, Hunterhill, Paisley. 1934–40
M. BOWIE, Easter Balmuidy, Maryhill, Glasgow. 1941–43
JACK BREWSTER, Boclair, Bearsden, Glasgow. 1943–87
J.A. BROWN, Gaindykehead, Airdrie, Lanarkshire. 1982–94
JOHN CALDWELL, Moorfield, Kilmarnock, Ayrshire. 1977–81
MRS C. CAMPBELL, 10 Westray Road, Cumbernauld,
Glasgow. (Appointed Member) 1982–90
HENRY CHRISTIE, Monreith Estate Office, Portwilliam,
Wigtownshire. 1980–88
J.W. CLEMENT, East Pitkierie, Anstruther, Fife. 1958–64
JOHN M. DAVIDSON, 11 Ravenstone Drive, Giffnock,
Glasgow. (Appointed Member.) 1957–61
SIR JAMES B. DOUGLAS, C.B.E.,Barstibly, Kirkcudbright 1936–62
JOHN DUNCAN, Castlehill, Maybole, Ayrshire. 1993–94

W.B.R. ELDER, M.B. Mid Glen Farm, Langbank, Glasgow. 1975–79
FRASER R. EVANS, Penkiln, Garlieston, Wigtownshire. 1987–94
W.L. FORREST, Mersington, Greenlaw, Berwickshire. 1968–80
A.G. GIBB-SHIRRA, Wyndhead, Lauder, Berwickshire. 1935–36
MRS A.M.GILCHRIST,46 Broompark Drive,Newton Meavns,
Glasgow. (Appointed Member) 1990–94
SIR ALEXANDER GLEN, K.B.E., C.B., M.C., 17 Merchiston
Gardens, Edinburgh.(Appointed Member.) 1960–63
W. GRAHAM, Lugate, Stow, Midlothian, 1937–41
ADAM GRAY, O.B.E., Ingleston of Borgue, Kirkcudbright. 1981–94
STEPHEN HARRISON,Airdrie Farm,Kirkbean,Dumfriesshire
1962–66
W.J.HARVEY, 29 Roseburn Terrace, Glasgow. 1934
W.C. HEWITT, 121 Dundonald Road, Kilmarnock. 1951–53
(Appointed Member.)
ANDREW L. HOWIE, C.B.E., Newmill House, Dunlop,
Ayrshire. 1980–94
ROBERT HOWIE, Drumfork Farm, Helensburgh. 1950.
PROF. T.L. Johnston, M.A., Ph.D. 14 Mansionhouse Road,
Edinburgh. (Appointed Member.) 1967–72
ROBERT A. LAMMIE, Low Dromore, Stranraer. 1966–82
W. LEITCH, M.B.E.12 Clarence Street, Clydebank, Glasgow 1953–57
(Appointed Member.)
SIR WILLIAM LITHGOW, Drums, Langbank, Glasgow. 1979–83
DAVID MARSHALL, O.B.E. East Port, Dunfermline. 1938–60
(Appointed Member.)
JOHN MARSHALL, Hardgrove, Carrutherston, Dumfriesshire
1969–81
JAMES McINTYRE, C.B.E., Barbeth, Stranraer. 1982–86
JAMES A. MINTO, Coulterhaugh, Biggar. 1966–82
MRS E. MUNDELL, Kilchamaig, Whitehouse Tarbet,Argyll. 1887–94
ALEXANDER NEWLANDS,31 Sutherland Avenue, Glasgow
(Appointed Member.) 1934
ROBERT PATE, Muirsland, Lesmahagow, Glasgow. 1962–66
Dr. J.D. POLLOCK,Manor House, Boswall Road, Edinburgh. 1936–38
(Appointed Member.)
SIR JOHN URE-PRIMROSE, Gannochy Farm, Perth. 1940–56
(Appointed Member.)
D.H. ROSS, T.D., M.A., B.L. Oillorn, Baldernock, Milngavie,
Glasgow. (Appointed Member.) 1961–67

A.D.S. ROWLAND, 24 Aytoun Road, Glasgow. 1984–94
(Appointed Member.)
F.A. ROTTENBURG, Lochlane House, Crieff, Perthshire. 1940–43
(Appointed Member.)
J. RUSSELL, Walston Mansion, Dunsyre, Stirlingshire. 1952–62
E. SANDYS, 40 Westbourne Crescent, Bearsden, Glasgow. 1974–78
(Appointed Member.)
A.R. SEMPLE, O.B.E., Charlesfield, Annan, Dumfriesshire. 1955–69
ROBERT SIMPSON, Duchlage, Crieff, Perthshire. 1888–94
JOHN SPEIR, Newton Farm, Hallside, Glasgow. 1935–39
THE EARL of STAIR, D.S.O. Lochinch Castle, Stranraer. 1934–45
J.S. STEVENSON, Balig, Ballantrae, Ayrshire. 1935–45
R.H.U. STEVENSON, Corseclays, Ballantrae, Ayrshire. 1953–77
D.A. ROSS STEWART, 13 Blacket Place, Edinburgh. 1969–75
(Appointed Member.)
D.T. STRATTON, Braehead, London Road, Kilmarnock. 1935–51
(Appointed Member.)
JOHN VALLANCE, Auchness, Ardwall, Wigtownshire. 1945–52
WILLIAM WEIR, Wheatrig, Kilmaurs, Ayrshire. 1981–93
JOHN WHITEFORD, Nether Southbar, Inchinnan, Paisley. 1944–75
DAVID YELLOWLEES, Muirhall Farm, Perth. 1964–88
A.S.L. YOUNG, Templeton Street, Glasgow. 1934
(Appointed Member.)
SIR WILLIAM YOUNG, C.B.E. Skerrington Mains, Hurlford,
Ayrshire. 1962–80
SIR GEORGE WILSON, Carbeth Home Farm, Balfron,
Stirlingshire. 1935–50
IAN WILSON, Drum, Beeswing, Kirkcudbrightshire. 1988–94
W.J.WRIGHT, C.B.E. The Heugh, Berwickshire. 1942–62

APPENDIX 2

SCHEME & PRINCIPAL AMENDING LEGISLATION

The Scottish Milk Marketing Scheme (Approval) Order 1933
The Scottish Milk Marketing Scheme (Coopted Members) Order 1934
The Scottish Milk Marketing Scheme (Amendment)Order 1935
The Scottish Milk Marketing Scheme (Amendment No. 2) Order 1935
The Scottish Milk Marketing Scheme (Amendment) Order 1937
The Scottish Milk Marketing Scheme (Amendment) Order 1950
The Scottish Milk Marketing Scheme Amendment (Approval) Order 1956
The Scottish Milk Marketing Scheme Amendment (Approval) Order 1968
The Scottish Milk Marketing Schemes Amendment Regulations 1978
The Scottish Milk Marketing Schemes Amendment Regulations 1979
The Scottish Milk Marketing Schemes Amendment Regulations 1981
The Agricultural Marketing Act 1958 and Milk Marketing Schemes Amendment Regulations 1981
The Scottish Milk Marketing Scheme Amendment (Approval) Order 1982
The Scottish Milk Marketing Schemes (Amendment) Regulations 1988
The Scottish Milk Marketing Scheme (Consolidation) Approval Order 1989
The Agricultural Act 1993. (Ending of Milk Marketing Schemes)

APPENDIX 3

PRODUCER NUMBERS IN SCOTLAND

Producer numbers in the S.M.M.B. are account for about 90% of all registered milk producers in U.K.

Their number has fallen by over 72% since the formation of the Boards in 1933. Over the last twenty years the rate of decline has averaged just under 3% per year.

SCOTLAND

1934	8991
1939	8945
1945	8926
1950	8754
1955	8678
1960	8012
1965	6892
1970	5383
1975	4120
1980	3330
1984	3051
1988	2705
1992	2508

TOTAL PRODUCTION IN SCOTLAND (Millions of litres)

SCOTLAND

1934	551
1939	606.2
1945	612.8
1950	830.5
1955	953.6
1960	1045.0
1965	1086.1
1970	132.3
1975	1187.4
1980	1258.0
1984	1406.1
1988	1192.9
1992	1193.0

AVERAGE MILK YIELD PER COW PER YEAR (litres) including estimates of the amount of milk retained on farms.

SCOTLAND

1939	2805
1945	2536
1950	2949
1955	3350
1960	3477
1965	3539
1970	3736
1975	4359
1980	4532
1984	5000
1988	5006
1992	5138

AVERAGE DAIRY HERD SIZE

SCOTLAND

1934	25.8
1942	31
1955	37
1960	39
1970	55
1975	71
1981	85
1984	90
1987	91
1990	91
1992	91

Scottish Milk

Product Knowledge

MILKS

COW'S MILK: the basic product.

Milk as from the cow, with no modification, has an average composition in the U.K. of: 3.9% fat, 3.2% protein, 4.6% lactose.

PROCESSED MILK:

Pasteurised milk: Heated to not less than 71.7°c for at least 15 seconds. This treatment will kill the most resistant pathogenic bacteria found in milk. 84% of the milk sold in the U.K. market is pasteurised.

Sterilised milk: Heated at over 100°c for a period, usually 20–45 minutes. This can extend shelf life to about one year.

U.H.T. treated milk: Heated to not less that 132°c for at least one second. The shelf is extended to about six months. The market share of this milk is about 4%.

Homogenised milk: This is milk which has been subjected to a mechanical treatment which breaks up the fat globules so that the cream is evenly dispersed throughout the milk and does not form a cream layer. There is no change in composition. This milk accounts for 4% of the consumer market.

Semi-skimmed milk: Standardised to a fat content of 1.6%, 3.8% protein and 4.7% lactose.

Skimmed milk: Cream is separated from the milk so that very little fat remains. The average composition is .1% fat, 3.3% protein and 4.8% lactose. Vitamins A and D having been removed with the fat can be replaced.

Drinking yoghurt: In making yoghurt, milk is cultured with a yoghurt starter (lactobaccilli and streptococci) to convert lactose into lactic acid, which causes some protein coagulation. Drinking yoghurts may be made by culturing low fat milk with added skimmed milk powder and adding sugar and flavouring, or they may be made by blending yoghurt, milk and fruit juice. A typical composition is: .3% fat, 3.2% protein and 14.9% carbohydrate (sugar plus lactose).

APPENDIX 4
BIBLIOGRAPHY

The following are the principal books that have been consulted and occasionally followed.

ABBREVIATIONS

O.S.A. Old Statistical Account, 21 volumes.

N.S.A. New Statistical Account.

T.H.A.S.S. = Transactions of the Highland and Agricultural Society of Scotland

1793–1816 Board of Agricultural Surveys of Agiculture of Great Britain by counties. Volumes on Scotland usually bear the title General View of the Agriculture of the County of...etc.

AGNEW, Sir ANDREW, 1893. *Hereditary Sheriffs of Galloway.*

AITON, Wm. 1811. *Agriculture in Ayrshire. Board of Agriculture,*

AITON, Wm. 1825. A Treatise of the Dairy Breed and Dairy Husbandry, with an Account of the Lanarkshire Breed of Horses. T.H.A.S.S.

BAKER STANLEY, 1973. *Milk to Market.* London.

BAKKER, Dr. D.L. 1948. *A History of the Dutch Cow.*

BAYNE, Rev. JOHN, 1935. *Dunlop Parish.*

BEATSON, ROBERT. 1794. *Agriculture in Fife.* Board of Agriculture

BECKER, R. 1973. *Dairy Cattle Breeds Origin and Development*, Florida.

BECKETT, J.V. 1990. *The Agricultural Revolution*

BIGGAR, JAMES. 1876. *Agriculture of Kirkcudbrightshire and Wigtownshire.*

BOUTFLOUR, MARY, 1965. *Bobby Boutflour. The Life and Reminiscences.*

BROWN, Hume, P. *Scotland before 1700.*

BURN, SCOTT. *Outlines of Modern Farming.* Lockwood

CAMPBELL, R.H. 1991. *Owners and Occupiers.*

CHEKE, V. 1959. *The Story of Cheesemaking in Britain*

CRAWLEY, JAMES, 1976. *Unpublished notes on the History of Creameries.*

CROCKETT, S.R. 1904. *Raiderland*

CUTFORTH COMMISSION, 1936. *Milk Report of the Reorganisation Commission for Great Britain.*

DEFOE, DANIEL. *Tours through England.*

DIXON, H.H. (1822–1870) *Known as the 'Druid'.* Field and Fern.

DONALDSON Rev. Wm. 1816. *A Report of the Machars and Rhins.*
DONALDSON, Rev. Wm. 1811.
A Report of the Southern District of Ayrshire.
DONNACHIE, Ian. 1971. *Industrial Archeology of Galloway.*
DOUGLAS, CHAS. T.H.A.S.S. 1919.
Scottish Agriculure during the War
DOUGLAS, CHAS. T.H.A.S.S. 1921. The Policy of the Agricultural Act.
ERNLE, LORD. 1961. *English Farming, Past and Present.*
FARRAR-HOCKLEY, A.H. 1964. *"The Somme."*
FARRAL, THOMAS. T.H.A.S.S. 1876. On the Ayrshire Breed of Cattle.
FAWCETT, A. 1988. *Women at War. Chronicle of the 20th Century.*
FENTON, ALEXANDER. 1976. *Scottish Country Life.*
FLINN, M.W. 1965.
The Economic and Social History of Britain.1066–1939
FRANKLIN, T.B. 1948 *A History of Agriculture.*
FRANKLIN, T.B. 1951. *A History of Scottish Farming.*
FOLEY, J. 1993. The Irish Dairy Industry: A Historical Perspective.
The Journal of the Society of Dairy Technology.
FREW, Rev. DAVID. 1909. *A History of the Parish of Urr.*
FULLARTON, Col. 1793. *Agriculture in Ayrshire.* Board of Agriculture
FUSSELL, G.E. 1952. *The Farmers' Tools.* London.
GARNER, F.H. 1946. *British Dairying.*
GRAHAM, HENRY. 1906.
The Social Life of Scotland in the 18th Century
GREEN,C.E.& YOUNG,D. 1907. *Encyclopaedia of Agriculture.*
GREENSHIELD, J.B. The art of Cheesemaking as practised in England,
1859. T.H.A.S.S. Pamphlet No. 39.
GRIGG COMMISSION. 1933.
Report of the Reorganisation Commission for Milk
HALDANE, A.R.B. 1952. *The Drove Roads of Scotland.* London.
HANDLEY, JAMES. 1953. *Scottish Farming in the 18th Century.*
HANDLEY, JAMES. 1963. *The Agricultural Revolution in Scotland.*
HALL,S.J.G.& CLUTTON-BROCK, J. *200 Years of British Livestock.*
HARLEY, WILLIAM. 1829. *The Harlian Dairy System.* London.
HENDERSON, T.G. T.H.A.S.S. 1929.
Agricultural Cooperation in Scotland.
HOARD'S DAIRYMAN, U.S.A.
HOBSON, GEORGE. T.H.A.S.S. 1918. British Friesian Cattle.
HOBSON, GEORGE. c.1921. *Livestock of the Farm, Vol.1.*
HOBSON, GEORGE. 1930. *History of British Cattle.*

HOUSTON, George. 1961. *Report for the Market of Scottish Cheese.*
HUTCHESON, A. The Past and Future of Scottish Agriculture. T.H.A.S.S. 1899.
JACKSON, JAMES. T.H.A.S.S. 1840. A Treatise on Agriculture and Dairy Husbandry.
JANSSON TAGE, 1973. *The Development of the Milking Machine.*
JENKINS, ALAN. 1970. *Drinka Pinta.* National Milk Publicity Council.
JOHNSTON, Rev. Bryce. 1794. *Agriculture in the County of Dumfries.*
JONES, C. BRYNER. (editor) c.1921. *Livestock of the Farm. 4vols.*
KNOWLES, L.A.C. 1944. *The Industrial and Commercial Revolutions during the 19th century.*
LAIRD, ROBERT. 1952. *The Economic Development of Dairy Farming in South West Scotland, 1919–1952.*
LAIRD, ROBERT. 1958. Farming in Ayrshire. Journal of Scottish Agriculture.
LAWRENCE, J. 1809. *A General Treatise on Cattle*
LEIGHTON, GERALD. T.H.A.S.S. 1921. Some Problems of the Dairy Industry.
LINDSAY, JEAN. 1968. *The Canals of Scotland.*
LOW, D. 1842. *The Breeds of Domestic Animals of the British Isles*
LUCAS REPORT. 1947. *Report of the Committee appointed to review the Working of the Agricultural Marketing Acts.*
McCULLOCH, JOHN, T.H.A.S.S. 1875. Dairy Management in Galloway.
MACDONALD, ALEX. 1887. T.H.A.S.S. Agriculture in the County of Renfrew
MACDONALD, Angus. 1993. *The Scottish Farmer. 100 years.*
MADONALD, James. T.H.A.S.S. 1876. Agriculture in the County of Fife.
MACFARLANE's *Geographical Collections.*
MACKENZIE, Rev. Wm. 1841. *History of Galloway.* 2 vols.
MacLELLAND, THOS. T.H.A.S.S. 1875, *Agriculture of the Stewartry of Kirkcudbright and Wigtownshire.*
MacLEOD, INNES. 1986. *Discovering Galloway.*
McMASTER, JOHN. T.H.A.S.S. 1885. Scotch cheesemaking.
MACNEILAGE, Archibald. T.H.A.S.S. 1912. Farming Methods in the West of Scotland.
McQUEEN, DONALD. 1960. *The Dairy Industry in South West Scotland.* (unpublished.)
MACTAGGART, JOHN. 1824. *Scottish Gallovidian Encyclopedia.*

MARSHALL, DAVID. T.H.A.S.S. 1946.
Scottish Agriculture during the War.
MARWICK W.H. 1946. *Scotland in Modern Times.*
MICHELLE & DEANE. 1962. *Abstract of British Historical Statistics.*
MINGAY, GEORGE. 1982. *British Friesians. An Epic in Progress.*
MITCHISON, ROSALIND. 1970. *A History of Scotland.*
MORTON, J.C. 1855. *Cyclopaedia of Agriculture.*
MURRAY, Sir KEITH. 1955.
History of the Second World War – Agriculture.
OJAL, E.M. 1952. *Agricultural & Industrial Progress.* (Oxford.)
ORR, J.B. T.H.A.S.S. 1931. *Development of Stock Farming in Scotland*
PERRY, P.J. 1973. *British Agriculture 1875-1914.*
PLUNKETT FOUNDATION. 1932.
Agricultural Cooperation in Scotland.
PRATT, J.B. 1858. *Buchan & Aberdeen.* Virtue & Co. Ltd. London.
RAISON,C. et al. 1933. *The Milk Trade.*
RALSTON, WILLIAM. T.H.A.S.S. 1885.
The Agriculture of Wigtownshire.
SHAW, JAMES, E. *Ayrshire, 1745-1950.*
SEDDON, QUINTIN. 1989. *The Silent Revolution.* B.B.C. Books.
SHELDON, J.P. c.1880 *Dairy Farming.*
SMITH, D.L. *Little Railways in South West Scotland*
SMITH, S. 1812. *Agriculture in Galloway.* Board of Agriculure.
SMOUT, T.C. 1969. *A History of the Scottish People 1560-1830.*
SMOUT, T.C. 1986. *A Century of the Scottish People 1830-1950.*
SPEIR JOHN. T.H.A.S.S. 1886. Dairying in Scotland.
STANFORD, J.K. 1956. *British Friesians. A History of the Breed.*
STREET, A.G. *Farmers' Glory.*
STURROCK, ARCHIBALD, 1866. T.H.A.S.S. Agriculture in Ayrshire.
STURTEVANT, L.& J. 1875
A Monograph of the Ayrshire Breed of Cattle.
SYMON, J.A. 1959. *Scottish Farming. Past and Present.*
SYMSON, ANDREW. *Large Description of Galloway.*
TROTTER ALEX. *East Galloway Sketches.*
TROW-SMITH, R. 1959.
A History of British Livestock Husbandry. 1700–1900.
TUCKELL,A.E. Dumfriesshire at the time of 'The '45'. Journal of
Scottish Agriculture: Winter 1970/71.
URE, Rev. David. T.H.A.S.S. 1794.
Agriculture in the County of Dumbarton.

URQUART, ROBERT. 1979.
History of the Scottish Milk Marketing Board.
WATSON,J.A. T.H.A.S.S. 1929.
Agricultural Revolution in Scotland 1750–1810
WATSON, J.A.S. & HOBBS, M.E. 1951. *Great Farmers.*
WINNIFRITH, Sir John. 1962.
The Ministry of Agriculture, Fisheries and Food.
WHETHAM, E.H. 1972. *The Agrarian History of England.* Vol.8.
WHITLOCK, RALPH. 1965. *A Short History of Farming in Britain.*
WHYTE, IAN. 1979.
Agriculture and Society in the 17th Century Scotland.
YOUATT, W. 1834. *Cattle: Their Breeds, Management,and Diseases.*
YOUATT, W. *The Complete Grazier.*
YOUATT, W. *Cattle.*
YOUNGSON,A.J. *The British Economy 1920–1957*
WATSON & HOBBS. 1951. *Great Farmers*
WILLIAMS. H.T. 1960. *Principles for Agricultural Policy.*
WOOD. Professor. 1921. *Rations for Livestock.* M.A.F.F.
ZEUNER. F. E. 1827. *A History of Domesticated Animals.*

List of Illustrations & Acknowledgements

Index

A

B

E

F

G

H

I

J

K

L

M

N

O

P

R

S

T

U

V

W

Y